THE THEORY OF ELECTRONS

THE THEORY OF ELECTRONS

AND ITS APPLICATIONS TO THE PHENOMENA OF LIGHT AND RADIANT HEAT

BY

H. A. LORENTZ

SECOND EDITION

DOVER PUBLICATIONS, INC.

NEW YORK

PRINTED AND BOUND IN THE UNITED STATES OF AMERICA

PREFACE.

The publication of these lectures, which I delivered in Columbia University in the spring of 1906, has been unduly delayed, chiefly on account of my wish to give some further development to the subject, so as to present it in a connected and fairly complete form; for this reason I have not refrained from making numerous additions. Nevertheless there are several highly interesting questions, more or less belonging to the theory of electrons, which I could but slightly touch upon. I could no more than allude in a note to Voigt's Treatise on magneto-optical phenomena, and neither Planck's views on radiation, nor Einstein's principle of relativity have received an adequate treatment.

In one other respect this book will, I fear, be found very deficient. No space could be spared for a discussion of the different ways in which the fundamental principles may be established, so that, for instance, there was no opportunity to mention the important share that has been taken in the development of the theory by Larmor and Wiechert.

It is with great pleasure that I express my thanks to Professor A. P. Wills for his kindness in reading part of the proofs, and to the publisher for the care he has bestowed on my work.

Leiden, January 1909.

H. A. Lorentz.

In this new edition the text has been left nearly unchanged. I have confined myself to a small number of alterations and additions in the foot-notes and the appendix.

Haarlem, December 1915.

H. A. L.

CONTENTS.

CHAPTER I.

GENERAL PRINCIPLES. THEORY OF FREE ELECTRONS.

The theory of electrons, on which I shall have the honor to lecture before you, already forms so vast a subject, that it will be impossible for me to treat it quite completely. Even if I confine myself to a general review of this youngest branch of the science of electricity, to its more important applications in the domain of light and radiant heat, and to the discussion of some of the difficulties that still remain, I shall have to express myself as concisely as possible, and to use to the best advantage the time at our disposal.

In this, as in every other chapter of mathematical physics, we may distinguish on the one hand the general ideas and hypotheses of a physical nature involved, and on the other the array of mathematical formulae and developments by which these ideas and hypotheses are expressed and worked out. I shall try to throw a clear light on the former part of the subject, leaving the latter part somewhat in the background and omitting all lengthy calculations, which indeed may better be presented in a book than in a lecture.[1]

1. As to its physical basis, the theory of electrons is an offspring of the great theory of electricity to which the names of Faraday and Maxwell will be for ever attached.

You all know this theory of Maxwell, which we may call the general theory of the electromagnetic field, and in which we constantly have in view the state of the matter or the medium by which the field is occupied. While speaking of this state, I must immediately call your attention to the curious fact that, although we never lose sight of it, we need by no means go far in attempting to form an image of it and, in fact, we cannot say much about it. It is true that we may represent to ourselves internal stresses existing in the

---

1) In this volume such calculations as I have only briefly indicated in my lectures are given at full length in the appendix at the end.

medium surrounding an electrified body or a magnet, that we may think of electricity as of some substance or fluid, free to move in a conductor and bound to positions of equilibrium in a dielectric, and that we may also conceive a magnetic field as the seat of certain invisible motions, rotations for example around the lines of force. All this has been done by many physicists and Maxwell himself has set the example. Yet, it must not be considered as really necessary; we can develop the theory to a large extent and elucidate a great number of phenomena, without entering upon speculations of this kind. Indeed, on account of the difficulties into which they lead us, there has of late years been a tendency to avoid them altogether and to establish the theory on a few assumptions of a more general nature.

The first of these is, that in an electric field there is a certain state of things which gives rise to a force acting on an electrified body and which may therefore be symbolically represented by the force acting on such a body per unit of charge. This is what we call the *electric force*, the symbol for a state in the medium about whose nature we shall not venture any further statement. The second assumption relates to a magnetic field. Without thinking of those hidden rotations of which I have just spoken, we can define this by the so called *magnetic force*, i. e. the force acting on a pole of unit strength.

After having introduced these two fundamental quantities, we try to express their mutual connexions by a set of equations which are then to be applied to a large variety of phenomena. The mathematical relations have thus come to take a very prominent place, so that Hertz even went so far as to say that, after all, the theory of Maxwell is best defined as the system of Maxwell's equations.

We shall not use these formulae in the rather complicated form in which they can be found in Maxwell's treatise, but in the clearer and more condensed form that has been given them by Heaviside and Hertz. In order to simplify matters as much as possible, I shall further introduce units[1]) of such a kind that we get rid of the larger part of such factors as 4π and $\sqrt{4\pi}$, by which the formulae were originally encumbered. As you well know, it was Heaviside who most strongly advocated the banishing of these superfluous factors and it will be well, I think, to follow his advice. Our unit of electricity will therefore be $\sqrt{4\pi}$ times smaller than the usual electrostatic unit.

1) The units and the notation of these lectures (with the exception of the letters serving to indicate vectors) have also been used in my articles on Maxwell's Theory and the Theory of Electrons, in the „Encyklopädie der mathematischen Wissenschaften", Vol. V, 13 and 14.

This choice having been made, we have at the same time fixed for every case the number by which the electric force is to be represented. As to the magnetic force, we continue to understand by it the force acting on a north pole of unit strength; the latter however is likewise $\sqrt{4\pi}$ times smaller than the unit commonly used.

2. Before passing on to the electromagnetic equations, it will be necessary to say a few words about the choice of the axes of coordinates and about our mathematical notation. In the first place, we shall always represent a line by s, a surface by σ and a space by S, and we shall write ds, $d\sigma$, dS respectively for an element of a line, a surface, or a space. In the case of a surface, we shall often have to consider the normal to it; this will be denoted by n. It is always to be drawn towards a definite side and we shall agree to draw it towards the outside, if we have to do with a closed surface.

The normal may be used for indicating the direction of a rotation in the surface. We shall say that the direction of a rotation in a plane and that of a normal to the plane correspond to each other, if an ordinary or right-handed screw turned in the direction of the rotation advances in that of the normal. This being agreed upon, we may add that the axes of coordinates will be chosen in such a manner that OZ corresponds to a rotation of 90^0 from OX towards OY.

We shall further find it convenient to use a simple kind of vector analysis and to distinguish vectors and scalar quantities by different sorts of letters. Conforming to general usage, I shall denote scalars by ordinary Latin or Greek letters. As to the vectors, I have, in some former publications, represented them by German letters. On the present occasion however, it seems to me that Latin letters, either capital or small ones, of the so called Clarendon type, e. g. $\mathbf{A}$, $\mathbf{P}$, $\mathbf{c}$ etc. are to be preferred. I shall denote by $\mathbf{A}_h$ the component of a vector $\mathbf{A}$ in the direction h, by $\mathbf{A}_x$, $\mathbf{A}_y$, $\mathbf{A}_z$ its components parallel to the axes of coordinates, by $\mathbf{A}_s$ the component in the direction of a line s and finally by $\mathbf{A}_n$ that along the normal to a surface.

The magnitude of a vector $\mathbf{A}$ will be represented by $|\mathbf{A}|$. For its square however we shall simply write $\mathbf{A}^2$.

Of the notions that have been introduced into vector analysis, I must recall to your minds those of the sum and of the difference of vectors, and those of the *scalar product* and the *vector product* of two vectors $\mathbf{A}$ and $\mathbf{B}$. The first of these „products“, for which we shall use the symbol

$$(\mathbf{A} \cdot \mathbf{B}),$$

is the scalar quantity defined by the formula

$$(\mathbf{A} \cdot \mathbf{B}) = |\mathbf{A}|\,|\mathbf{B}| \cos(\mathbf{A}, \mathbf{B}) = \mathbf{A}_x\mathbf{B}_x + \mathbf{A}_y\mathbf{B}_y + \mathbf{A}_z\mathbf{B}_z$$

The vector product, for which we shall write

$$[\mathbf{A} \cdot \mathbf{B}],$$

is a vector perpendicular to the plane through $\mathbf{A}$ and $\mathbf{B}$, whose direction corresponds to a rotation by less than 180^0 from the direction of $\mathbf{A}$ towards that of $\mathbf{B}$, and whose magnitude is given by the area of the parallelogram described with $\mathbf{A}$ and $\mathbf{B}$ as sides. Its components are

$$[\mathbf{A} \cdot \mathbf{B}]_x = \mathbf{A}_y \mathbf{B}_z - \mathbf{A}_z \mathbf{B}_y, \quad [\mathbf{A} \cdot \mathbf{B}]_y = \mathbf{A}_z \mathbf{B}_x - \mathbf{A}_x \mathbf{B}_z,$$
$$[\mathbf{A} \cdot \mathbf{B}]_z = \mathbf{A}_x \mathbf{B}_y - \mathbf{A}_y \mathbf{B}_x.$$

In many cases we have to consider a scalar quantity φ or a vector $\mathbf{A}$ which is given at every point of a certain space. If φ is a continuous function of the coordinates, we can introduce the vector having for its components

$$\frac{\partial \varphi}{\partial x}, \quad \frac{\partial \varphi}{\partial y}, \quad \frac{\partial \varphi}{\partial z}.$$

This can easily be shown to be perpendicular to the surface

$$\varphi = \text{const.}$$

and we may call it the *gradient* of φ, which, in our formulae, we shall shorten to „grad φ“.

A space at every point of which a vector $\mathbf{A}$ has a definite direction and a definite magnitude may be called a vector field, and the lines which at every point indicate the direction of $\mathbf{A}$ may be spoken of as vector- or direction-lines. In such a vector field, if $\mathbf{A}_x, \mathbf{A}_y, \mathbf{A}_z$ are continuous functions of the coordinates, we can introduce for every point a certain scalar quantity and a certain new vector, both depending on the way in which $\mathbf{A}$ changes from point to point, and both having the property of being independent of the choice of the axes of coordinates. The scalar quantity is called the *divergence* of $\mathbf{A}$ and defined by the formula

$$\operatorname{div} \mathbf{A} = \frac{\partial \mathbf{A}_x}{\partial x} + \frac{\partial \mathbf{A}_y}{\partial y} + \frac{\partial \mathbf{A}_z}{\partial z}.$$

The vector is called the *rotation* or the ***curl*** of $\mathbf{A}$; its components are

$$\frac{\partial \mathbf{A}_z}{\partial y} - \frac{\partial \mathbf{A}_y}{\partial z}, \quad \frac{\partial \mathbf{A}_x}{\partial z} - \frac{\partial \mathbf{A}_z}{\partial x}, \quad \frac{\partial \mathbf{A}_y}{\partial x} - \frac{\partial \mathbf{A}_x}{\partial y},$$

and it will be represented by the symbol „rot $\mathbf{A}$“.

If the divergence of a vector is 0 at all points, its distribution over space is said to be *solenoidal.* On the other hand, we shall speak of an *irrotational* distribution, if at all points we have rot $\mathbf{A} = 0$.

In order to complete our list of notations, I have only to add that the symbol Δ is an abbreviation for

$$\frac{\partial^2}{\partial x^2}+\frac{\partial^2}{\partial y^2}+\frac{\partial^2}{\partial z^2},$$

and that not only scalars but also vectors may be differentiated with respect to the coordinates or the time. For example, $\frac{\partial \mathbf{A}}{\partial x}$ means a vector whose components are

$$\frac{\partial \mathbf{A}_x}{\partial x},\quad \frac{\partial \mathbf{A}_y}{\partial x},\quad \frac{\partial \mathbf{A}_z}{\partial x},$$

and $\frac{\partial \mathbf{A}}{\partial t}$ has a similar meaning. A differentiation with respect to the time t will be often represented by a dot, a repeated differentiation of the same kind by two dots, etc.

3. We are now prepared to write down the fundamental equations for the electromagnetic field in the form which they take for the ether. We shall denote by $\mathbf{d}$ the electric force, the same symbol serving for the dielectric displacement, because in the ether this has the same direction and, on account of the choice of our units, the same numerical magnitude as the electric force. We shall further represent by $\mathbf{h}$ the magnetic force and by c a constant depending on the properties of the ether. A third vector is the current $\mathbf{c}$, which now consists only of the displacement current of Maxwell. It exists wherever the dielectric displacement $\mathbf{d}$ is a function of the time, and is given by the formula

$$\mathbf{c}=\dot{\mathbf{d}}. \tag{1}$$

In the form of differential equations, the formulae of the electromagnetic field may now be written as follows:

$$\operatorname{div} \mathbf{d}=0, \tag{2}$$

$$\operatorname{div} \mathbf{h}=0, \tag{3}$$

$$\operatorname{rot} \mathbf{h}=\frac{1}{c}\mathbf{c}=\frac{1}{c}\dot{\mathbf{d}}, \tag{4}$$

$$\operatorname{rot} \mathbf{d}=-\frac{1}{c}\dot{\mathbf{h}}. \tag{5}$$

The third equation, conjointly with the second, determines the magnetic field that is produced by a given distribution of the current $\mathbf{c}$. As to the last equation, it expresses the law according to which electric forces are called into play in a system with a variable magnetic field, i. e. the law of what is ordinarily called electromagnetic induction. The formulae (1), (4) and (5) are vector equations and may each be replaced by three scalar equations relating to the separate axes of coordinates.

Thus (1) is equivalent to

$$\mathbf{c}_x = \frac{\partial \mathbf{d}_x}{\partial t}, \quad \mathbf{c}_y = \frac{\partial \mathbf{d}_y}{\partial t}, \quad \mathbf{c}_z = \frac{\partial \mathbf{d}_z}{\partial t},$$

and (4) to

$$\frac{\partial \mathbf{h}_z}{\partial y} - \frac{\partial \mathbf{h}_y}{\partial z} = \frac{1}{c}\frac{\partial \mathbf{d}_x}{\partial t}, \quad \text{etc.}$$

The state of things that is represented by our fundamental equations consists, generally speaking, in a propagation with a velocity c. Indeed, of the six quantities $\mathbf{d}_x$, $\mathbf{d}_y$, $\mathbf{d}_z$, $\mathbf{h}_x$, $\mathbf{h}_y$, $\mathbf{h}_z$, five may be eliminated[1]), and we then find for the remaining one ψ an equation of the form

$$\Delta\psi - \frac{1}{c^2}\frac{\partial^2\psi}{\partial t^2} = 0. \tag{6}$$

This is the typical differential equation for a disturbance of the state of equilibrium, travelling onwards with the speed c.

Though all the solutions of our equations have this general character, yet there are a very large variety of them. The simplest corresponds to a system of polarized plane waves. For waves of this kind, we may have for example

$$\mathbf{d}_y = a \cos n\left(t - \frac{x}{c}\right), \quad \mathbf{h}_z = a \cos n\left(t - \frac{x}{c}\right), \tag{7}$$

all other components of $\mathbf{d}$ and $\mathbf{h}$ being 0.

I need not point out to you that really, in the state represented by these formulae, the values of $\mathbf{d}_y$ and $\mathbf{h}_z$, which for a certain value of t exist at a point with the coordinate x, will after a lapse of time δt be found in a point whose coordinate is $x + c\delta t$. The constant a is the amplitude and n is the frequency, i. e. the number of vibrations in a time 2π. If n is high enough, we have to do with a beam of plane polarized light, in which, as you know already, the electric and the magnetic vibrations are perpendicular to the ray as well as to each other.

Similar, though perhaps much more complicated formulae may serve to represent the propagation of Hertzian waves or the radiation which, as a rule, goes forth from any electromagnetic system that is not in a steady state. If we add the proper boundary conditions, such phenomena as the diffraction of light by narrow openings or its scattering by small obstacles may likewise be made to fall under our system of equations.

The formulae for the ether constitute the part of electromagnetic theory that is most firmly established. Though perhaps the way in which they are deduced will be changed in future years, it is

1) See Note 1 (Appendix).

hardly conceivable that the equations themselves will have to be altered. It is only when we come to consider the phenomena in ponderable bodies, that we are led into uncertainties and doubts.

4. There is one way of treating these phenomena that is comparatively safe and, for many purposes, very satisfactory. In following it, we simply start from certain relations that may be considered as expressing, in a condensed form, the more important results of electromagnetic experiments. We have now to fix our attention on *four* vectors, the electric force $\mathbf{E}$, the magnetic force $\mathbf{H}$, the current of electricity $\mathbf{C}$ and the magnetic induction $\mathbf{B}$. These are connected by the following fundamental equations:

$$\operatorname{div} \mathbf{C} = 0, \tag{8}$$

$$\operatorname{div} \mathbf{B} = 0, \tag{9}$$

$$\operatorname{rot} \mathbf{H} = \frac{1}{c}\mathbf{C}, \tag{10}$$

$$\operatorname{rot} \mathbf{E} = -\frac{1}{c}\dot{\mathbf{B}}, \tag{11}$$

presenting the same form as the formulae we have used for the ether.

In the present case however, we have to add the relation between $\mathbf{E}$ and $\mathbf{C}$ on the one hand, and that between $\mathbf{H}$ and $\mathbf{B}$ on the other. Confining ourselves to isotropic bodies, we can often describe the phenomena with sufficient accuracy by writing for the dielectric displacement

$$\mathbf{D} = \varepsilon \mathbf{E}, \tag{12}$$

a vector equation which expresses that the displacement has the same direction as the electric force and is proportional to it. The current in this case is again Maxwell's displacement current

$$\mathbf{C} = \dot{\mathbf{D}}. \tag{13}$$

In conducting bodies on the other hand, we have to do with a current of conduction, given by

$$\mathbf{J} = \sigma \mathbf{E}, \tag{14}$$

where σ is a new constant. This vector is the only current and therefore identical to what we have called $\mathbf{C}$, if the body has only the properties of a conductor. In some cases however, one has been led to consider bodies endowed with the properties of both conductors and dielectrics. If, in a substance of this kind, an electric force is supposed to produce a dielectric displacement as well as a current of conduction, we may apply at the same time (12) and (14), writing for the total current

$$\mathbf{C} = \dot{\mathbf{D}} + \mathbf{J} = \varepsilon \dot{\mathbf{E}} + \sigma \mathbf{E}. \tag{15}$$

Finally, the simplest assumption we can make as to the relation between the magnetic force and the magnetic induction is expressed by the formula

$$\mathbf{B} = \mu \mathbf{H}, \tag{16}$$

in which μ is a new constant.

5. Though the equations (12), (14) and (16) are useful for the treatment of many problems, they cannot be said to be applicable to all cases. Moreover, even if they were so, this general theory, in which we express the peculiar properties of different ponderable bodies by simply ascribing to each of them particular values of the dielectric constant ε, the conductivity σ and the magnetic permeability μ, can no longer be considered as satisfactory, when we wish to obtain a deeper insight into the nature of the phenomena. If we want to understand the way in which electric and magnetic properties depend on the temperature, the density, the chemical constitution or the crystalline state of substances, we cannot be satisfied with simply introducing for each substance these coefficients, whose values are to be determined by experiment; we shall be obliged to have recourse to some hypothesis about the mechanism that is at the bottom of the phenomena.

It is by this necessity, that one has been led to the conception of *electrons*, i. e. of extremely small particles, charged with electricity, which are present in immense numbers in all ponderable bodies, and by whose distribution and motions we endeavor to explain all electric and optical phenomena that are not confined to the free ether. My task will be to treat some of these phenomena in detail, but I may at once say that, according to our modern views, the electrons in a conducting body, or at least a certain part of them, are supposed to be in a free state, so that they can obey an electric force by which the positive particles are driven in one, and the negative electrons in the opposite direction. In the case of a non-conducting substance, on the contrary, we shall assume that the electrons are bound to certain positions of equilibrium. If, in a metallic wire, the electrons of one kind, say the negative ones, are travelling in one direction, and perhaps those of the opposite kind in the opposite direction, we have to do with a current of conduction, such as may lead to a state in which a body connected to one end of the wire has an excess of either positive or negative electrons. This excess, the charge of the body as a whole, will, in the state of equilibrium and if the body consists of a conducting substance, be found in a very thin layer at its surface.

In a ponderable dielectric there can likewise be a motion of the electrons. Indeed, though we shall think of each of them as having a definite position of equilibrium, we shall not suppose them to be wholly immovable. They can be displaced by an electric force exerted by the ether, which we conceive to penetrate all ponderable matter, a point to which we shall soon have to revert. Now, however, the displacement will immediately give rise to a new force by which the particle is pulled back towards its original position, and which we may therefore appropriately distinguish by the name of *elastic force*. The motion of the electrons in non-conducting bodies, such as glass and sulphur, kept by the elastic force within certain bounds, together with the change of the dielectric displacement in the ether itself, now constitutes what Maxwell called the displacement current. A substance in which the electrons are shifted to new positions is said to be electrically polarized.

Again, under the influence of the elastic forces, the electrons can vibrate about their positions of equilibrium. In doing so, and perhaps also on account of other more irregular motions, they become the centres of waves that travel outwards in the surrounding ether and can be observed as light if the frequency is high enough. In this manner we can account for the emission of light and heat. As to the opposite phenomenon, that of absorption, this is explained by considering the vibrations that are communicated to the electrons by the periodic forces existing in an incident beam of light. If the motion of the electrons thus set vibrating does not go on undisturbed, but is converted in one way or another into the irregular agitation which we call heat, it is clear that part of the incident energy will be stored up in the body, in other terms that there is a certain absorption. Nor is it the absorption alone that can be accounted for by a communication of motion to the electrons. This optical resonance, as it may in many cases be termed, can likewise make itself felt even if there is no resistance at all, so that the body is perfectly transparent. In this case also, the electrons contained within the molecules will be set in motion, and though no vibratory energy is lost, the oscillating particles will exert an influence on the velocity with which the vibrations are propagated through the body. By taking account of this reaction of the electrons we are enabled to establish an electromagnetic theory of the refrangibility of light, in its relation to the wave-length and the state of the matter, and to form a mental picture of the beautiful and varied phenomena of double refraction and circular polarization.

On the other hand, the theory of the motion of electrons in metallic bodies has been developed to a considerable extent. Though here also much remains to be done, new questions arising as we proceed, we can already mention the important results that have been reached by Riecke, Drude and J. J. Thomson.[1]) The fundamental idea of the modern theory of the thermic and electric properties of metals is, that the free electrons in these bodies partake of the heat-motion of the molecules of ordinary matter, travelling in all directions with such velocities that the mean kinetic energy of each of them is equal to that of a gaseous molecule at the same temperature. If we further suppose the electrons to strike over and over again against metallic atoms, so that they describe irregular zigzag-lines, we can make clear to ourselves the reason that metals are at the same time good conductors of heat and of electricity, and that, as a general rule, in the series of the metals, the two conductivities change in nearly the same ratio. The larger the number of free electrons, and the longer the time that elapses between two successive encounters, the greater will be the conductivitv for heat as well as that for electricity.

6. This rapid review will suffice to show you that the theory of electrons is to be regarded as an extension to the domain of electricity of the molecular and atomistic theories that have proved of so much use in many branches of physics and chemistry. Like these, it is apt to be viewed unfavourably by some physicists, who prefer to push their way into new and unexplored regions by following those great highways of science which we possess in the laws of thermodynamics, or who arrive at important and beautiful results, simply by describing the phenomena and their mutual relations by means of a system of suitable equations. No one can deny that these methods have a charm of their own, and that, in following them, we have the feeling of treading on firm ground, whereas in the molecular theories the too adventurous physicist often runs the risk of losing his way and of being deluded by some false prospect of success. We must not forget, however, that these molecular hypotheses can boast of some results that could never have been attained by pure thermodynamics, or by means of the equations of the electromagnetic field in their most general form, results that are well known to all who have studied the kinetic theory of gases, the theories of

---

1) E. Riecke, Zur Theorie des Galvanismus und der Wärme, Ann. Phys. Chem. **66** (1898), p. 353, 545, 1199; Über das Verhältnis der Leitfähigkeiten der Metalle für Wärme und für Elektrizität, Ann. Phys. **2** (1900), p. 835. P. Drude, Zur Elektronentheorie der Metalle, Ann. Phys. **1** (1900), p. 566; **3** (1900), p. 369. J. J. Thomson, Indications relatives à la constitution de la matière fournies par les recherches récentes sur le passage de l'électricité à travers les gaz, Rapports du Congrès de physique de 1900, Paris, **3**, p. 138. See also H. A. Lorentz, The motion of electrons in metallic bodies, Amsterdam Proc. 1904—1905, p. 438, 588, 684.

dilute solutions, of electrolysis and of the genesis of electric currents by the motion of ions. Nor can the fruitfulness of these hypotheses be denied by those who have followed the splendid researches on the conduction of electricity through gases of J. J. Thomson[1]) and his fellow workers.

7. I have now to make you acquainted with the equations forming the foundation of the mathematical theory of electrons. Permit me to introduce them by some preliminary remarks.

In the first place, we shall ascribe to each electron certain finite dimensions, however small they may be, and we shall fix our attention not only on the exterior field, but also on the interior space, in which there is room for many elements of volume and in which the state of things may vary from one point to another. As to this state, we shall suppose it to be of the same kind as at outside points. Indeed, one of the most important of our fundamental assumptions must be that the ether not only occupies all space between molecules, atoms or electrons, but that it pervades all these particles. We shall add the hypothesis that, though the particles may move, *the ether always remains at rest.* We can reconcile ourselves with this, at first sight, somewhat startling idea, by thinking of the particles of matter as of some local modifications in the state of the ether. These modifications may of course very well travel onward while the volume-elements of the medium in which they exist remain at rest.

Now, if within an electron there is ether, there can also be an electromagnetic field, and all we have got to do is to establish a system of equations that may be applied as well to the parts of the ether where there is an electric charge, i. e. to the electrons, as to those where there is none. As to the distribution of the charge, we are free to make any assumption we like. For the sake of convenience we shall suppose it to be distributed over a certain space, say over the whole volume occupied by the electron, and we shall consider the volume-density ρ as a continuous function of the coordinates, so that the charged particle has no sharp boundary, but is surrounded by a thin layer in which the density gradually sinks from the value it has within the electron to 0. Thanks to this hypothesis of the continuity of ρ, which we shall extend to all other quantities occurring in our equations, we have never to trouble ourselves about surfaces of discontinuity, nor to encumber the theory by separate equations relating to these. Moreover, if we suppose the difference between the ether within and without the electrons to be caused, at least so

---

1) J. J. Thomson, Conduction of electricity through gases, Cambridge, 1903.

far as we are concerned with it, only by the existence of the volume-density in the interior, the equations for the external field must be got from those for the internal one by simply putting $\varrho = 0$, so that we have only to write down *one* system of differential equations.

Of course, these must be obtained by a suitable modification, in which the influence of the charge is expressed, of the equations (2)—(5) which we have established for the free, i. e. for the uncharged ether. It has been found that we can attain our object by the slightest modification imaginable, and that we can assume the following system

$$\operatorname{div} \mathbf{d} = \varrho, \tag{17}$$

$$\operatorname{div} \mathbf{h} = 0, \tag{18}$$

$$\operatorname{rot} \mathbf{h} = \frac{1}{c} \mathbf{c} = \frac{1}{c} (\dot{\mathbf{d}} + \varrho \mathbf{v}), \tag{19}$$

$$\operatorname{rot} \mathbf{d} = -\frac{1}{c} \dot{\mathbf{h}}, \tag{20}$$

in which the first and the third formula are the only ones that have been altered.

In order to justify these modifications, I must in the first place recall to your minds the general relation existing in **Maxwell's** theory between the dielectric displacement across a closed surface and the amount of charge e contained within it. It is expressed by the equation

$$\int \mathbf{d}_n \, d\sigma = e, \tag{21}$$

in which the integral relates to the closed surface, each element $d\sigma$ of it being multiplied by the component of $\mathbf{d}$ along the normal n, which, as we have already said, is drawn towards the outside. Using a well known form of speech and comparing the state of things with one in which there would be no dielectric displacement at all, we may say that the total quantity of electricity that has been displaced across the surface (a quantity that has been shifted in an outward direction being reckoned as positive), is equal to the charge e. Now, if we apply this to an element of space $dx\,dy\,dz$, taken at a point where there is a volume-density ϱ, we have

$$e = \varrho \, dx \, dy \, dz$$

and, since the integral in (21) reduces to

$$\operatorname{div} \mathbf{d} \cdot dx \, dy \, dz,$$

we are at once led to the formula (17).

In the second place, we must observe that a moving charge constitutes what is called a convection current and produces the same magnetic effects as a common current of conduction; this was first shown by Rowland's celebrated and well known experiment. Now, if $\mathbf{v}$ is the velocity of the charge, it is natural to write $\rho\mathbf{v}$ for the convection current; indeed, the three components $\rho\mathbf{v}_x$, $\rho\mathbf{v}_y$, $\rho\mathbf{v}_z$ represent the amounts of charge, reckoned per unit of area and unit of time, which are carried across elements of surface perpendicular to the axes of coordinates. On the other hand, if in the interior of an electron there is an electromagnetic field, there will also be a displacement current $\dot{\mathbf{d}}$. We are therefore led to assume as the expression for the total current

$$\mathbf{c} = \dot{\mathbf{d}} + \rho\mathbf{v}, \tag{22}$$

and to use the equation (19) in order to determine the magnetic field. Of course, this is again a vector equation. In applying it to special problems, it is often found convenient to replace it by the three scalar differential equations

$$\frac{\partial \mathbf{h}_z}{\partial y} - \frac{\partial \mathbf{h}_y}{\partial z} = \frac{1}{c}\left(\frac{\partial \mathbf{d}_x}{\partial t} + \rho\mathbf{v}_x\right), \quad \frac{\partial \mathbf{h}_x}{\partial z} - \frac{\partial \mathbf{h}_z}{\partial x} = \frac{1}{c}\left(\frac{\partial \mathbf{d}_y}{\partial t} + \rho\mathbf{v}_y\right),$$
$$\frac{\partial \mathbf{h}_y}{\partial x} - \frac{\partial \mathbf{h}_x}{\partial y} = \frac{1}{c}\left(\frac{\partial \mathbf{d}_z}{\partial t} + \rho\mathbf{v}_z\right).$$

You see that by putting $\rho = 0$, in the formulae (17) and (19), we are led back to our former equations (2) and (4).

8. There is one more equation to be added, in fact one that is of equal importance with (17)—(20). It will have been noticed that I have carefully abstained from saying anything about the nature of the electric charge represented by ρ. Speculations on this point, or attempts to reduce the idea of a charge to others of a different kind, are entirely without the scope of the present theory; we do not pretend to say more than this, that ρ is a quantity, belonging to a certain point in the ether and connected with the distribution of the dielectric displacement in the neighbourhood of that point by the equation (17). We may say that the ether can be the seat of a certain state, determined by the vector $\mathbf{d}$ which we call the dielectric displacement, that in general this vector is solenoidally distributed, but that there are some places which form an exception to this rule, the divergence of $\mathbf{d}$ having a certain value ρ, different from 0. In such a case, we speak of an electric charge and understand by its density the value of div $\mathbf{d}$.

As to the statement that the charges can move through the ether, the medium itself remaining at rest, if reduced to its utmost simplicity, it only means that the value of div $\mathbf{d}$ which at one moment exists at a point P, will the next moment be found at another place P'.

Yet, in order to explain electromagnetic phenomena, we are obliged to go somewhat further. It is not quite sufficient to consider ϱ as merely the symbol for a certain state of the ether. On the contrary, we must invest the charges with a certain degree of substantiality, so far at least that we recognize the possibility of *forces* acting on them and producing or modifying their motion. The word „force“ is here taken in the ordinary sense it has in dynamics, and we should easily become accustomed to the idea of forces acting on the charges, if we conceived these latter as fixed to what we are accustomed to call matter, or as being a property of this matter. This is the idea underlying the name of „charged particle“ which we have already used and shall occasionally use again for an electron. We shall see later on that, in some cases at least, the fitness of the name is somewhat questionable.

However this may be, we must certainly speak of such a thing as the force acting on a charge, or on an electron, on charged matter, whichever appellation you prefer. Now, in accordance with the general principles of Maxwell's theory, we shall consider this force as caused by the state of the ether, and even, since this medium pervades the electrons, as exerted by the ether on all internal points of these particles where there is a charge. If we divide the whole electron into elements of volume, there will be a force acting on each element and determined by the state of the ether existing within it. We shall suppose that this force is proportional to the charge of the element, so that we only want to know the force acting per unit charge. This is what we can now properly call *the electric force.* We shall represent it by $\mathbf{f}$. The formula by which it is determined, and which is the one we still have to add to (17)—(20), is as follows:

$$\mathbf{f} = \mathbf{d} + \frac{1}{c}[\mathbf{v} \cdot \mathbf{h}]. \tag{23}$$

Like our former equations, it is got by generalizing the results of electromagnetic experiments. The first term represents the force acting on an electron in an electrostatic field; indeed, in this case, the force per unit of charge must be wholly determined by the dielectric displacement. On the other hand, the part of the force expressed by the second term may be derived from the law according to which an element of a wire carrying a current is acted on by a magnetic field with a force perpendicular to itself and the lines of force, an action, which in our units may be represented in vector notation by

$$\mathbf{F} = \frac{s}{c}[\mathbf{i} \cdot \mathbf{h}],$$

where $\mathbf{i}$ is the intensity of the current considered as a vector, and s the length of the element. According to the theory of electrons, $\mathbf{F}$ is made up of all the forces with which the field $\mathbf{h}$ acts on the separate electrons moving in the wire. Now, simplifying the question by the assumption of only one kind of moving electrons with equal charges e and a common velocity $\mathbf{v}$, we may write

$$s\mathbf{i} = Ne\mathbf{v},$$

if N is the whole number of these particles in the element s. Hence

$$\mathbf{F} = \frac{Ne}{c}[\mathbf{v}\cdot\mathbf{h}],$$

so that, dividing by Ne, we find for the force per unit charge

$$\frac{1}{c}[\mathbf{v}\cdot\mathbf{h}].$$

As an interesting and simple application of this result, I may mention the explanation it affords of the induction current that is produced in a wire moving across the magnetic lines of force. The two kinds of electrons having the velocity $\mathbf{v}$ of the wire, are in this case driven in opposite directions by forces which are determined by our formula.

9. After having been led in one particular case to the existence of the force $\mathbf{d}$, and in another to that of the force $\frac{1}{c}[\mathbf{v}\cdot\mathbf{h}]$, we now combine the two in the way shown in the equation (23), going beyond the direct result of experiments by the assumption that in general the two forces exist at the same time. If, for example, an electron were moving in a space traversed by Hertzian waves, we could calculate the action of the field on it by means of the values of $\mathbf{d}$ and $\mathbf{h}$, such as they are at the point of the field occupied by the particle.

Of course, in cases like this, in which we want to know the force exerted by an external field, we need not distinguish the directions and magnitudes of $\mathbf{f}$ at different points of the electron, at least if there is no rotation of the particle; the velocity $\mathbf{v}$ will be the same for all its points and the external field may be taken as homogeneous on account of the smallness of the electron. If however, for an electron having some variable motion, we are required to calculate the force that is due to its own field, our analysis must be pushed further. The field is now far from homogeneous, and after having divided the particle into elements of volume, we must determine the action of the field on each of them. Finally, if the electron is treated as a rigid body, we shall have to calculate in the ordinary way the resultant force and the resultant couple.

10. While I am speaking so boldly of what goes on in the interior of an electron, as if I had been able to look into these small particles, I fear one will feel inclined to think I had better not try to enter into all these details. My excuse must be that one can scarcely refrain from doing so, if one wishes to have a perfectly definite system of equations; moreover, as we shall see later on, our experiments can really teach us something about the dimensions of the electrons. In the second place, it may be observed that in those cases in which the internal state of the electrons can make itself felt, speculations like those we have now entered upon, are at all events interesting, be they right or wrong, whereas they are harmless as soon as we may consider the internal state as a matter of little importance.

It must also be noticed that our assumptions by no means exclude the possibility of certain distributions of charge which we have not at first mentioned. By indefinitely diminishing the thickness of the transition layer in which ϱ passes from a finite value to 0, we can get as a limiting case that of an electron with a sharp boundary. We can also conceive the charge to be present, not throughout the whole extent of the particle, but only in a certain layer at its surface, whose thickness may be made as small as we like, so that after all we can speak of a surface-charge. Indeed, in some of our formulae we shall have in view this special case.

11. Since our equations form the real foundation-stones of the structure we are going to build, it will be well to examine them somewhat more closely, so that we may be sure that they are consistent with each other. They are easily shown to be so, provided only the charge of an element of volume remain constant during its motion.[1]) If we regard the electrons as rigid bodies, as we shall almost always do, this of course means that ϱ is constant at every point of a particle. However, we might also suppose the electrons to change their shape and volume; only, in this case, the value of ϱ for an element of volume ought to be considered as varying in the inverse ratio as the magnitude of the element.

It is also important to remark that our formulae are applicable to a system in which the charges, instead of being concentrated in certain small particles, are spread over larger spaces in any way you like. We may even go a step further and imagine any number of charges with the densities ϱ_1, ϱ_2 etc., which are capable of penetrating each other and therefore of occupying the same part of space, and which move, each with its own velocity. This would require us to

---

1) Note 2.

replace the terms ϱ and $\varrho\mathbf{v}$ in (17) and (19) by $\varrho_1 + \varrho_2 + \cdots$ and $\varrho_1\mathbf{v}_1 + \varrho_2\mathbf{v}_2 + \cdots$, the vectors $\mathbf{v}_1, \mathbf{v}_2, \ldots$ being the velocities of the separate charges. An assumption of this kind, artificial though it may seem, will be found of use in one of the problems we shall have to examine.

12. I have now to call your attention to some of the many beautiful results that may be derived from our fundamental equations, in the first place to the way in which the electromagnetic field is determined by the formulae (17)—(20), if the distribution and the motion of the charges are supposed to be given. The possibility of this determination is due to the fact that we can eliminate five of the six quantities $\mathbf{d}_x$, $\mathbf{d}_y$, $\mathbf{d}_z$, $\mathbf{h}_x$, $\mathbf{h}_y$, $\mathbf{h}_z$, exactly as we could do, when we treated the equations for the free ether, and to the remarkable form in which the final equation presents itself.[1] We have, for example, three equations for the components of $\mathbf{d}$, which we may combine into the vector formula

$$\Delta \mathbf{d} - \frac{1}{c^2}\ddot{\mathbf{d}} = \operatorname{grad} \varrho + \frac{1}{c^2}\frac{\partial}{\partial t}(\varrho \mathbf{v}), \tag{24}$$

and the similar condition for the magnetic force

$$\Delta \mathbf{h} - \frac{1}{c^2}\ddot{\mathbf{h}} = -\frac{1}{c}\operatorname{rot}(\varrho \mathbf{v}). \tag{25}$$

It will not be necessary to write down the six scalar equations for the separate components; we can confine ourselves to the formulae for $\mathbf{d}_x$ and $\mathbf{h}_x$, viz.

$$\Delta \mathbf{d}_x - \frac{1}{c^2}\ddot{\mathbf{d}}_x = \frac{\partial \varrho}{\partial x} + \frac{1}{c^2}\frac{\partial(\varrho \mathbf{v}_x)}{\partial t}, \tag{26}$$

$$\Delta \mathbf{h}_x - \frac{1}{c^2}\ddot{\mathbf{h}}_x = -\frac{1}{c}\left\{\frac{\partial(\varrho \mathbf{v}_z)}{\partial y} - \frac{\partial(\varrho \mathbf{v}_y)}{\partial z}\right\}. \tag{27}$$

In order to express myself more clearly, it will be proper to introduce a name for the left-hand sides of these equations. The result of the operation Δ, applied to a quantity ψ that is a function of the coordinates x, y, z, has been called the Laplacian of ψ. Similarly, the result of the operation $\Delta - \frac{1}{c^2}\cdot\frac{\partial^2}{\partial t^2}$ may be given the name of the Dalembertian of the original quantity, in commemoration of the fact that the mathematician d'Alembert was the first to solve a partial differential equation, occurring in the theory of a vibrating string, which contains this operation, or rather the operation $\frac{\partial^2}{\partial x^2} - \frac{1}{c^2}\frac{\partial^2}{\partial t^2}$, which is a special case of it. Of course, since vectors can be differentiated with respect to time and place, we may as well

1) Note 3.

speak of the Dalembertian of a vector as of that of a scalar quantity. Accordingly, since, for a given distribution and motion of the charges, the right-hand members of our last equations are known functions of x, y, z, t, we see that the vectors $\mathbf{d}$ and $\mathbf{h}$, as well as each of their components, are determined by the values of their Dalembertians. We have therefore to look into the question, what will be the value of a quantity ψ whose Dalembertian has a given value ω. This is a problem which admits a simple solution. In the ordinary theory of the potential it is proved that a function ψ whose Laplacian has a given value ω, may be found by the formula

$$\psi = -\frac{1}{4\pi}\int\frac{\omega}{r}\,dS, \tag{28}$$

where r is the distance from an element of volume dS to the point P for which we want to calculate ψ, ω the value of the Laplacian in this element, and where we have to integrate over all parts of space in which ω is different from 0.

Now, it is very remarkable that a function ψ satisfying the equation

$$\left(\Delta - \frac{1}{c^2}\frac{\partial^2}{\partial t^2}\right)\psi = \omega, \tag{29}$$

may be found by a calculation very like that indicated in (28)[1]. The only difference is that, if we are asked to determine the value of ψ at the point P for the instant t, we must take for ω the value of this function existing in the element dS at the time $t - \frac{r}{c}\cdot$ We shall henceforth include in square brackets quantities whose values must be taken, not for the time t, but for the previous time $t - \frac{r}{c}\cdot$ Using this notation, we may say that the function

$$\psi = -\frac{1}{4\pi}\int\frac{[\omega]}{r}\,dS \tag{30}$$

is a solution of the differential equation (29). It should be observed that this also holds when ω is a vector quantity; $[\omega]$ and $\frac{[\omega]}{r}\,dS$ will then be so likewise, and the integration in (30) is to be understood as the addition of an infinite number of infinitely small vectors. For purposes of actual computation, the vector equation may again be split up into three scalar ones, containing the components of ω, and giving us those of ψ.

---

1) Note 4.

13. The above method of calculation might be applied to the equations (24) and (25) or (26) and (27). Since, however, the second members of these formulae are somewhat complicated, we prefer not directly to determine **d** and **h**, but to calculate in the first place certain auxiliary functions on which the electric and magnetic forces may be made to depend, and which are called *potentials*. The first is a scalar quantity, which I shall denote by φ, the second a vector for which I shall write **a**.

If the potentials are subjected to the relations

$$\Delta\varphi - \frac{1}{c^2}\ddot{\varphi} = -\varrho \tag{31}$$

and

$$\Delta \mathbf{a} - \frac{1}{c^2}\ddot{\mathbf{a}} = -\frac{1}{c}\varrho\mathbf{v}, \tag{32}$$

one can show[1]), by means of (17)—(20), that the dielectric displacement is given by

$$\mathbf{d} = -\frac{1}{c}\dot{\mathbf{a}} - \text{grad}\,\varphi \tag{33}$$

and the magnetic force by

$$\mathbf{h} = \text{rot}\,\mathbf{a}. \tag{34}$$

You see that the equations (31) and (32) are again of the form (29), so that the two potentials are determined by the condition that their Dalembertians must have the simple values $-\varrho$ and $-\frac{1}{c}\varrho\mathbf{v}$. Therefore, on account of (30), we may write

$$\varphi = \frac{1}{4\pi}\int \frac{1}{r}[\varrho]\,dS \tag{35}$$

and

$$\mathbf{a} = \frac{1}{4\pi c}\int \frac{1}{r}[\varrho\mathbf{v}]\,dS. \tag{36}$$

By these equations, combined with (33) and (34), our problem is solved. They show that, in order to calculate the field, we have to proceed as follows: Let P be the point for which we wish to determine the potentials at the time t. We must divide the whole surrounding space into elements of volume, any one of which is called dS. Let it be situated at the point Q and let the distance QP be denoted by r. In this element of space there may or may not be a part of an electron at a certain time. We are only concerned with the question whether it contains a charge at the time $t - \frac{r}{c}$. Indeed, the brackets serve to remind us that we are to understand

1) Note 5.

by ϱ the density existing in dS at the particular instant $t-\frac{r}{c}$ and by $\varrho\mathbf{v}$ the product of this density and the velocity of the charge within dS at that same instant. These values $[\varrho]$ and $[\varrho\mathbf{v}]$ must be multiplied by dS and divided by r. Finally, we have to do for all elements what we have done for the one dS and to add all the results. Of course there may be many elements which do not contribute anything to the integrals, viz. all those which at the time $t-\frac{r}{c}$ did not contain any charge.

14. What has been said calls forth some further remarks. In the first place, you see that the factor $\frac{1}{4\pi}$, which we have been so anxious to get rid of, has again appeared. We cannot prevent it from doing so, but fortunately it is now confined to a few of our equations. In the second place, it is especially important to observe that the values of ϱ and $\varrho\mathbf{v}$ existing at a certain point Q at the time $t-\frac{r}{c}$ do not make themselves felt at the point P at the same moment $t-\frac{r}{c}$, but at the later time t. We may therefore really speak of a propagation taking place with the velocity c. The parts of φ and $\mathbf{a}$ which are due to the several elements dS correspond to states existing in these elements at times which are the more remote, the farther these elements are situated from the point P considered.

On account of this special feature of our result, the potentials φ and $\mathbf{a}$, given by (35) and (36), are often called *retarded* potentials.

I must add that the function (30) is not the most general solution of (29), and that for this reason the values of (33) and (34) derived from (35) and (36) are not the only ones satisfying the fundamental equations. We need not however speak of other solutions, if we assume that an electromagnetic field in the ether is never produced by any other causes than the presence and motion of electrons.[1]

15. The case of a single electron furnishes a good example for the application of our general formulae. Let us suppose in the first place that the particle never has had nor will have any motion. Then we have $\mathbf{a}=0$, and since ϱ is the same at all instants, the scalar potential is given by

$$\varphi=\frac{1}{4\pi}\int\frac{\varrho}{r}\,dS.$$

The equations (33) and (34) becoming

$$\mathbf{d}=-\operatorname{grad}\varphi,\quad \mathbf{h}=0,$$

we fall back on the ordinary formulae of electrostatics.

1) Note 6.

We shall next consider an electron having (from $t = -\infty$ until $t = +\infty$) a translation with constant velocity w along a straight line. Let P and P' be two points in such positions that the line PP' is in the direction of the motion of the particle. It is easily seen that, if we wish to calculate φ, $\mathfrak{a}$, $\mathfrak{d}$ and $\mathfrak{h}$, first for the point P and the time t, and then for the point P' and the time $t + \frac{PP'}{w}$, we shall have to repeat exactly the same calculations. If, for example, dS is an element of space contributing a part to the integrals (35) and (36) in the first problem, the corresponding integrals in the second will contain equal parts due to an element dS' which may be got by shifting dS in the direction of translation over a distance equal to PP'.

It appears from this that the electron is continually surrounded by the same field, which it may therefore be said to carry along with it. As to the nature of this field, one can easily deduce from (33)—(36) that, in the case of a spherical electron with a charge symmetrically distributed around the centre, if s is the path of the centre, the electric lines of force are curves situated in planes passing through s, and the magnetic lines circles having s as axis.[1]) The field is distinguished from that of an electron without translation, not only by the presence of the magnetic force, but also by an alteration in the distribution of the dielectric displacement.

We shall finally take a somewhat less simple case. Let us suppose that, from $t = -\infty$ until a certain instant t_1, the electron is at rest in a position A, and that, in a short interval of time beginning at t_1, it acquires a velocity w which remains constant in magnitude and direction until after some time, in a short interval ending at the instant t_2, the motion is stopped. Let B be the final position in which the electron remains for ever afterwards.

If P is any point in the surrounding ether, we can consider two distances l_1 and l_2, the first of which is the shortest of all the lines drawn from P to the points of the electron in the position A, and the second the longest of all the lines joining P to the electron in the position B. We shall suppose the interval $t_2 - t_1$ to be so long that $t_2 + \frac{l_2}{c} > t_1 + \frac{l_1}{c}$.

It will be clear that in performing the calculation of φ and $\mathfrak{a}$, for the point P and for an instant previous to $t_1 + \frac{l_1}{c}$, we shall get a result wholly independent of the motion of the electron. This motion can by no means make itself felt at P during this first period, which will therefore be characterized by the field belonging

1) Note 7.

to the immovable electron. A similar field will exist at P after the time $t_2 + \frac{l_2}{c}$, every influence that has been emitted by the particle while moving, having already, in its outward progress, passed over the point considered.

Between $t_1 + \frac{l_1}{c}$ and $t_2 + \frac{l_2}{c}$ the field at P will be due to the moving electron. If we suppose the dimensions of the particle to be very small in comparison with the distances l_1, l_2, and the velocity w to be acquired and lost in intervals of time much shorter than $t_2 - t_1$, we may be sure that during the larger part of the interval between $t_1 + \frac{l_1}{c}$ and $t_2 + \frac{l_2}{c}$ the field at P will be what it would have been, had a constant velocity w existed for ever. Of course, immediately after $t_1 + \frac{l_1}{c}$ and shortly before $t_2 + \frac{l_2}{c}$ it will be otherwise; then, there will be a gradual transition from one state of things to the other. It is clear also that these periods of transition, taken for different points P, will not be found to coincide. If S_1, S_2, S_3 are parts of space at different distances from the line AB, S_1 being the most remote and S_3 the nearest, it may very well be that, at some particular instant, S_1 is occupied by the field belonging to the electron while at rest in the position A, S_2 by the field of the moving electron, and S_3 by the final field.

16. Thus far we have only used the equations (17)—(20). Adding to these the formula (23) for the electric force, and supposing the forces of any other nature which may act on the electrons to be given, we have the means of determining, not only the field, but also the motion of the charges. For our purpose however, it is not necessary to enter here into special problems of this kind. We shall concentrate our attention on one or two general theorems holding for any system of moving electrons.

In the first place, suitable transformations of the fundamental formulae lead to an equation expressing the law of conservation of energy.[1]) If we confine ourselves to the part of the system lying within a certain closed surface σ, this equation has the form

$$\int \varrho(\mathbf{f} \cdot \mathbf{v}) dS + \frac{d}{dt}\left\{\frac{1}{2}\int (\mathbf{d}^2 + \mathbf{h}^2) dS\right\} + c\int [\mathbf{d} \cdot \mathbf{h}]_n d\sigma = 0, \quad (37)$$

which we shall now try to interpret. Since $\mathbf{f}$ is the force with which the ether acts on unit charge, $\varrho \mathbf{f} dS$ will be the force acting on the element dS of the charge, and

$$(\varrho dS \mathbf{f} \cdot \mathbf{v}) = \varrho(\mathbf{f} \cdot \mathbf{v}) dS$$

1) Note 8.

its work per unit of time. The first integral in (37) is thus seen to represent the work done by the ether on the electrons per unit of time. Combined with the work of other forces to which the electrons may be subjected, this term will therefore enable us to calculate the change of the kinetic energy of the electrons.

Of course, if the ether does work on the electrons, it must lose an equivalent amount of energy, a loss for which a supply of energy from the part of the system outside the surface σ may make up, or which may be accompanied by a transfer of energy to that part. We must therefore consider

$$\tfrac{1}{2}(\mathbf{d}^2 + \mathbf{h}^2)\,dS \tag{38}$$

as the expression for the energy contained within an element of volume of the ether, and

$$c\int [\mathbf{d}\cdot\mathbf{h}]_n\,d\sigma \tag{39}$$

as that for an amount of energy that is lost by the system within the surface and gained by the surrounding ether.

The two parts into which (38) can be divided may properly be called the electric and the magnetic energy of the ether. Reckoned per unit of volume the former is seen to be

$$w = \tfrac{1}{2}\mathbf{d}^2, \tag{40}$$

and the latter

$$w_m = \tfrac{1}{2}\mathbf{h}^2. \tag{41}$$

These values are equivalent to those that were given long ago by Maxwell. That the coefficients are $\tfrac{1}{2}$ and not 2π or something of the kind, is due to the choice of our new units and will certainly serve to recommend them.

As to the transfer of energy represented by (39), it must necessarily take place at the points of the surface σ itself, because our theory leaves no room for any action at a distance. Further, we are naturally led to suppose that the actions by which it is brought about are such that, for each element $d\sigma$, the quantity $c[\mathbf{d}\cdot\mathbf{h}]_n d\sigma$ may be said to represent the amount of energy that is transmitted across this particular element. In this way we come to the conception, first formulated by Poynting[1]), of a *current* or *flow* of energy. It is determined by the vector product of $\mathbf{d}$ and $\mathbf{h}$, multiplied by the constant c, so that we can write for it

$$\mathbf{s} = c[\mathbf{d}\cdot\mathbf{h}], \tag{42}$$

1) J. H. Poynting, On the transfer of energy in the electromagnetic field, London Trans. 175 (1884), p. 343.

the meaning being that, for any element $d\sigma$, the amount of energy by which it is traversed, is given for unit of time and unit of area by the component $\mathbf{s}_n$ of the vector $\mathbf{s}$ along the normal to the element.

17. It is interesting to apply the above results to the beam of polarized light represented by our equations (7). We find for the energy which it contains per unit of space

$$\frac{1}{2}(\mathbf{d}^2 + \mathbf{h}^2) = a^2 \cos^2 n\left(t - \frac{x}{c}\right),$$

and for the flow of energy across a plane perpendicular to the axis of x

$$c\mathbf{d}_y\mathbf{h}_z = ca^2 \cos^2 n\left(t - \frac{x}{c}\right).$$

The mean values of these expressions for a full period are

$$\tfrac{1}{2}a^2$$

and

$$\tfrac{1}{2}ca^2.$$

Indeed, by a well known theorem, the mean value of $\cos^2 n\left(t - \frac{x}{c}\right)$ is $\frac{1}{2}$.

It is easily seen that the expression $\frac{1}{2}ca^2$ may also be used for calculating the flow of energy during any lapse of time that is very long compared with a period.

If the beam of light is laterally limited by a cylindrical surface whose generating lines are parallel to OX, as it may be if we neglect diffraction phenomena, and if a normal section has the area Σ, the flow of energy across a section is given by $\frac{1}{2}ca^2\Sigma$. It is equal for any two sections and must indeed be so, because the amount of energy in the part of the beam between them remains constant.

The case of a single electron having a uniform translation likewise affords a good illustration of what has been said about the flow of energy. After having determined the internal and the external field by means of the formulae (33)—(36), we can deduce the total electromagnetic energy from (40) and (41). I shall later on have occasion to mention the result. For the present I shall only say that, considering the course of the electric and the magnetic lines of force, which intersect each other at right angles, we must conclude that there is a current of energy, whose general direction is that of the translation of the electron. This should have been expected, since the moving electron is constantly surrounded by the same field. The energy of this field may be said to accompany the particle in its motion.

Other examples might likewise show us how **Poynting's** theorem throws a clear light on many questions. Indeed, its importance can hardly be overestimated, and it is now difficult to recall the state of electromagnetic theory of some thirty years ago, when we had to do without this beautiful theorem.

18. Before leaving this subject I will, with your permission, call attention to the question, as to how far we can attach a definite meaning to a flow of energy. It must, I believe, be admitted that, as soon as we know the mutual action between two particles or elements of volume, we shall be able to make a definite statement as to the energy given by one of them to the other. Hence, a theory which explains things by making definite assumptions as to the mutual action of the parts of a system, must at the same time admit a transfer of energy, concerning whose intensity there can be no doubt. Yet, even if this be granted, we can easily see that in general it will not be possible to trace the paths of parts or elements of energy in the same sense in which we can follow in their course the ultimate particles of which matter is made up.

In order to show this, I shall understand by P a particle or an element of volume and by $A, B, C, \ldots, A', B', C', \ldots$ a certain number of other particles or elements, between which and P there is some action resulting in a transfer of energy and, in accordance with what has just been said, I shall suppose these actions to be so far known that we can distinctly state what amount of energy is interchanged between any two particles. Let, for example, P receive from $A, B, C, \ldots$ the quantities $a, b, c, \ldots$ of energy, and let it give to $A', B', C', \ldots$ the quantities $a', b', c', \ldots$, gaining for itself a certain amount p. Then we shall have the equation

$$a + b + c + \cdots = p + a' + b' + c' + \cdots.$$

Now, though in our imaginary case each term in this equation would be known, we should have no means for determining in what way the quantities of energy contained in $a, b, c, \ldots$, say the individual units of energy, are distributed among $p, a', b', c', \ldots$. If, for example, there are only two terms on each side of the equation, all of the same value, so that it takes the form

$$a + b = a' + b',$$

we can neither conclude that a' is the same energy as a and b' the same as b, nor that a' is identical to b, and b' to a. There would be no means of deciding between these two views and others that likewise suggest themselves.

For this reason, the flow of energy can, in my opinion, never have quite the same distinct meaning as a flow of material particles, which, by our imagination at least, we can distinguish from each other and follow in their motion. It might even be questioned whether, in electromagnetic phenomena, the transfer of energy really takes place in the way indicated by Poynting's law, whether, for example, the heat developed in the wire of an incandescent lamp is really due to energy which it receives from the surrounding medium, as the theorem teaches us, and not to a flow of energy along the wire itself. In fact, all depends upon the hypotheses which we make concerning the internal forces in the system, and it may very well be, that a change in these hypotheses would materially alter our ideas about the path along which the energy is carried from one part of the system to another. It must be observed however that there is no longer room for any doubt, so soon as we admit that the phenomena going on in some part of the ether are *entirely* determined by the electric and magnetic force existing in that part. No one will deny that there is a flow of energy in a beam of light; therefore, if all depends on the electric and magnetic force, there must also be one near the surface of a wire carrying a current, because here, as well as in the beam of light, the two forces exist at the same time and are perpendicular to each other.

19. Results hardly less important than the equation of energy, and of the same general character, are obtained when we consider the resultant of all the forces exerted by the ether on the electrons of a system. For this system we can take a ponderable body which is in a peculiar electromagnetic state or in which electromagnetic phenomena are going on. In our theory the ponderomotive force exerted on a charged conductor, a magnet or a wire carrying a current, is made up of all the forces with which the ether acts on the electrons of the body.

Let σ again be a closed surface, and $\mathbf{F}$ the resultant force on all the electrons contained within it. Then, on account of (23), we may write

$$\mathbf{F} = \int \varrho \left\{ \mathbf{d} + \frac{1}{c} [\mathbf{v} \cdot \mathbf{h}] \right\} dS, \tag{43}$$

extending the integral to all the electrons, or as we may do as well (ϱ being 0 in the space between the particles), to the whole space S. Now, by the application of the equations (17)—(20)[1]), this force $\mathbf{F}$ may be shown to be equal to the sum of two vectors

$$\mathbf{F} = \mathbf{F}_1 + \mathbf{F}_2, \tag{44}$$

which are determined by the equations

1) Note 9.

$$\mathsf{F}_{1x} = \tfrac{1}{2}\int \{ 2\mathsf{d}_x\mathsf{d}_n - \mathsf{d}^2 \cos(n, x) \} \, d\sigma$$

$$+ \tfrac{1}{2}\int \{ 2\mathsf{h}_x\mathsf{h}_n - \mathsf{h}^2 \cos(n, x) \} \, d\sigma \text{ etc.} \qquad (45)$$

and

$$\mathsf{F}_2 = -\frac{1}{c^2}\int \dot{\mathsf{s}}\, dS. \qquad (46)$$

The first part of the force is represented by an integral over the surface σ, its components, of which only one is given here, being determined by the values of d_x, d_y, d_z, h_x, etc. at the surface. The second part of the force, on the contrary, presents itself as an integral over the space S, not only over those parts of it where there is an electric charge, but also over those where there is none.

20. In discussing the above result we must distinguish several cases.

a) In all phenomena in which the system is in a stationary state, the force F_2, for which we may write

$$\mathsf{F}_2 = -\frac{1}{c^2}\frac{d}{dt}\int \mathsf{s}\, dS, \qquad (47)$$

disappears, and the whole force F is reduced to an integral over the surface σ. In other terms, the ponderomotive action can be regarded as the sum of certain infinitely small parts, each of which belongs to one of the surface-elements $d\sigma$ and depends on the state existing at that element. A very natural way of interpreting this is to speak of each of these parts as of a *stress* in the ether, acting on the element considered.

The stress depends on the orientation of the element. If this is determined by the normal n, and if, using a common notation, we write X_n, Y_n, Z_n for the components of the force per unit area, exerted by the part of the medium on the positive side of the surface on the part lying on the negative side, we shall have

$$X_n = \tfrac{1}{2}\{ 2\mathsf{d}_x\mathsf{d}_n - \mathsf{d}^2 \cos(n, x) \} + \tfrac{1}{2}\{ 2\mathsf{h}_x\mathsf{h}_n - \mathsf{h}^2 \cos(n, x) \} \text{ etc.} \qquad (48)$$

From these formulae we can easily deduce the components X_x, Y_x, Z_x, X_y etc. of the stresses acting on elements whose normal is parallel to one of the axes of coordinates. We find

$$X_x = \tfrac{1}{2}(\mathsf{d}_x^2 - \mathsf{d}_y^2 - \mathsf{d}_z^2) + \tfrac{1}{2}(\mathsf{h}_x^2 - \mathsf{h}_y^2 - \mathsf{h}_z^2) \text{ etc.,} \qquad (49)$$

$$X_y = Y_x = \mathsf{d}_x\mathsf{d}_y + \mathsf{h}_x\mathsf{h}_y \text{ etc.,} \qquad (50)$$

precisely the values of the stresses by which Maxwell long ago accounted for the ponderomotive forces observed in electric and magnetic fields.

This method of calculating the resultant force is often very convenient, the more so because we can take for σ any surface surrounding the body for which we have to solve the problem.

b) We are led to similar conclusions if we consider a system that is the seat of periodical phenomena, confining ourselves to the mean value of the force taken for a complete period T. The mean value being given by

$$\frac{1}{T}\int_0^T \mathbf{F}\, dt,$$

the last term in (44) disappears. Indeed, by (47) the time integral of $\mathbf{F}_2$ is equal to the difference of the values of

$$-\frac{1}{c^2}\int \mathbf{s}\, dS$$

for $t = 0$ and $t = T$, and these values are equal on account of the periodicity of the changes.

Hence, in this case also, the resultant force is reduced to surface-integrals, or, as we may say, to stresses in the ether.

It can easily be shown that the mean value of $\mathbf{F}$ (and of periodically changing quantities in general) during a lapse of time that is very much longer than a period T, is equal to the mean value during a period, even though the interval considered is not exactly a multiple of T.

21. An interesting example is furnished by the pressure of radiation. Let (Fig. 1) AB be a plane disk, receiving in a normal direction a beam of light L, which, taking OX in the direction shown in the diagram, we can represent by our formulae (7). Let us take for σ the surface of the flat cylindrical box $CDEF$, whose plane sides lie before and behind the disk and are parallel to it. Then, if the plate is perfectly opaque, we have only to consider the stress on CD. Moreover, if the disk is supposed to be perfectly black, so that there is no reflected beam, there is only the electromagnetic field represented by the equations (7). Hence, since a normal to the plane CD, drawn towards the outside of the box $CDEF$, has a direction opposite to that of OX, the force acting on the absorbing body in the direction of OX per unit area is given by

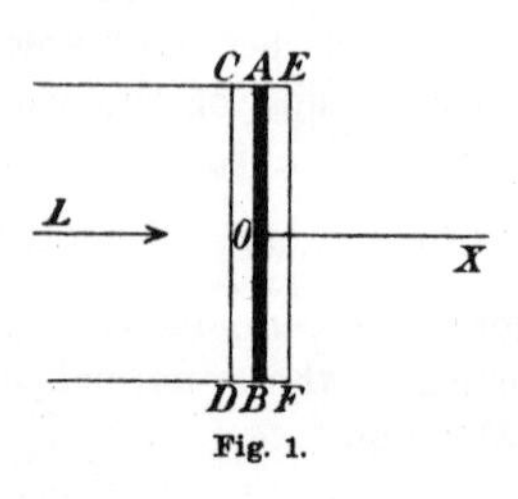

Fig. 1.

$$-X_x = \tfrac{1}{2}(\mathfrak{d}_y^2 + \mathfrak{h}_z^2),$$

and its mean value by

$$\tfrac{1}{2}a^2.$$

Comparing this with the value of the energy and attending to the direction of the force, we conclude that the beam of light produces a normal pressure on the absorbing body, the intensity of the pressure per unit of surface being numerically equal to the electromagnetic energy which the beam contains per unit of volume.

The same method can be applied to a body which transmits and reflects a certain amount of light, and to a disk on which a beam of light falls in an oblique direction. In all cases in which there is no light behind the disk, the force in the direction of the normal will be a pressure $-X_x$ on the illuminated side, if the axis of x is directed as stated above.

We shall apply this to a homogeneous and isotropic state of radiation, existing in a certain space that is enclosed by perfectly reflecting walls. By homogeneous and isotropic we mean that the space is traversed by rays of light or heat of various directions, in such a manner that the radiation is of equal intensity in different parts of the space and in all directions, and that all directions of $\mathfrak{d}$ and $\mathfrak{h}$ are equally represented in it. It can easily be shown that in this case there is no tangential stress on an element $d\sigma$ of the wall. As to the normal pressure, which is represented by $-X_x$, if the axis of x is made to coincide with the normal, we may write for it

$$p = \tfrac{1}{2}(\overline{\mathfrak{d}_y^2} + \overline{\mathfrak{d}_z^2} - \overline{\mathfrak{d}_x^2}) + \tfrac{1}{2}(\overline{\mathfrak{h}_y^2} + \overline{\mathfrak{h}_z^2} - \overline{\mathfrak{h}_x^2}),$$

where the horizontal bars are intended to indicate the mean values, over the space considered, of the several terms.[1]) But, on account of our assumptions regarding the state of radiation,

$$\overline{\mathfrak{d}_x^2} = \overline{\mathfrak{d}_y^2} = \overline{\mathfrak{d}_z^2}.$$

Each of these quantities is therefore equal to one third of their sum, i. e. to $\tfrac{1}{3}\overline{\mathfrak{d}^2}$. Similarly

$$\overline{\mathfrak{h}_x^2} = \overline{\mathfrak{h}_y^2} = \overline{\mathfrak{h}_z^2} = \tfrac{1}{3}\overline{\mathfrak{h}^2}.$$

Hence, if the formulae (40) and (41) are taken into account,

$$p = \tfrac{1}{6}(\overline{\mathfrak{d}^2} + \overline{\mathfrak{h}^2}) = \tfrac{1}{3}(w_e + w_m).$$

In this case, the pressure on the walls per unit of surface is equal to one third of the electromagnetic energy per unit of volume.

Later on, the problem of radiation pressure will be treated by a different method.

---

1) Note **10**

22. Thus far we have simplified the equation (44) by supposing the last term to vanish. In general, however, this term may not be omitted, and the force $\mathbf{F}$ cannot be accounted for by a system of stresses acting on the surface σ.

This conclusion takes a remarkable form, if the surface σ is supposed to enclose no electrons at all. Of course, the total force $\mathbf{F}$ must be 0 in this case, as may be seen from the original expression (43). Nevertheless, the force due to the stresses is not generally 0, having the value

$$\mathbf{F}_1 = -\mathbf{F}_2 = \frac{1}{c^2}\int \dot{\mathbf{s}}\, dS. \qquad (51)$$

It is worthy of notice that this last equation is quite independent of the theory of electrons, being a consequence of the fundamental equations for the case $\varrho = 0$, i. e. of the equations for the free ether. It has indeed been known for a long time.[1])

In the mind of Maxwell and of many writers on the theory there seems to have been no doubt whatever as to the real existence of the ether stresses determined by the formulae (49) and (50). Considered from this point of view, the equation (51) tells us that in general the resultant force $\mathbf{F}_1$ of all the stresses acting on a part of the ether will not be 0. This was first pointed out by Helmholtz.[2]) He inferred from it that the ether cannot remain at rest, and established a system of equations by which its motion can be determined. I shall not enter upon these, because no experiment has ever shown us any trace of a motion of the ether in an electromagnetic field.

We may sum up by saying that a theory which admits the existence of Maxwell's stresses leads to the following conclusions:

1. A portion of the ether is not in equilibrium under the stresses acting on its surface.

2. The stresses acting on the elements of a surface which surrounds a ponderable body will, in general, produce a resultant force different from the force acting on the electrons of the body according to our theory.

23. Having got thus far, we may take two different courses. In the first place, bearing in mind that the ether is undoubtedly widely different from all ordinary matter, we may make the assumption that this medium, which is the receptacle of electromagnetic energy and the vehicle for many and perhaps for all the forces acting on ponderable matter, is, by its very nature, never put in motion,

---

1) Note **11**.

2) Helmholtz, Folgerungen aus Maxwell's Theorie über die Bewegungen des reinen Äthers, Ann. Phys. Chem. **53** (1894), p. 135.

that it has neither velocity nor acceleration, so that we have no reason to speak of its mass or of forces that are applied to it. From this point of view, the action on an electron must be considered as primarily determined by the state of the ether in the interior of each of its elements of volume, and the equation (43) as the direct and immediate expression for it. There is no reason at all why the force should be due to pressures or stresses in the universal medium. If we exclude the idea of forces acting *on* the ether, we cannot even speak of these stresses, because they would be forces exerted by one part of the ether on the other.

I should add that, while thus denying the real existence of ether stresses, we can still avail ourselves of all the mathematical transformations by which the application of the formula (43) may be made easier. We need not refrain from reducing the force to a surface-integral, and for convenience's sake we may continue to apply to the quantities occurring in this integral the name of stresses. Only, we must be aware that they are only imaginary ones, nothing else than auxiliary mathematical quantities.

Perhaps all this that has now been said about the absolute immobility of the ether and the non-existence of the stresses, may seem somewhat startling. If it is thought too much so, one may have recourse to the other conception to which I have alluded. In choosing this, we recognize the real existence of Maxwell's internal forces, and we regard the ether as only *approximately* immovable.

Let us admit that between adjacent parts of the ether there is an action determined by the equations (48), so that an element of volume of the free ether experiences a force

$$\frac{1}{c^2}\dot{\mathbf{s}}\, dS,$$

and let us suppose the medium to move in such a way that it has a momentum

$$\frac{1}{c^2}\mathbf{s}\, dS, \tag{52}$$

or $\frac{1}{c^2}\mathbf{s}$ per unit of volume. Let us further imagine that the density of the ether is so great that only a very small velocity, too small to be detected by any means at our disposal, is required for the momentum (52). Then, the formula (51) which, applied to an element of the ether, takes the form

$$\mathbf{F}_1 = \frac{1}{c^2}\dot{\mathbf{s}}\, dS$$

tells us that the assumed state of motion can really exist. This is clear because for very small velocities the resultant force acting on the ether contained in a *fixed* element of volume may be said to be equal to the rate of change of the momentum that is found *within* that element.[1])

On the other hand, in the case of an element dS occupied by a charge, the formula

$$\mathbf{F} = \mathbf{F}_1 - \frac{1}{c^2}\dot{\mathbf{s}}\,dS$$

may be interpreted as follows. The ether within the element is subject to a force $\mathbf{F}_1$, due to the stresses on the surface. Of this force, the part

$$\frac{1}{c^2}\dot{\mathbf{s}}\,dS$$

goes to produce the change of momentum of the ether, the remaining part $\mathbf{F}$ being transferred to the charge.

You will readily pêrceive that, after all, the difference between the two modes of view consists mainly in the different interpretations given to the same equations.

24. Whatever may be our opinion about the questions we have now touched upon, our discussion shows the importance of the vector

$$\frac{1}{c^2}\mathbf{s}\,dS,$$

which has a definite direction and magnitude for every element of volume, and of the vector

$$\mathbf{G} = \frac{1}{c^2}\int \mathbf{s}\,dS \tag{53}$$

that may be derived from it by integration. Abraham[2]) of Göttingen has applied to these quantities the name of *electromagnetic momentum*. We may term them so, even if we do not wish to convey the idea that they represent a real momentum, as they would according to the second of the two lines of thought we have just followed.

The way in which the conception of electromagnetic momentum may be of use for the elucidation of electromagnetic phenomena comes out most clearly if, in dealing with a system of finite dimensions, as the systems in our experiments actually are, we make the enclosing surface σ recede on all sides to an infinite distance. It may be shown that the surface-integrals in (45) then become 0, so that, if the integration is extended to all space, we shall have

$$\mathbf{F} = -\frac{d\mathbf{G}}{dt}, \tag{54}$$

1) Note **12**.

2) M. Abraham, Prinzipien der Dynamik des Elektrons, Ann. Phys. **10** (1903), p. 105.

or in words: the force exerted by the ether on a system of electrons, or, as we may say, on the ponderable matter containing these electrons, is equal and opposite to the change per unit of time of the electromagnetic momentum. Now, since the action tends to produce a change equal to the force itself in the momentum (in the ordinary sense of the word) of the ponderable matter, we see that the sum of this momentum and the electromagnetic one will not be altered by the actions exerted by the ether.

Before passing on to one or two applications, I must call your attention to the intimate connexion between the momentum and the flow of energy $\mathbf{s}$. The equation (53) at once shows us that every part of space in which there is a flow of energy contributes its part to the vector $\mathbf{G}$; hence, in order to form an idea of this vector and of its changes, we have in the first place to fix our attention on the radiation existing in different parts of space. If, in course of time, the flow of energy reaches new parts of space or leaves parts in which it was at first found, this will cause the vector $\mathbf{G}$ to change from one moment to another.

It must also be kept in mind that (53) is a vector equation and that (54) may be decomposed into three formulae giving us the components $\mathbf{F}_x$, $\mathbf{F}_y$, $\mathbf{F}_z$ of the resultant force.

25. Very interesting illustrations of the preceding theory may be taken from the phenomena of radiation pressure, to which I shall therefore return for a moment. Let us consider, for example, a source of light sending out its rays in a single direction, which may be brought about by suitable arrangements, and let us suppose this radiation to have begun at a certain instant, so that we can speak of the *first* wave or of the *front* of the train of waves that have been emitted. This front is a plane at right angles to the beam and advancing with the velocity c. Hence, if Σ is the normal section of the beam, the volume occupied by the radiation increases by $c\Sigma$ per unit of time. As we have seen, the flow of energy has the direction of the beam. In making the following calculation, we shall reason as if, at every point, the flow were constantly equal to the mean flow $\overline{\mathbf{s}}$ taken for a full period. If the magnitude of this mean flow, which relates to unit of area, is $|\overline{\mathbf{s}}|$, we shall find that of the electromagnetic momentum, whose direction is likewise that of the beam, if we multiply $\frac{1}{c^2}|\overline{\mathbf{s}}|$ by the volume occupied by the light. It appears from this that the change of $\mathbf{G}$ per unit of time is

$$|\dot{\mathbf{G}}| = \frac{1}{c}|\overline{\mathbf{s}}|\,\Sigma;$$

consequently, since this vector has the direction of the rays, there will be a force on the source of light of the same intensity and in a direction opposite to that in which the rays are emitted. This force of recoil, which, however, is extremely small, may be compared with the reaction that would exist if the rays of light consisted of a stream of material particles. By similar reasoning we can determine the pressure on the black disk we have formerly considered. But, in this case, it is best to imagine the radiation of the source to have been *stopped* at a certain moment, so that there is a plane which we may call the *rear* of the progression of waves. It approaches the black disk with the velocity c, and if Σ and $|\bar{\mathbf{s}}|$ have the same meaning as just now, the magnitude of the electromagnetic momentum will diminish by

$$\frac{1}{c}|\bar{\mathbf{s}}|\Sigma$$

per unit of time. Consequently, there will be a normal pressure of this intensity acting on the disk. The result agrees with what we have deduced from the value of the stress in the ether, the quantity $|\bar{\mathbf{s}}|$ being related to the amplitude a by the equation

$$|\bar{\mathbf{s}}| = \tfrac{1}{2} c a^2.$$

It is easy to extend these results to a more general case. Let a plane disk receive, from any direction we like, a beam of parallel rays, and let one part of these be reflected, another absorbed and the remaining part transmitted. Let the vectors $\mathbf{s}$, $\mathbf{s}'$ and $\mathbf{s}''$ be the flows of energy per unit of area in the incident, reflected and transmitted beams, $\bar{\mathbf{s}}$, $\bar{\mathbf{s}}'$, $\bar{\mathbf{s}}''$ the mean flows taken for a full period, Σ, Σ', Σ'' the normal sections of the beams. Then, if we imagine the space occupied by the light to be limited by two fronts, one in the reflected and one in the transmitted beam, and by a rear plane in the incident one, all these planes travelling onward with the velocity c, the change of electromagnetic momentum will be given by the vector expression

$$\frac{1}{c}(\Sigma'\bar{\mathbf{s}}' + \Sigma''\bar{\mathbf{s}}'' - \Sigma\bar{\mathbf{s}}),$$

and the force on the plate by

$$\frac{1}{c}(\Sigma\bar{\mathbf{s}} - \Sigma'\bar{\mathbf{s}}' - \Sigma''\bar{\mathbf{s}}'').$$

It must here be mentioned that the radiation pressure has been observed by Lebedew[1]) and by E. F. Nichols and Hull[2]), and that the theoretical predictions as to its intensity have been verified to within one percent by the measurements of the last named physicists.

1) P. Lebedew, Untersuchungen über die Druckkräfte des Lichtes, Ann. Phys. **6** (1901), p. 433.

2) E. F. Nichols and G. F. Hull, The pressure due to radiation, Astrophysical Journ. **17** (1903), p. 315; also Ann. Phys. **12** (1903), p. 225.

26. The theory of electromagnetic momentum, which we have found of so much use in the case of beams of light that are emitted, reflected or absorbed by a body, is also applicable to the widely different case of a moving electron. We may therefore, without too abrupt a transition, turn once more to some questions belonging to what we can call the dynamics of an electron, and in which we are concerned with the field the particle produces and the force exerted on it by the ether. We shall in this way be led to the important subject of the *electromagnetic mass* of the electrons.

To begin with, I shall say some words about the field of a system of electrons or of charges distributed in any way, having a constant velocity of translation w, say in the direction of the axis of x, smaller than the speed of light c. We shall introduce axes of coordinates moving with the system, and we shall simplify our formulae by putting

$$\frac{w}{c} = \beta. \tag{55}$$

Now, we have already seen that the field is carried along by the system. The same may be said of the potentials φ and $\mathbf{a}$, which serve to determine it, and it may easily be inferred from this[1]) that the values of $\frac{\partial \varphi}{\partial t}$ and $\frac{\partial \mathbf{a}}{\partial t}$ in a fixed point of space are given by

$$-w\frac{\partial \varphi}{\partial x}, \quad -w\frac{\partial \mathbf{a}}{\partial x}.$$

Similarly

$$\frac{\partial^2 \varphi}{\partial t^2} = w^2\frac{\partial^2 \varphi}{\partial x^2}, \quad \frac{\partial^2 \mathbf{a}}{\partial t^2} = w^2\frac{\partial^2 \mathbf{a}}{\partial x^2}.$$

Thus the equation (31) takes the form

$$(1-\beta^2)\frac{\partial^2 \varphi}{\partial x^2} + \frac{\partial^2 \varphi}{\partial y^2} + \frac{\partial^2 \varphi}{\partial z^2} = -\varrho, \tag{56}$$

whereas (32) may be replaced by the formula

$$(1-\beta^2)\frac{\partial^2 \mathbf{a}_x}{\partial x^2} + \frac{\partial^2 \mathbf{a}_x}{\partial y^2} + \frac{\partial^2 \mathbf{a}_x}{\partial z^2} = -\beta\varrho, \tag{57}$$

the components $\mathbf{a}_y$ and $\mathbf{a}_z$ being both 0, as is seen directly from (36).

Comparing (56) and (57), we conclude that

$$\mathbf{a}_x = \beta\varphi,$$

so that we have only to determine the scalar potential.

This can be effected by a suitable change of independent variables. If a new variable x' is defined by

$$x' = (1-\beta^2)^{-1/2}x, \tag{58}$$

1) Note **13**.

(56) becomes

$$\frac{\partial^2 \varphi}{\partial x'^2} + \frac{\partial^2 \varphi}{\partial y^2} + \frac{\partial^2 \varphi}{\partial z^2} = -\varrho, \tag{59}$$

having the well known form of Poisson's equation. Since this equation occurs in the determination of the field for charges that are at rest, the problem is hereby reduced to an ordinary problem of electrostatics. Only, the value of φ in our moving system S is connected with the potential, not of the same system when at rest, but of a system in which all the coordinates parallel to OX have been changed in the ratio determined by (58).[1]

The result may be expressed as follows. Let S' be a system having no translation, and which we obtain by enlarging the dimensions of S in the direction of OX in the ratio of 1 to $(1-\beta^2)^{-1/2}$. Then, if a point with the coordinates x, y, z in S and a point with the coordinates x', y, z in S' are said to correspond to each other, if the charges of corresponding elements of volume are supposed to be equal, and if φ' is the potential in S', the scalar potential in the moving system is given by

$$\varphi = (1-\beta^2)^{-1/2}\varphi'. \tag{60}$$

Let us now take for the moving system a single electron, to which we shall ascribe the form of a sphere with radius R and a uniformly distributed surface-charge e. The corresponding system S' is an elongated ellipsoid of revolution, and its charge happens to be distributed according to the law that holds for a conductor of the same form. Therefore, the field of the moving spherical particle and all the quantities belonging to it, can be found by means of the ordinary theory of a charged ellipsoid that is given in many treatises. I shall only mention the results obtained for the more important quantities.

The total electric energy is given by

$$U = \frac{e^2}{32\pi R}\left[\frac{3-\beta^2}{\beta}\log\frac{1+\beta}{1-\beta} - 2\right], \tag{61}$$

and the magnetic energy by

$$T = \frac{e^2}{32\pi R}\left[\frac{1+\beta^2}{\beta}\log\frac{1+\beta}{1-\beta} - 2\right]. \tag{62}$$

As to the electromagnetic momentum, this has the direction of the translation, as may at once be deduced from (53), because we know already that the general direction of the flow of energy coincides with that of the motion of the particle. The formula for the magnitude of the electromagnetic momentum, calculated for the first time by Abraham, is

$$|\mathbf{G}| = \frac{e^2}{16\pi Rc}\left[\frac{1+\beta^2}{\beta^2}\log\frac{1+\beta}{1-\beta} - \frac{2}{\beta}\right]. \tag{63}$$

1) Note **14**.

All these values U, T, $|\mathbf{G}|$ increase when the velocity is augmented. They become infinite for $\beta = 1$, i. e. when the electron reaches a velocity equal to that of light.[1])

27. According to our fundamental assumptions, each element of volume of an electron experiences a force due to the field produced by the particle itself, and the question now arises whether there will be any resultant force acting on the electron as a whole. The consideration of the electromagnetic momentum will enable us to decide this question.

If the velocity w is constant in magnitude and direction, as it has been supposed to be in what precedes, the vector $\mathbf{G}$ will likewise be constant and there will be no resultant force. This is very important; it shows that, if free from all external forces, an electron, just like a material point, will move with constant velocity, notwithstanding the presence of the surrounding ether. In all other cases however there is an action of the medium.

It must be observed that, in the case of a variable velocity, the above formulae for U, T and $|\mathbf{G}|$ do not, strictly speaking, hold. However, if the variation of the state of motion is so slow that the change taking place in a time $\frac{R}{c}$ may be neglected, one may apply the formula (63) for every moment, and use it to determine the change $\mathbf{G}$ of the momentum per unit of time.[2]) As the result depends on the acceleration of the electron, the force exerted by the ether is likewise determined by the acceleration.

Let us first take the case of a rectilinear translation with variable velocity w. The vector $\dot{\mathbf{G}}$ is directed along the line of motion, and its magnitude is given by

$$\frac{d\,|\mathbf{G}|}{dt} = \frac{d\,|\mathbf{G}|}{dw}\,\dot{w} = \frac{1}{c}\,\frac{d\,|\mathbf{G}|}{d\beta}\,\dot{w}.$$

Putting

$$\frac{d\,|\mathbf{G}|}{dw} = \frac{1}{c}\,\frac{d\,|\mathbf{G}|}{d\beta} = m', \tag{64}$$

we conclude that there is a force acting on the electron, opposite to its acceleration and equal to the product of the latter and the coefficient m'.

In the second place, I shall consider an electron having a velocity $\mathbf{w}$ of constant magnitude, but of varying direction. The acceleration is then normal to the path and it is convenient to use vector equations. Let $\mathbf{w}$ be the velocity, $\mathbf{w}$ the acceleration, and

1) Note **15**. 2) See § **37**.

let us take into account that in this case there is a constant ratio between $|\mathbf{G}|$ and $|\mathbf{w}|$, for which I shall write

$$\frac{|\mathbf{G}|}{|\mathbf{w}|} = \frac{|\mathbf{G}|}{c\beta} = m''. \tag{65}$$

We have also

$$\mathbf{G} = m''\mathbf{w},$$

and the force exerted by the ether is given by

$$-\dot{\mathbf{G}} = -m''\dot{\mathbf{w}}.$$

It is opposite in direction to the normal acceleration $\dot{\mathbf{w}}$ and has an intensity equal to the product of this acceleration with the coefficient m''.

In the most general case the acceleration $\mathbf{j}$ will be directed neither along the path nor normally to it. If we decompose it into two components, the one $\mathbf{j}'$ in the line of motion and the other $\mathbf{j}''$ at right angles to it, we shall have, for the force on the electron due to its own electromagnetic field, in vector notation[1])

$$-m'\mathbf{j}' - m''\mathbf{j}''. \tag{66}$$

28. The way in which these formulae are usually interpreted will become clear to us, if we suppose the electron to have a certain mass m_0 in the ordinary sense of the word, and to be acted on, not only by the force that is due to its own field, but also by a force $\mathbf{K}$ of any other kind. The total force being

$$\mathbf{K} - m'\mathbf{j}' - m''\mathbf{j}'',$$

the equation of motion, expressed in the language of vector analysis, will be

$$\mathbf{K} - m'\mathbf{j}' - m''\mathbf{j}'' = m_0(\mathbf{j}' + \mathbf{j}''). \tag{67}$$

Instead of this we can write

$$\mathbf{K} = (m_0 + m')\mathbf{j}' + (m_0 + m'')\mathbf{j}'',$$

from which it appears that the electron moves, as if it had *two* different masses $m_0 + m'$ and $m_0 + m''$, the first of which comes into play when we are concerned with an acceleration in the line of motion, and the second when we consider the normal acceleration. By measuring the force $\mathbf{K}$ and the accelerations $\mathbf{j}'$ and $\mathbf{j}''$ in different cases, we can determine both these coefficients. We shall call them the *effective* masses, m_0 the *material* mass, and m', m'' the *electromagnetic* masses. In order to distinguish m' and m'', we can apply the name of *longitudinal* electromagnetic mass to the first, and

1) Note **16**.

that of *transverse* electromagnetic mass to the second of these coefficients.[1])

From what has been said one finds the following formulae for m' and m'':

$$m' = \frac{e^2}{8\pi R\beta^3 c^2}\left[\frac{2\beta}{1-\beta^2} - \log\frac{1+\beta}{1-\beta}\right], \tag{68}$$

$$m'' = \frac{e^2}{16\pi R\beta^3 c^2}\left[-2\beta + (1+\beta^2)\log\frac{1+\beta}{1-\beta}\right], \tag{69}$$

or, expanded in series,

$$m' = \frac{e^2}{4\pi Rc^2}\left(\frac{2}{3} + \frac{4}{5}\beta^2 + \frac{6}{7}\beta^4 + \cdots\right), \tag{70}$$

$$m'' = \frac{e^2}{8\pi Rc^2}\left[\left(1+\frac{1}{3}\right) + \left(\frac{1}{3}+\frac{1}{5}\right)\beta^2 + \left(\frac{1}{5}+\frac{1}{7}\right)\beta^4 + \cdots\right]. \tag{71}$$

For small velocities the two masses have the same value

$$m' = m'' = \frac{e^2}{6\pi Rc^2}, \tag{72}$$

whereas for larger velocities the longitudinal mass always surpasses the transverse one. Both increase with β, until for $\beta = 1$, i. e. for a velocity equal to the speed of light, they become infinite.

If, for a moment, we confine ourselves to a rectilinear motion of an electron, the notion of electromagnetic mass can be derived from that of electromagnetic energy. Indeed, this latter is larger for a moving electron than for one that is at rest. Therefore, if we are to put the particle in motion by an external force **K**, we must not only produce the ordinary kinetic energy $\frac{1}{2}m_0 w^2$ but, in addition to this, the part of the electromagnetic energy that is due to the velocity. The effect of the field will therefore be that a larger amount of work is required than if we had to do with an ordinary material particle m_0; it will be just the same as if the mass were larger than m_0.

By reasoning of this kind we can also easily verify the formula (68). If the velocity is changing very slowly, we may at every instant apply the formulae (61) and (62). Since the total energy $T + U$ is a function of the velocity w, its rate of change is given by

$$\frac{d(T+U)}{dw}\dot{w} = \frac{d(T+U)}{d\beta}\frac{1}{c}\dot{w}. \tag{73}$$

This must be equal to the work done per unit of time by the moving force, or rather by the part of it that is required on account of the

---

1) The notion of (longitudinal) electromagnetic mass was introduced for the first time by J. J. Thomson in his paper „On the electric and magnetic effects produced by the motion of electrified bodies", Phil. Mag. (5) **11** (1881), p. 227. The result of his calculation is, however, somewhat different from that to which one is led in the modern theory of electrons.

electromagnetic field. Consequently, dividing (73) by w, we find the intensity of this part, and if next we divide by $\dot{w}$, the acceleration, the result must be the longitudinal electromagnetic mass. If one calculates

$$m' = \frac{1}{cw}\frac{d(T+U)}{d\beta} = \frac{1}{\beta c^2}\frac{d(T+U)}{d\beta}$$

by means of the formulae (61) and (62), one really finds exactly the value (68).

29. A close analogy to this question of electromagnetic mass is furnished by a simple hydrodynamical problem. A solid, perfectly smooth sphere, moving with the velocity $\mathbf{w}$ in an incompressible perfect fluid which extends on all sides to infinite distance, produces in this fluid a state of motion characterized by a kinetic energy for which we may write

$$T = \tfrac{1}{2}\alpha \mathbf{w}^2,$$

if α is a constant, depending on the radius of the ball and on the density of the fluid. Under the influence of an external force applied to the ball in the direction of the translation, its velocity will change as if it had, not only its true mass m_0, but besides this an apparent mass m', whose value is given by

$$m' = \frac{1}{|\mathbf{w}|}\frac{dT}{d|\mathbf{w}|} = \alpha,$$

a formula corresponding to the last equation of § 28.

We could have obtained the same result if we had first calculated the momentum of the fluid. We should have found for it

$$\mathbf{G} = \alpha \mathbf{w},$$

an expression from which we can also infer that the transverse apparent mass has the same value α as the longitudinal one.

This is shown by the equation

$$m'' = \frac{|\mathbf{G}|}{|\mathbf{w}|}.$$

30. If, in the case of the ball moving in the perfect fluid, we were obliged to confine ourselves to experiments in which we measure the external forces applied to the body and the accelerations produced by them, we should be able to determine the effective mass $m_0 + m'$ (or $m_0 + m''$), but it would be impossible to find the values of m_0 and m' (or m'') separately. Now, it is very important that, in the experimental investigation of the motion of an electron, we can go a step farther. This is due to the fact that the electromagnetic mass is not a constant, but increases with the velocity.

Suppose we can make experiments for two different known velocities of an electron, and that by this means we can find the ratio k between the effective transverse masses which come into play in the two cases. Let $\varkappa$ be the ratio between the electromagnetic transverse masses, calculated, as can really be done, by the formula (69). Then, distinguishing by the indices I and II the quantities relating to the two cases, we shall have the formulae

$$\frac{m_0 + m''_I}{m_0 + m''_{II}} = k, \quad \frac{m''_I}{m''_{II}} = \varkappa,$$

and the ratio between the true mass m_0 and the electromagnetic mass m''_I will be given by

$$\frac{m''_I}{m_0} = \frac{\varkappa(k-1)}{\varkappa - k}.$$

If the experimental ratio k differed very little from the ratio $\varkappa$ that is given by the formula (69), m_0 would come out much smaller than m''_I and we should even have to put $m_0 = 0$, if k were *exactly* equal to $\varkappa$.

I have spoken here of the transverse electromagnetic mass, because this is the one with which we are concerned in the experiments I shall now have to mention.

31. You all know that the cathode rays and the β-rays of radio-active bodies are streams of negative electrons, and that Goldstein's canal rays and the α-rays consist of similar streams of positively charged particles. In all these cases it has been found possible to determine the ratio between the numerical values of the charge of a particle and its transverse effective mass. The chief method by which this has been achieved is based on the measurement, for the same kind of rays, of the deflections from their rectilinear course that are produced by known external electric and magnetic forces.

The theory of the method is very simple. If, in the first place, an electron having a charge e and an effective mass m, moves in an electric field $\mathbf{d}$, with a velocity w perpendicular to the lines of force, the acceleration is given by $\frac{e\mathbf{d}}{m}$; hence, if r is the radius of curvature of the path,

$$\frac{w^2}{r} = \frac{e|\mathbf{d}|}{m},$$

so that, if $|\mathbf{d}|$ and r have been measured, we can calculate the value of

$$\frac{e}{m w^2}. \qquad (74)$$

Let us consider in the second place an electron moving in a magnetic field $\mathbf{h}$, and let us suppose the velocity w to be perpendicular to the magnetic force. Then, the field will exert on the particle a force $\frac{e w |\mathbf{h}|}{c}$, as is seen from the last term of (23). This force being perpendicular to the velocity, we shall have, writing r' for the radius of curvature of the path,

$$\frac{w^2}{r'} = \frac{e w |\mathbf{h}|}{cm}.$$

The determination of $|\mathbf{h}|$ and r' can therefore lead to a knowledge of the expression

$$\frac{e}{mw},$$

and, by combining this with (74), we shall be enabled to find both w and $\frac{e}{m}$.

32. I shall not speak of the large number of determinations of this kind that have been made by several physicists, and will only say a few words relative to the important work of Kaufmann[1]) on the β-rays of radium. These rays appear to contain negative electrons with widely different velocities, so that it is possible to examine the question whether $\frac{e}{m}$ is a function of the velocity or a constant. Kaufmann's experiments were arranged in such a manner that the electric and the magnetic deflection, belonging to the same electrons, could be measured, so that the values both of w and of $\frac{e}{m}$ could be deduced from them. Now, it was found that, while the velocity w ranges from about 0,5 to more than 0,9 of the velocity of light, the value of $\frac{e}{m}$ diminishes considerably. If we suppose the charge to be equal for all the negative electrons constituting the rays, this diminution of $\frac{e}{m}$ must be due to an increase of the mass m. This proves that at all events the electromagnetic mass has an appreciable influence. It must even greatly predominate. Indeed, Kaufmann's numbers show no trace of an influence of the material mass m_0, his ratio k of effective masses for two different velocities (a ratio which is the inverse of that of the values of $\frac{e}{m}$) agreeing within the limits of experimental errors with the ratio $\varkappa$ between the electromagnetic masses, as deduced from Abraham's formula (69).

1) W. Kaufmann, Über die Konstitution des Elektrons, Ann. Phys. **19** (1906), p. 487.

Of course, we are free to believe, if we like, that there is some small material mass attached to the electron, say equal to one hundredth part of the electromagnetic one, but with a view to simplicity, it will be best to admit Kaufmann's conclusion, or hypothesis, if we prefer so to call it, that the negative electrons have no material mass at all.

This is certainly one of the most important results of modern physics, and I may therefore be allowed to dwell upon it for a short time and to mention two other ways in which it can be expressed. We may say that, in the case of a moving negative electron, there is no energy of the ordinary form $\frac{1}{2} m_0 w^2$, but merely the electromagnetic energy $T + U$, which may be calculated by means of the formulae (61) and (62). For high velocities this energy is a rather complicated function of the velocity, and it is only for velocities very small compared with that of light, that the part of it which depends on the motion, can be represented by the expression $\frac{1}{2} m' w^2$, where m' has the value given by (72). This is found by expanding $T + U$ in a series similar to (70) and (71).

We obtain another remarkable form of our result, if in the equation of motion (67), which for $m_0 = 0$ becomes

$$\mathbf{K} - m'\mathbf{j}' - m''\mathbf{j}'' = 0,$$

we attach to the two last terms their original meaning of forces exerted by the ether. The equation tells us that the *total* force acting on the particle is always 0. An electron, for example, which has an initial velocity in an external electromagnetic field, will move in such a manner that the force due to the external field is exactly counterbalanced by the force that is called forth by the electron's own field, or, what amounts to the same thing, that the force exerted by the resulting field is 0.

After all, by our negation of the existence of material mass, the negative electron has lost much of its substantiality. We must make it preserve just so much of it, that we can speak of forces acting on its parts, and that we can consider it as maintaining its form and magnitude. This must be regarded as an inherent property, in virtue of which the parts of the electron cannot be torn asunder by the electric forces acting on them (or by their mutual repulsions, as we may say).

33. In our preceding reasoning we have admitted the equality of the charges of all the negative electrons given off by the radium salt that has been used in Kaufmann's experiments. We shall now pass on to a wide generalization of this hypothesis.

As is well known, Faraday's law of electrolysis proves that all monovalent electrolytic ions have exactly equal charges, and that, if this is denoted by e, the charges of bivalent, trivalent ions etc. are $2e$, $3e$ etc. Thus the conception has arisen that this e, say the charge of an ion of hydrogen, is the smallest quantity of electricity that ever occurs in physical phenomena, an atom of electricity, as we may call it, which can only present itself in whole numbers. Experimental determinations by J. J. Thomson[1]) of the charges carried by the ions in conducting gases, and certain speculations about the electrons which are vibrating in a body traversed by a beam of light, have made it highly probable that this same amount of charge e occurs in these cases, that it is, so to say, a real natural unit of electricity, and that all charged particles, all electrons and ions carry one such unit or a multiple of it. The negative electrons which constitute the β-rays and the cathode rays are undoubtedly the simplest of all these charged particles, and there are good reasons for supposing their charge to be equal to one unit of electricity, i. e. to the charge of an ion of hydrogen.[2])

Leaving aside the case of multiple charges, and ascribing to all electrons or ions, whether they be positive or negative, the same amount of electricity, we can say that the masses m of different particles are inversely proportional to the values that have been found for $\frac{e}{m}$.

Now, for the negative electrons of the cathode rays and of the β-rays, this latter value is, for small velocities nearly[3])

$$1.77 \,.\, 10^7 c\sqrt{4\pi}.$$

For an ion of hydrogen, the corresponding number can be drawn from the electrochemical equivalent of the gas. It is found to be

$$9650 \cdot c\sqrt{4\pi},$$

nearly 1800 times smaller than the number for the free negative electrons. Hence, the mass of a negative electron is about the 1800th part of that of an atom of hydrogen.

---

1) See J. J. Thomson, Conduction of electricity through gases, and The corpuscular theory of matter, London, 1907, by the same author.

2) Note **16***.

3) I write it in this form in order to show that the number is $1,77 \cdot 10^7$, if the ordinary electromagnetic units are used. It may be mentioned here that Simon's measurements on cathode rays [Ann. Phys. Chem. **69** (1899), p. 589] lead to the value $1,878 \cdot 10^7$, and that Kaufmann, calculating his results by means of Abraham's formulae, finds $1,823 \cdot 10^7$. Later experiments on β-rays by Bestelmeyer [Ann. Phys. **22** (1907), p. 429], however, have given the number $1,72 \cdot 10^7$. The number given in the text is taken from Bucherer, who found 1,763 [Ann. Phys. **28** (1909), p. 513] and Wolz, whose result was 1,767 [Ann. Phys. **30** (1909), p. 273].

It must be noticed especially that the values of $\frac{e}{m}$ obtained for different negative electrons are approximately equal. This lends a strong support to the view that all negative electrons are equal to each other. On the contrary, there are great differences between the positive electrons, such as we find in the canal rays and the α-rays of radio-active substances. The values of $\frac{e}{m}$ belonging to these rays are widely divergent. They are however all of the same order of magnitude as the values holding for electrolytic ions. Consequently, the masses of the positive electrons must be comparable with those of chemical atoms. We can therefore imagine the free electrons to be the product of a disintegration of atoms, of a division into a positively and a negatively charged particle, the first having nearly the whole mass of the atom, and the second only a very small part of it.

34. Of late the question has been much discussed, as to whether the idea that there is no material but only electromagnetic mass, which, in the case of negative electrons, is so strongly supported by Kaufmann's results, may not be extended to positive electrons and to matter in general. On this subject of an electromagnetic theory of matter we might observe that, if we suppose atoms to contain negative electrons, of which one or more may be given off under certain circumstances, as they undoubtedly are, and if the part that remains after the loss of a negative particle is called a positive electron, then certainly all matter may be said to be made up of electrons. But this would be mere words. What we really want to know is, whether the mass of the positive electron can be calculated from the distribution of its charge in the same way as we can determine the mass of a negative particle. This remains, I believe, an open question, about which we shall do well to speak with some reserve.

In a more general sense, I for one should be quite willing to adopt an electromagnetic theory of matter and of the forces between material particles. As regards matter, many arguments point to the conclusion that its ultimate particles always carry electric charges and that these are not merely accessory but very essential. We should introduce what seems to me an unnecessary dualism, if we considered these charges and what else there may be in the particles as wholly distinct from each other.

On the other hand, I believe every physicist feels inclined to the view that all the forces exerted by one particle on another, all molecular actions and gravity itself, are transmitted in some way by the ether, so that the tension of a stretched rope and the elasticity of an iron bar must find their explanation in what goes on in the ether between the molecules. Therefore, since we can hardly admit that one and the same medium is capable of transmitting two or more actions by wholly different mechanisms, all forces may be regarded as connected more or less intimately with those which we study in electromagnetism.

For the present, however, the nature of this connexion is entirely unknown to us and we must continue to speak of many kinds of forces without in the least being able to account for their origin. We shall even be obliged to subject the negative electrons to certain forces, about whose mode of action we are in the dark. Such are, for example, the forces by which the electrons in a ponderable dielectric are driven back to their positions of equilibrium, and the forces that come into play when an electron moving in a piece of metal has its course changed by an impact against a metallic atom.

35. The universal unit of electricity of which we have spoken can be evaluated as soon as we have formed an estimate of the mass of the chemical atoms. This has been done fairly well in different ways, and we shall not be far from the truth if we take

$$1{,}5 \cdot 10^{-24} \text{ gramm}$$

for the mass of an atom of hydrogen. Combining this with the electrochemical equivalent of this element, which in our units is $\frac{0{,}0001036}{c\sqrt{4\pi}}$, we find for the charge of an ion of hydrogen

$$1{,}5 \cdot 10^{-20}\, c\sqrt{4\pi}.$$

This number must also represent the charge of a negative electron. Therefore, the value of $\frac{e}{m}$ (for small velocities) being

$$1{,}77 \cdot 10^{7}\, c\sqrt{4\pi},$$

we find

$$m = 7 \cdot 10^{-28} \text{ gramm}.$$

Now, this must be the mass given by the formula (72). Substituting also the value of e, we get the following number for the radius

$$R = 1{,}5 \cdot 10^{-13} \text{ cm}.$$

We may compare this with the estimates that have been formed in the kinetic theory of gases. The distance of neighboring molecules in the atmospheric air is probably about

$$3 \cdot 10^{-7} \text{ cm}$$

and the diameter of a molecule of hydrogen may be taken to be

$$2 \cdot 10^{-8}$$

You see that, compared with these lengths, the electron is quite microscopical. Probably it is even much smaller than a single atom, so that, if this contains a certain number of negative electrons, these may be likened to spheres placed at distances from each other that are high multiples of their diameters.

36. Before closing our discussion on the subject of electromagnetic mass, I must call your attention to the question as to whether, in a system composed of a certain number of electrons, the electromagnetic mass is the sum of the electromagnetic masses of the separate particles, or, as I shall rather put it, whether, if the system moves with a common velocity of translation, the electromagnetic energy, in so far as it depends on the motion, can be made up of parts, each belonging to one electron, so that, for small velocities, it can be represented by

$$\sum \tfrac{1}{2} m' v^2.$$

This will, of course, be the case, if the electrons are so far apart that their fields may be said not to overlap. If, however, two electrons were brought into immediate contact, the total energy could not be found by an addition, for the simple reason, that, being a quadratic function of **d** and **h**, the energy due to the superposition of two fields is not equal to the sum of the energies which would be present in each of the two, if it existed by itself.

We have now to bethink ourselves of the extreme smallness of the electrons. It is clear that the larger part of the electromagnetic energy belonging to a particle will be found in a very small part of the field lying quite near it, within a distance from the centre that is a moderate multiple of the radius. Therefore, it may very well be that a number of electrons are so widely dispersed that the effective parts of their fields lie completely outside each other. In such a case the system may be said to have an electromagnetic mass equal to the sum of the masses of the individual electrons.

Yet there are important cases in which we are not warranted in asserting this. In order to make this clear, I shall call F_1 the part of the field of an electron which lies nearest to the particle, and F_2 the more distant part, the surface of separation between the two being a sphere whose radius is rather large in comparison with that of the electron. Then, if the electron is taken by itself, the part E_1 of the energy contained within F_1 far surpasses the energy E_2 which has its seat in F_2. Now, if we have N electrons at such distances from each other that their fields F_1 do not overlap, we shall have to add to each other the amounts of energy E_1. The quantities E_2 on the contrary must not be simply added, for the remoter fields F_2 will certainly cover, partly at least, the same space S. If, in this space, the dielectric displacements or the magnetic forces due to the individual electrons have directions making rather small angles with each other, all the fields F_2, feeble though they are, may very well produce a resulting field of appreciable energy. We have an example of this in the electric field of a charged conductor, and in the magnetic field around a wire carrying a current. The energy of this magnetic field may be shown to be, in very common cases, considerably larger than the sum of all the amounts of energy which I have called E_1, at least in as much as these depend on the motion of the electrons. The possibility of this will be readily understood, if one thinks of the extreme case that, at a point of the space S, all electrons produce a magnetic force in exactly the same direction. Then, if each of these forces has the magnitude $|\mathbf{h}|$, the resultant magnetic force has the magnitude $N|\mathbf{h}|$, so that the magnetic energy per unit of volume becomes $\frac{1}{2}N^2\mathbf{h}^2$. This is proportional to the square of the number N which we shall suppose to be very large. On the other hand, the sum of the quantities E_1 may be reckoned to be proportional to the first power of N.

This digression was necessary in order to point out the connexion between the electromagnetic mass of electrons and the phenomena of self-induction. In these latter it is the magnetic energy due to the overlapping of the feeble fields F_2 that makes itself felt. In dealing with effects of induction we can very well speak of the electromagnetic inertia of the current, or of the electromagnetic mass of the electrons moving in it, but we must keep in mind that this mass is very much larger than the sum of those we should associate with the separate particles. This large value is brought about (as are all effects of the current) by the cooperation of an immense number of electrons of the same kind moving in the same direction.[1])

37. In our treatment of the electromagnetic mass of electrons we have started from the expression (66) for the force to which an electron is subjected on account of its own field. However, this expression is not quite exact. It is based on the assumption that the equation (63) may be applied to a case of non-uniform motion, and we observed already that this may be done only if the state of motion changes very little during the time an electromagnetic disturbance would take to travel over a distance equal to the dimensions of the electron. This amounts to saying that, if l is one of these dimensions, and τ a time during which the state of motion is sensibly altered, the quantity

$$\frac{l}{c\tau} \tag{75}$$

must be very small.

1) Note 17.

In reality, the force (66) is only the first term of a series in which, compared with the preceding one, each term is of the order of magnitude (75).

In some phenomena the next term of the series makes itself felt it is therefore necessary to indicate its value. By a somewhat laborious calculation it is found to be

$$\frac{e^2}{6\pi c^3}\ddot{\mathbf{v}}, \tag{76}$$

where the vector $\mathbf{v}$ is twice differentiated with respect to the time. I may mention by the way that this formula holds for any distribution of the electric charge e.[1])

In many cases the new force represented by (76) may be termed a *resistance* to the motion. This is seen, if we calculate the work of the force during an interval of time extending from $t = t_1$ to $t = t_2$. The result is

$$\frac{e^2}{6\pi c^3}\int_{t_1}^{t_2}(\mathbf{v}\cdot\ddot{\mathbf{v}})\,dt = \frac{e^2}{6\pi c^3}\Big|(\mathbf{v}\cdot\dot{\mathbf{v}})\Big|_{t_1}^{t_2} - \frac{e^2}{6\pi c^3}\int_{t_1}^{t_2}\dot{\mathbf{v}}^2\,dt.$$

Here the first term disappears if, in the case of a periodic motion, the integration is extended to a full period; also, if at the instants t_1 and t_2 either the velocity or the acceleration is 0. We have an example of the latter case in those phenomena in which an electron strikes against a ponderable body and is thrown back by it.

Whenever the above formula reduces to the last term, the work of the force is seen to be negative, so that the name of resistance is then justly applied. This is also confirmed by the form our formula takes for an electron having a simple harmonic motion. The velocity being given by

$$\mathbf{v} = \mathbf{b}\cos nt,$$

where n is a constant, we may write $\ddot{\mathbf{v}} = -n^2\mathbf{v}$, and, instead of (76),

$$-\frac{n^2e^2}{6\pi c^3}\mathbf{v}, \tag{77}$$

so that, in this particular case, the force is opposite to the velocity and proportional to it.

The work of (77) during a full period T is

$$-\frac{n^2e^2}{6\pi c^3}\int_{t_1}^{t_1+T}\mathbf{v}^2\,dt = -\frac{n^2e^2}{12\pi c^3}\mathbf{b}^2T. \tag{78}$$

38. In all cases in which the work of the force (76) is negative, the energy of the electron (if not kept at a constant value by

---

1) Note **18**.

the action of some other cause) must diminish, and that of the ether must increase. This means that there is a continous *radiation* from the particle outwards, such as cannot be said to exist when the velocity is constant and the electron simply carries its field along with it.

For the purpose of getting a clear idea of the radiation, it is well to consider the field at a very large distance from the particle. We shall see that, if the distance is large enough, the radiation field gets, so to say, disentangled from the field we have formerly considered, which is carried along by the moving particle.

In order to determine the field at a large distance, we can avail ourselves of the following formulae for the scalar and the vector potential, which hold for all points whose distance from the electron is very large compared with its dimensions:

$$\varphi = \frac{e}{4\pi\left[r\left(1-\frac{\mathbf{v}_r}{c}\right)\right]}, \quad \mathbf{a} = \frac{e[\mathbf{v}]}{4\pi c\left[r\left(1-\frac{\mathbf{v}_r}{c}\right)\right]}. \tag{79}$$

Here, the square brackets have a meaning similar to that which we gave them in the general equations (35) and (36). If one wishes to determine the potentials at a point P for the time t, one must first seek the position M of the electron, which satisfies the condition that, if it is reached at the time t_0, previous to t,

$$MP = c(t - t_0).$$

The distance MP is denoted by r, and $[\mathbf{v}]$ means the velocity in the position M, $\mathbf{v}_r$ its component in the direction MP.

The formulae have been deduced from (35) and (36); the vector $1 - \frac{\mathbf{v}_r}{c}$ in the denominators shows, however, that the problem is not quite so simple as might be expected at first sight. A complication arises from the circumstance that we must not integrate over the space occupied by the electron *at the particular instant which we have denoted by* t_0. On the contrary, according to the meaning of (35) and (36), we must fix our attention on the different points of the electron and choose for each of them, among all its successive positions, the one M' which is determined by the condition, that, if it is reached at the time t_0',

$$M'P = c(t - t_0').$$

The time t_0' is slightly different for the different points of the electron and therefore the space over which we have to integrate (which contains all the points M') cannot be said to coincide with the space occupied by the electron at any particular instant.[1])

1) Note 19.

39. Leaving aside these rather complicated calculations, I proceed to the determination of the field at very large distances. The formulae (33) and (34) which we must use for this purpose require us to differentiate φ and $\mathbf{a}$. In doing so I shall omit all terms in which the square and the higher powers of the distance r appear in the denominator. I shall therefore treat as a constant the factor r in the denominators of (79), so that only $\mathbf{v}_r$ has to be differentiated in the expression for φ and, if we also neglect terms in which a component of the velocity is multiplied by one of the acceleration, only $[\mathbf{v}]$ in the second formula. Performing all operations and denoting by x, y, z the coordinates of P with respect to the point M as origin, and by $\mathbf{j}$ the acceleration of the electron in the position M, I find[1])

$$\mathbf{d}_x = \frac{e}{4\pi c^2 r}\left\{-\mathbf{j}_x + \frac{x}{r}\mathbf{j}_r\right\}, \text{ etc.} \tag{80}$$

$$\mathbf{h}_x = \frac{e}{4\pi c^2 r}\left\{\mathbf{j}_y \frac{z}{r} - \mathbf{j}_z \frac{y}{r}\right\}, \text{ etc.} \tag{81}$$

The three formulae for $\mathbf{d}$ can be interpreted as follows. If the acceleration $\mathbf{j}$ is decomposed into $\mathbf{j}_r$ in the direction of MP and $\mathbf{j}_p$ perpendicular to it, the dielectric displacement in P is parallel to $\mathbf{j}_p$ and its magnitude is given by

$$-\frac{e}{4\pi c^2 r}\mathbf{j}_p.$$

In order to see the meaning of the equations for $\mathbf{h}$, we can introduce a vector $\mathbf{k}$ of unit length in the direction from M towards P. The components of this vector being $\frac{x}{r}$, $\frac{y}{r}$, $\frac{z}{r}$, we have

$$\mathbf{h} = \frac{e}{4\pi c^2 r}[\mathbf{j}\cdot\mathbf{k}].$$

The magnitude of $\mathbf{h}$ is therefore

$$\frac{e}{4\pi c^2 r}\mathbf{j}_p,$$

equal to that of the dielectric displacement. Further, the magnetic force is seen to be perpendicular both to the line MP and to the dielectric displacement. Consequently there is a flow of energy along MP. It is easily seen that this flow is directed away from the position M of the electron, and that its intensity is given by

$$\frac{e^2}{16\pi^2 c^3 r^2}\mathbf{j}_p^2 = \frac{e^2}{16\pi^2 c^3 r^2}\mathbf{j}^2 \sin^2\vartheta,$$

if ϑ is the angle between MP and the acceleration $\mathbf{j}$.[2])

1) Note **20**. 2) Note **21**.

The result may be applied to any point of a spherical surface σ described around the centre M with r as radius. The total outward flow of energy across this sphere is given by

$$\frac{e^2}{16\pi^2 c^3 r^2}\,\mathfrak{j}^2 \int \sin^2\vartheta\, d\sigma = \frac{e^2}{6\pi c^3}\,\mathfrak{j}^2. \tag{82}$$

The reason for my former assertion that, at very large distances from the electron, the radiation field predominates over the field considered in § 26, lies in the fact that, in the latter, $\mathbf{d}$ and $\mathbf{h}$ diminish as $\frac{1}{r^2}$ and in the radiation field only as $\frac{1}{r}$.

We can sum up the preceding considerations by saying that an electron does not emit energy so long as it has a uniform rectilinear motion, but that it does as soon as its velocity changes either in magnitude or in direction.

40. The theory of the production of Röntgen rays, first proposed by Wiechert and Stokes, and worked out by J. J. Thomson[1]), affords a very interesting application of our result. According to it, these rays consist of a rapid and irregular succession of sharp electromagnetic impulses, each of which is due to the change of velocity which an electron of the cathode rays undergoes when it impinges against the anti-cathode.[2]) I cannot however dwell upon this subject, having too much to say about the emission of light-vibrations with which we shall be often concerned.

If an electron has a simple harmonic motion, the velocity is continually changing, and, by what has been said, there must be a continous emission of energy. It will also be clear that, at each point of the surrounding field, the state is periodically changing, keeping time with the electron itself, so that we shall have a radiation of homogeneous light. Before going into some further details, I shall first consider the total amount of energy emitted during a full period.

Let us choose the position of equilibrium as origin of coordinates and let the vibration take place along the axis of x, the displacement at the time t being given by

$$\mathbf{x} = a\cos(nt + p).$$

Then the acceleration is

$$-an^2\cos(nt + p).$$

---

1) E. Wiechert, Die Theorie der Elektrodynamik und die Röntgen'sche Entdeckung, Abh. d. Phys.-ökon. Ges. zu Königsberg i. Pr. (1896), p. 1; Über die Grundlagen der Elektrodynamik, Ann. Phys. Chem. **59** (1896), p. 283; G. G. Stokes, On the nature of the Röntgen rays, Manch. Memoirs **41** (1897), Mem. 15; J. J. Thomson, A theory of the connexion between cathode and Röntgen rays, Phil. Mag. (5) **45** (1898), p. 172.

2) Note **21***.

If the amplitude a is very small, the sphere of which we have spoken in the preceding paragraph may be considered as having its centre, not in M, one of the positions of the electron, but in the origin O, and we may understand by $\mathbf{j}$ the acceleration of the electron at the time $t - \frac{r}{c}$, r being the distance from O. Therefore, on account of (82), the flow of energy across the sphere will be per unit of time

$$\frac{e^2}{6\pi c^3} a^2 n^4 \cos^2 \left\{ n\left(t - \frac{r}{c}\right) + p \right\}.$$

Integrating this over a full period T we get

$$\frac{e^2}{12\pi c^3} a^2 n^4 T. \tag{83}$$

Now, if the amplitude is to remain constant, the electron must be acted on by an external force equal and opposite to the resistance (77). The work of this force is given by (78) with the sign reversed. Since the amplitude of the velocity is equal to the amplitude a of the elongation, multiplied by n, the work of the force corresponds exactly to the amount of energy (83) that is emitted.[1])

41. For the sake of further examining the field produced by an electron having a simple harmonic motion, we shall go back to the formulae (79). Let us first only suppose that the motion of the electron is confined to a certain very small space $\mathbf{S}$, one point of which is chosen as origin of coordinates. Let $\mathbf{x}$, $\mathbf{y}$, $\mathbf{z}$ be the coordinates of the electron, $\dot{\mathbf{x}}$, $\dot{\mathbf{y}}$, $\dot{\mathbf{z}}$ its velocities and $\ddot{\mathbf{x}}$, $\ddot{\mathbf{y}}$, $\ddot{\mathbf{z}}$ the components of its acceleration. We shall consider all these quantities as infinitely small of the first order, and neglect all terms containing the product of any two of them. We shall further denote by x, y, z the coordinates of the point P for which we wish to determine the field, and by r_0 its distance from the origin. Now, if M is the position of the electron of which we have spoken in our explanation of the equations (79), the distance $MP = r$ will be infinitely near the distance r_0, and the time t_0 infinitely near the time $t - \frac{r_0}{c}$. The changes in the position and the velocity of the electron in an infinitely small time being quantities of the second order, we may therefore understand by M the position at the instant $t - \frac{r_0}{c}$, and by $\mathbf{v}$ the velocity at that time. Further:

$$\frac{1}{r} = \frac{1}{r_0} - \frac{\partial}{\partial x}\left(\frac{1}{r_0}\right)[\mathbf{x}] - \frac{\partial}{\partial y}\left(\frac{1}{r_0}\right)[\mathbf{y}] - \frac{\partial}{\partial z}\left(\frac{1}{r_0}\right)[\mathbf{z}],$$

1) Note **22**.

because, as is easily seen, the change in the distance between O and P, due to a shifting of the first point towards M, is equal to the change that would take place, if O remained where it was, but P were given a displacement $-\mathbf{x}, -\mathbf{y}, -\mathbf{z}$. The square brackets now serve to indicate the values at the time $t - \frac{r_0}{c}$; they will have this meaning in all formulae that are now to be developed.

Substituting the above value of $\frac{1}{r}$, and

$$\frac{1}{1 - \frac{[\mathbf{v}_r]}{c}} = 1 + \frac{[\mathbf{v}_r]}{c},$$

where $\mathbf{v}_r$ may be considered as the component along OP, we find for the scalar potential

$$\varphi = \frac{e}{4\pi}\left\{\frac{1}{r_0} - \frac{\partial}{\partial x}\left(\frac{1}{r_0}\right)[\mathbf{x}] - \frac{\partial}{\partial y}\left(\frac{1}{r_0}\right)[\mathbf{y}] - \frac{\partial}{\partial z}\left(\frac{1}{r_0}\right)[\mathbf{z}] + \frac{[\mathbf{v}_r]}{c r_0}\right\}.$$

Having got thus far, we can omit the index $_0$, so that r now means the distance from the origin O to a point with the coordinates x, y, z. As regards the last term, we can use the transformation

$$\frac{[\mathbf{v}_r]}{c} = \frac{1}{c}\frac{x}{r}[\mathbf{v}_x] + \frac{1}{c}\frac{y}{r}[\mathbf{v}_y] + \frac{1}{c}\frac{z}{r}[\mathbf{v}_z] = \frac{1}{c}\frac{x[\dot{\mathbf{x}}] + y[\dot{\mathbf{y}}] + z[\dot{\mathbf{z}}]}{r}$$

$$= -\left(\frac{\partial[\mathbf{x}]}{\partial x} + \frac{\partial[\mathbf{y}]}{\partial y} + \frac{\partial[\mathbf{z}]}{\partial z}\right),$$

the last step in which will be clear, if we attend to the meaning of $\frac{\partial[\mathbf{x}]}{\partial x}$ etc. The symbol $[\mathbf{x}]$ represents the value of $\mathbf{x}$ at the time $t - \frac{r}{c}$ which we shall, for a moment, denote by t'. This time t' depends in its turn on the distance r, which again is a function of the coordinates x, y, z of the external point. Hence

$$\frac{\partial[\mathbf{x}]}{\partial x} = \frac{\partial[\mathbf{x}]}{\partial t'}\frac{\partial t'}{\partial r}\frac{\partial r}{\partial x} = [\dot{\mathbf{x}}] \cdot -\frac{1}{c}\frac{x}{r}, \quad \text{etc.}$$

Finally, the scalar potential becomes

$$\varphi = \frac{e}{4\pi}\left\{\frac{1}{r} - \frac{\partial}{\partial x}\frac{[\mathbf{x}]}{r} - \frac{\partial}{\partial y}\frac{[\mathbf{y}]}{r} - \frac{\partial}{\partial z}\frac{[\mathbf{z}]}{r}\right\}. \tag{84}$$

The expression for the vector potential is even more simple, viz.

$$\mathbf{a} = \frac{e[\mathbf{v}]}{4\pi c r}. \tag{85}$$

The radiation field, which predominates at large distances, and in which we find the flow of energy of which we have already spoken, is determined by the three last terms of φ and by the vector potential. At smaller distances it is superposed on the field represented by the first term of φ, which is the same that would surround the electron if it were at rest.

42. By a slight change in the circumstances of the case, we can do away with the electrostatic field altogether. Let us suppose the electron to perform its vibrations in the interior of an atom or a molecule of matter, to which we shall now give the name of *particle* and which occupies the small space $\mathbf{S}$. If the particle as a whole is not charged, it must contain, besides our movable electron, a charge $-e$, either in the form of one or more electrons, or distributed in any other manner. We shall suppose that this complementary charge $-e$ remains at rest, and that, if the electron e did so likewise, in a determinate position, which we shall take as origin of coordinates, there would be no external field at all, at least not at a distance that is large in comparison with the dimensions of $\mathbf{S}$. This being admitted, the immovable charge $-e$ must produce a scalar potential equal and opposite to the first term in (84), so that, if we consider the field of the whole particle, this term will be cancelled. Our assumption amounts to this, that the charge $-e$ is equivalent to a single electron $-e$ at the point O, so that, if the electron $+e$ has the coordinates $\mathbf{x}, \mathbf{y}, \mathbf{z}$, things will be as if we had two equal and opposite charges at a small distance from each other. We express this by saying that the particle is electrically polarized, and we define its electric moment by the equation

$$\mathbf{p} = e\mathbf{r}, \tag{86}$$

where $\mathbf{r}$ is the vector drawn from O towards the position of the movable electron. The components of $\mathbf{p}$ are

$$\mathbf{p}_x = e\mathbf{x}, \quad \mathbf{p}_y = e\mathbf{y}, \quad \mathbf{p}_z = e\mathbf{z}, \tag{87}$$

and from (84) and (85) we find the following expressions for the potentials in the field surrounding the polarized particle

$$\varphi = -\frac{1}{4\pi}\left\{\frac{\partial}{\partial x}\frac{[\mathbf{p}_x]}{r} + \frac{\partial}{\partial y}\frac{[\mathbf{p}_y]}{r} + \frac{\partial}{\partial z}\frac{[\mathbf{p}_z]}{r}\right\}, \tag{88}$$

$$\mathbf{a} = \frac{[\dot{\mathbf{p}}]}{4\pi c r}. \tag{89}$$

These relations also hold in the case of a polarized particle whose state is somewhat more complicated. Let us imagine that it contains a certain number of electrons, any part of which may be movable. We shall find the potentials by calculating (84) and (85) for the separate electrons and adding the results. Using the sign Σ for this last operation, and keeping in mind that

$$\Sigma e = 0, \tag{90}$$

we shall again find the formulae (88) and (89), if we define the moment of the particle by the formula

$$\mathbf{p} = \Sigma e\mathbf{r}, \tag{91}$$

or its components by

$$\mathfrak{p}_x = \Sigma e\mathbf{x}, \quad \mathfrak{p}_y = \Sigma e\mathbf{y}, \quad \mathfrak{p}_z = \Sigma e\mathbf{z}. \tag{92}$$

It is even unnecessary that the charges should be concentrated in separate electrons. We can as well suppose them to be continuously distributed, but of course capable of moving or fluctuating in one way or another. Then the sums in the last formulae must be replaced by integrals. We shall have

$$\int \varrho\, dS = 0 \tag{93}$$

and for the components of the moment

$$\mathfrak{p}_x = \int \varrho \mathbf{x}\, dS, \quad \mathfrak{p}_y = \int \varrho \mathbf{y}\, dS, \quad \mathfrak{p}_z = \int \varrho \mathbf{z}\, dS, \tag{94}$$

the integration being extended over the space S occupied by the particle. It must be noticed that on account of (90) and (93), the vectors (91) and (94) are independent of the choice of the point O.

43. The formulae (88) and (89) show that the particle is a centre of radiation whenever the moment $\mathfrak{p}$ is changing, and that it emits regular vibrations if $\mathfrak{p}$ is a periodic function of the time.

We shall suppose for example that

$$\mathfrak{p}_x = b \cos (nt + p), \quad \mathfrak{p}_y = 0, \quad \mathfrak{p}_z = 0,$$

b, n and p being constants. Then we have

$$\frac{[\mathfrak{p}_x]}{r} = \frac{b}{r} \cos\left\{n\left(t - \frac{r}{c}\right) + p\right\},$$

and the field is easily determined by means of (88) and (89).

I shall not write down the general formulae but only those which hold for values of r that are very large compared with the wave-length, and which are obtained by the omission of all terms of the order $\frac{1}{r^2}$. They are as follows:

$$\left.\begin{aligned}
\mathfrak{d}_x &= \frac{n^2 b}{4\pi c^2 r} \cdot \frac{r^2 - x^2}{r^2} \cos\left\{n\left(t - \frac{r}{c}\right) + p\right\}, \\
\mathfrak{d}_y &= -\frac{n^2 b}{4\pi c^2 r} \cdot \frac{xy}{r^2} \cos\left\{n\left(t - \frac{r}{c}\right) + p\right\}, \\
\mathfrak{d}_z &= -\frac{n^2 b}{4\pi c^2 r} \cdot \frac{xz}{r^2} \cos\left\{n\left(t - \frac{r}{c}\right) + p\right\}, \\
\mathfrak{h}_x &= 0, \\
\mathfrak{h}_y &= \frac{n^2 b}{4\pi c^2 r} \cdot \frac{z}{r} \cos\left\{n\left(t - \frac{r}{c}\right) + p\right\}, \\
\mathfrak{h}_z &= -\frac{n^2 b}{4\pi c^2 r} \cdot \frac{y}{r} \cos\left\{n\left(t - \frac{r}{c}\right) + p\right\},
\end{aligned}\right\} \tag{95}$$

corresponding to (80) and (81).[1]

1) Note **23**.

I must add that our formulae for the field around a particle whose state of polarization is periodically changing, agree with those by which Hertz represented the state of the field around his vibrator.[1])

44. We shall now pass on to certain equations that will be of use to us when we come to speak of the influence of the Earth's translation on optical phenomena. They relate to the electromagnetic phenomena in a system of bodies having a common uniform translation, whose velocity we shall denote by $\mathbf{w}$, and are derived from our original equations by a change of variables. Indeed, it is very natural to refer the phenomena in a moving system, not to a system of axes of coordinates that is at rest, but to one that is fixed to the system and shares its translation; these new coordinates will be represented by x', y', z'. They are given by

$$x' = x - \mathbf{w}_x t, \quad y' = y - \mathbf{w}_y t, \quad z' = z - \mathbf{w}_z t. \tag{96}$$

It will also be found useful to fix our attention on the velocity $\mathbf{u}$ of the charges relatively to the moving axes, so that in our fundamental equations we have to put

$$\mathbf{v} = \mathbf{w} + \mathbf{u}.$$

Now it has been found that in those cases in which the velocity of translation $\mathbf{w}$ is so small that its square $\mathbf{w}^2$, or rather the fraction $\frac{\mathbf{w}^2}{c^2}$, may be neglected, the differential equations referred to the moving axes take almost the same form as the original formulae, if, instead of t, we introduce a new independent variable t', and if, at the same time, the dielectric displacement and the magnetic force are replaced by certain other vectors which we shall call $\mathbf{d}'$ and $\mathbf{h}'$.

The variable t' is defined by the equation

$$t' = t - \frac{1}{c^2}(\mathbf{w}_x x' + \mathbf{w}_y y' + \mathbf{w}_z z'), \tag{97}$$

and the vectors $\mathbf{d}'$ and $\mathbf{h}'$ by

$$\mathbf{d}' = \mathbf{d} + \frac{1}{c}[\mathbf{w} \cdot \mathbf{h}], \tag{98}$$

$$\mathbf{h}' = \mathbf{h} - \frac{1}{c}[\mathbf{w} \cdot \mathbf{d}]. \tag{99}$$

We can regard t' as the time reckoned from the instant

$$\frac{1}{c^2}(\mathbf{w}_x x' + \mathbf{w}_y y' + \mathbf{w}_z z'),$$

---

1) H. Hertz, Die Kräfte elektrischer Schwingungen, behandelt nach der Maxwell'schen Theorie, Ann. Phys. Chem. **36** (1888), p. 1.

which changes from one point to the other. This variable is therefore properly called the *local* time, in order to distinguish it from the *universal* time t.

As to the vectors $\mathbf{d}'$ and $\mathbf{h}'$, the difference between them and $\mathbf{d}$, $\mathbf{h}$ is but small, since the fraction $\frac{|\mathbf{w}|}{c}$ is so. Even if we have to do with the translation of the Earth, the value of $|\mathbf{w}|$ is no more than one ten-thousandth part of the velocity of light.

Neglecting terms with the square of $\frac{|\mathbf{w}|}{c}$, as has already been said, one finds the following system of transformed equations:

$$\operatorname{div} \mathbf{d}' = \left\{1 - \frac{(\mathbf{w} \cdot \mathbf{u})}{c^2}\right\} \varrho, \tag{100}$$

$$\operatorname{div} \mathbf{h}' = 0, \tag{101}$$

$$\operatorname{rot} \mathbf{h}' = \frac{1}{c}(\dot{\mathbf{d}}' + \varrho \mathbf{u}), \tag{102}$$

$$\operatorname{rot} \mathbf{d}' = -\frac{1}{c}\dot{\mathbf{h}}'. \tag{103}$$

The dot means a differentiation with respect to t', and the symbols div and rot (and, in the next paragraph, grad) serve to indicate differentiations with respect to x', y', z' in exactly the same manner as they formerly indicated differentiations with respect to x, y, z. Rot $\mathbf{h}'$, for example, now means a vector whose components are

$$\frac{\partial \mathbf{h}'_z}{\partial y'} - \frac{\partial \mathbf{h}'_y}{\partial z'}, \quad \frac{\partial \mathbf{h}'_x}{\partial z'} - \frac{\partial \mathbf{h}'_z}{\partial x'}, \quad \frac{\partial \mathbf{h}'_y}{\partial x'} - \frac{\partial \mathbf{h}'_x}{\partial y'}.$$

You see that the formulae have nearly, but not quite, the same form as (17)—(20), the difference consisting in the term $\frac{(\mathbf{w} \cdot \mathbf{u})}{c^2}$ in the first equation.[1])

45. Starting from the new system of equations, we can now repeat much of what has been said in connexion with the original one. For a given distribution and motion of the charges, the field is entirely determined, and here again the problem can be considerably simplified by the introduction of two potentials, a scalar and a vector one. These are given by the equations

$$\varphi' = \frac{1}{4\pi}\int \frac{1}{r}[\varrho]\, dS \tag{104}$$

and

$$\mathbf{a}' = \frac{1}{4\pi c}\int \frac{1}{r}[\varrho \mathbf{u}]\, dS, \tag{105}$$

where however the symbols $[\varrho]$ and $[\varrho \mathbf{u}]$ require some explanation. If we want to calculate φ' and $\mathbf{a}'$ for a point P, for the moment at

1) Note **24**. See also Note **72***.

which the local time of this point has a definite value t', we must, for each element dS situated at a distance r from P, take the values of ϱ and $\varrho \mathbf{u}$ such as they are at the instant at which the local time of the element is

$$t' - \frac{r}{c}.$$

Finally, we have the following formulae for the determination of the field by means of the potentials[1]):

$$\mathbf{d}' = -\frac{1}{c}\dot{\mathbf{a}}' - \text{grad}\,\varphi' + \frac{1}{c}\text{grad}\,(\mathbf{w}\cdot\mathbf{a}'), \tag{106}$$

$$\mathbf{h}' = \text{rot}\,\mathbf{a}'. \tag{107}$$

Here again, if we compare with (33) and (34), we notice a slight difference. In (33) there is no term corresponding to the last one in (106).[2])

Notwithstanding the two differences I have pointed out, there is a large variety of cases, in which a state of things in a system at rest has its exact analogue in the same system with a translation. I shall give two examples that are of interest.

In the first place, the values of $\mathbf{d}'$ and $\mathbf{h}'$ produced by a particle moving with the velocity $\mathbf{w}$, and having a variable electric moment, are given by formulae similar to those we formerly found for the radiation from a particle without a translation, und which I therefore need not even write down.

If the moment of a particle placed at the origin of coordinates is represented by

$$\mathbf{p}_x = b\cos(nt' + p), \quad \mathbf{p}_y = 0, \quad \mathbf{p}_z = 0, \tag{108}$$

all we have to do is to replace, in (95), $\mathbf{d}, \mathbf{h}, x, y, z, t$ by $\mathbf{d}', \mathbf{h}', x', y', z', t'$.[3])

In order to show the meaning of this result, I shall consider the field at a point situated on the positive axis of y'. It is determined by

$$\mathbf{d}'_x = \frac{n^2 b}{4\pi c^2 r}\cos\left\{n\left(t' - \frac{y'}{c}\right) + p\right\}, \quad \mathbf{h}'_z = -\frac{n^2 b}{4\pi c^2 r}\cos\left\{n\left(t' - \frac{y'}{c}\right) + p\right\},$$

all other components being 0. Since, neglecting terms of the second order, we may write

$$\mathbf{d} = \mathbf{d}' - \frac{1}{c}[\mathbf{w}\cdot\mathbf{h}']$$

instead of (98), we have

$$\mathbf{d}_x = \mathbf{d}'_x - \frac{\mathbf{w}_y}{c}\mathbf{h}'_z,$$

from which it appears that the dielectric displacement takes the form

$$\mathbf{d}_x = \alpha\cos\left\{n\left(t' - \frac{y'}{c}\right) + p\right\},$$

in which α is a constant.

---

1) Note **25**. 2) See however Note **72***. 3) Note **26**.

By substitution of the value of the local time and of the value (96) for y', this becomes

$$\mathbf{d}_x = a \cos\left\{n\left(1 + \frac{\mathbf{w}_y}{c}\right)\left(t - \frac{y}{c}\right) + p\right\}.$$

Thus we see that, at a fixed point of space, i. e. for a definite value of y, the frequency of the vibrations is given by

$$n\left(1 + \frac{\mathbf{w}_y}{c}\right).$$

If the radiating particle has a positive velocity $\mathbf{w}_y$, i. e. one that is directed towards the point considered, this frequency is higher than that of the particle itself, which, as is shown by (108), still has the value n. This is the well known change of frequency which, according to Doppler's principle, is caused by a motion of the source of light.

46. Our second example relates to the reflexion of a beam of light by a perfectly reflecting mirror, for instance by one that consists of a perfectly conducting substance. We shall suppose the incidence to be normal, and begin with the case of a mirror having no translation, so that we have to use the original equations. Let the beam of light be represented by (7) and let the surface of the mirror coincide with the plane YOZ. Then, the reflected beam, which we shall distinguish by the suffix (r), is given by

$$\mathbf{d}_{y(r)} = -a \cos n\left(t + \frac{x}{c}\right), \quad \mathbf{h}_{z(r)} = a \cos n\left(t + \frac{x}{c}\right).$$

Indeed, these values satisfy the condition that, at the mirror, there be no dielectric displacement along its surface. If we put $x = 0$, we really find

$$\mathbf{d}_y + \mathbf{d}_{y(r)} = 0.$$

The case of reflexion by a mirror moving with the velocity $\mathbf{w}_x$, in the direction of the axis of x, i. e. in the direction of its normal, can be treated by the same formulae, provided only we change $x, t, \mathbf{d}, \mathbf{h}$ into $x', t', \mathbf{d}', \mathbf{h}'$.[1]) Therefore, if the incident beam is now represented by

$$\mathbf{d}_y' = a \cos n\left(t' - \frac{x'}{c}\right), \quad \mathbf{h}_z' = a \cos n\left(t' - \frac{x'}{c}\right),$$

we shall have for the reflected light

$$\mathbf{d}'_{y(r)} = -a \cos n\left(t' + \frac{x'}{c}\right), \quad \mathbf{h}'_{z(r)} = a \cos n\left(t' + \frac{x'}{c}\right).$$

Let us now examine the values of $\mathbf{d}_y$, $\mathbf{h}_z$, $\mathbf{d}_{y(r)}$ and $\mathbf{h}_{z(r)}$ in this case. The only component of $\mathbf{w}$ being $\mathbf{w}_x$, we find

1) Note 27.

$$\mathbf{d}_y = \mathbf{d}'_y + \frac{1}{c}\mathbf{w}_x\mathbf{h}'_z,\ \mathbf{h}_z = \mathbf{h}'_z + \frac{1}{c}\mathbf{w}_x\mathbf{d}'_y,$$

so that the incident rays are given by

$$\mathbf{d}_y = a\left(1+\frac{\mathbf{w}_x}{c}\right)\cos n\left(t'-\frac{x'}{c}\right),$$

$$\mathbf{h}_z = a\left(1+\frac{\mathbf{w}_x}{c}\right)\cos n\left(t'-\frac{x'}{c}\right),$$

and the reflected rays by

$$\mathbf{d}_{y(r)} = -a\left(1-\frac{\mathbf{w}_x}{c}\right)\cos n\left(t'+\frac{x'}{c}\right),$$

$$\mathbf{h}_{z(r)} = a\left(1-\frac{\mathbf{w}_x}{c}\right)\cos n\left(t'+\frac{x'}{c}\right).$$

In these formulae we shall now express t' and x' in terms of t and x.

The value of the local time is

$$t' = t - \frac{\mathbf{w}_x x'}{c^2},$$

and

$$x' = x - \mathbf{w}_x t.$$

Hence

$$t' - \frac{x'}{c} = \left(1+\frac{\mathbf{w}_x}{c}\right)\left(t-\frac{x}{c}\right),$$

$$t' + \frac{x'}{c} = \left(1-\frac{\mathbf{w}_x}{c}\right)\left(t+\frac{x}{c}\right).$$

The formulae are simplified if we put

$$a\left(1+\frac{\mathbf{w}_x}{c}\right) = \mathrm{a},\quad n\left(1+\frac{\mathbf{w}_x}{c}\right) = \mathrm{n}.$$

Continuing to neglect the square of $\frac{\mathbf{w}_x}{c}$, we infer from this

$$a\left(1-\frac{\mathbf{w}_x}{c}\right) = \mathrm{a}\left(1-\frac{2\mathbf{w}_x}{c}\right),\ n\left(1-\frac{\mathbf{w}_x}{c}\right) = \mathrm{n}\left(1-\frac{2\mathbf{w}_x}{c}\right),$$

so that the final formulae for the incident rays are

$$\mathbf{d}_y = \mathrm{a}\cos \mathrm{n}\left(t-\frac{x}{c}\right),\ \mathbf{h}_z = \mathrm{a}\cos \mathrm{n}\left(t-\frac{x}{c}\right),$$

and those for the reflected light

$$\mathbf{d}_{y(r)} = -\mathrm{a}\left(1-\frac{2\mathbf{w}_x}{c}\right)\cos \mathrm{n}\left(1-\frac{2\mathbf{w}_x}{c}\right)\left(t+\frac{x}{c}\right),$$

$$\mathbf{h}_{z(r)} = \mathrm{a}\left(1-\frac{2\mathbf{w}_x}{c}\right)\cos \mathrm{n}\left(1-\frac{2\mathbf{w}_x}{c}\right)\left(t+\frac{x}{c}\right).$$

These equations show that both the frequency and the amplitude of the reflected beam are changed by the motion of the mirror. The frequency is now $n\left(1-\frac{2\mathbf{w}_x}{c}\right)$, smaller than n, if the mirror recedes from the source. These changes might have been predicted on the ground of Doppler's principle. As to the amplitude, it is changed in exactly the same ratio as the frequency, so that the reflected intensity is diminished by a motion in one direction and increased by a motion in the other direction.

It is interesting to verify these results by considering the energy of the system. This may easily be done, if we fix our attention, not on the fluctuations of the electromagnetic energy, but on its mean value, so that, at every point of the beam, w_e and w_m (§ 16) are considered as constants. Let the rays occupy a cylinder whose generating lines are parallel to OX and whose normal section is Σ. Let P be a plane perpendicular to OX at some distance before the mirror and having a fixed position in the ether. If $\mathbf{w}_x$ is positive, so that the mirror recedes, the space between the mirror and the plane P increases by $\mathbf{w}_x\Sigma$ per unit of time, so that the energy contained in that space increases by

$$(w_e + w_m)\mathbf{w}_x\Sigma.$$

Again, if p is the pressure on the mirror, the work done by the field will be

$$p\mathbf{w}_x\Sigma.$$

Consequently, if S is the current of energy towards the mirror per unit of area of the plane P, we must have

$$S\Sigma = (w_e + w_m)\mathbf{w}_x\Sigma + p\mathbf{w}_x\Sigma. \tag{109}$$

We can easily calculate the quantities occurring in this equation. In the incident beam there is a flow of energy (§ 17)

$$\tfrac{1}{2}\mathrm{a}^2 c$$

towards the mirror, and in the reflected light a flow

$$\tfrac{1}{2}\mathrm{a}^2\left(1-\frac{2\mathbf{w}_x}{c}\right)^2 c = \tfrac{1}{2}\mathrm{a}^2\left(1-\frac{4\mathbf{w}_x}{c}\right)c$$

away from it, so that

$$S = 2\mathrm{a}^2\mathbf{w}_x. \tag{110}$$

As to w_e, w_m and p, we may take for them the values that would hold if the mirror where at rest, because these quantities have to be multiplied by $\mathbf{w}_x$. Therefore, since the value of $w_e + w_m$ consists of two equal parts, one belonging to the incident and the other to the reflected light[1]),

$$w_e + w_m = \mathrm{a}^2. \tag{111}$$

1) Note 28.

Finally, by what has been said in § 25,

$$p = a^2. \tag{112}$$

The values (110), (111) and (112) really satisfy the condition (109).

47. I shall close this chapter by a short account of the application of the theory of electrons to the motion of electricity in metallic bodies. In my introductory remarks, I have already alluded to the researches of Riecke, Drude and J. J. Thomson. I now wish especially to call your attention to the views that have been put forward by the second of these physicists.

In his theory, every metal is supposed to contain a large number of free electrons, which are conceived to partake of the heat-motion of the ordinary atoms and molecules. Further, a well known theorem of the kinetic theory of matter, according to which, at a given temperature, the mean kinetic energy is the same for all kinds of particles, leads to the assumption that the mean kinetic energy of an electron is equal to that of a molecule of a gas taken at the same temperature. Though the velocity required for this is very considerable, yet the electrons are not free to move away in a short time to a large distance from their original positions. They are prevented from doing so by their impacts against the atoms of the metal itself.

For the sake of simplicity we shall assume only one kind of free electrons, the opposite kind being supposed to be fixed to the ponderable matter. Now, if the metal is not subjected to an electric force, the particles are moving indiscriminately towards all sides; there is no transfer of electricity in a definite direction. This changes however as soon as an electric force is applied. The velocities of the electrons towards one side are increased, those towards the other side diminished, so that an electric current is set up, the intensity of which can be calculated by theoretical considerations. The formula to which one is led, of course contains the electric force, the number N of electrons per unit of volume, the charge e and the mass m of each of them. In the first place, the force acting on an electron is found if we multiply by e the electric force. Next dividing by m, we shall find the velocity given to the electron per unit of time. The velocity acquired by the electrons will further depend on the time during which they are exposed to the undisturbed action of the electric force, a time for which we may take the interval that elapses between two successive impacts against a metallic atom. During this interval, the length of which is given by $\frac{l}{u}$, if l is the path between the two encounters, and u the velocity of the electron, the electric force produces a certain velocity which we can take to be lost again at the next collision.

These considerations will suffice for the explanation of the formula

$$\sigma = \frac{e^2 N l}{2 m u}, \tag{113}$$

which Drude has established for the electric conductivity of the metal, and in which we must understand by u the mean velocity of the electrons in their irregular heat-motion, and by l their mean length of free path. Now, as I said already, the mean kinetic energy of an electron, for which we may write $\frac{1}{2}mu^2$, is supposed to be equal to the mean kinetic energy of a gaseous molecule. The latter is proportional to the absolute temperature T, and may therefore be represented by

$$\alpha T,$$

where α is a universal constant. If we use this notation, (113) takes the form

$$\sigma = \frac{e^2 N l u}{4 \alpha T}. \tag{114}$$

48. In order to show you all the beauty of Drude's theory, I must also say a few words about the conductivity for heat. This can be calculated in a manner much resembling that in which it is determined in the kinetic theory of gases. Indeed, a bar of metal whose ends are maintained at different temperatures, may be likened to a colum of a gas, placed, for example, in a vertical position, and having a higher temperature at its top than at its base. The process by which the gas conducts heat consists, as you know, in a kind of diffusion between the upper part of the column, in which we find larger, and the lower one in which there are smaller molecular velocities; the amount of this diffusion, and the intensity of the flow of heat that results from it, depend on the mean distance over which a molecule travels between two successive encounters. In Drude's theory of metals, the conduction of heat goes on in a way that is exactly similar. Only, the carriers by which the heat is transferred from the hotter towards the colder parts of the body, now are the free electrons, and the length of their free paths is limited, not, as in the case of a gas, by the mutual encounters, but by the impacts against the metallic atoms, which we may suppose to remain at rest on account of their large masses.

Working out these ideas, Drude finds for the coefficient of conductivity for heat

$$k = \tfrac{1}{3} \alpha N l u. \tag{115}$$

49. It is highly interesting to compare the two conductivities, that for heat and that for electricity. Dividing (115) by (114), we get

$$\frac{k}{\sigma} = \frac{4}{3}\left(\frac{\alpha}{e}\right)^2 T, \tag{116}$$

which shows that the ratio must be equal for all metals. As a rough approximation this is actually the case.

We see therefore that Drude has been able to account for the important fact that, as a general rule, the metals which present the greatest conductivity for heat are also the best conductors of electricity.

Going somewhat deeper into details, I can point out to you two important verifications of the equation (116).

In the first place, measurements by Jaeger and Diesselhorst[1]) have shown that the ratio $\frac{k}{\sigma}$ between the two conductivities varies approximately as the absolute temperature, the ratio between the values of $\frac{k}{\sigma}$ for 100^0 and 18^0 ranging, for the different metals, between 1,25 and 1,12, whereas the ratio between the absolute temperatures is 1,28.

In the second place, the right-hand member of (116) can be calculated by means of data taken from other phenomena.[2]) In order to see this, we shall consider an amount of hydrogen, equal to an electrochemical equivalent of this substance, and we shall suppose this quantity to occupy, at the temperature T, a volume of one cubic centimetre. It will then exert a pressure that can easily be calculated, and which I shall denote by p.

We have already seen that the charge e which occurs in the formula (116), may be reckoned to be equal to the charge of an atom of hydrogen in an electrolytic solution. Therefore, the number of atoms in one electrochemical equivalent of hydrogen is $\frac{1}{e}\cdot$ The gas being diatomic, the number of molecules is $\frac{1}{2e}$, and the total kinetic energy of their progressive motion is

$$\frac{\alpha T}{2e}$$

per cubic centimetre.

By the fundamental formula of the kinetic theory of gases the

1) W. Jaeger und H. Diesselhorst, Wärmeleitung, Elektrizitätsleitung, Wärmekapazität und Thermokraft einiger Metalle, Sitzungsber. Berlin 1899, p. 719.

2) See M. Reinganum, Theoretische Bestimmung des Verhältnisses von Wärme- und Elektrizitätsleitung der Metalle aus der Drudeschen Elektronentheorie, Ann. Phys. 2 (1900), p. 398.

pressure per unit area is numerically equal to two thirds of this, so that

$$p = \frac{\alpha T}{3e}.$$

The equation (116) therefore takes the form

$$\frac{k}{\sigma} = 12 \frac{p^2}{T},$$

or

$$p = \sqrt{\tfrac{1}{12} \frac{k}{\sigma} T}. \tag{117}$$

This relation between the conductivities of a metal and other quantities derived from phenomena which, at first sight, have no connexion at all, neither with the conduction of heat, nor with that of electricity, has been verified in a very satisfactory way.

The electrochemical equivalent of hydrogen being

$$\frac{0{,}000104}{c\sqrt{4\pi}}$$

in our units, and the mass of a cubic centimetre of the gas at 0° and under a pressure of 76 cm of mercury being 0,0000896 gramm, one finds for the temperature of 18° ($T = 273 + 18$),

$$p = \frac{12{,}5 \times 10^5}{c\sqrt{4\pi}}. \tag{118}$$

On the other hand, expressing σ in the ordinary electromagnetic units, Jaeger and Diesselhorst have found for silver at 18°

$$\frac{k}{\sigma} = 686 \times 10^8.$$

In our units this becomes

$$\frac{k}{\sigma} = \frac{686 \times 10^8}{4\pi c^2},$$

by which we find for the quantity on the right hand side of (117)

$$\frac{12{,}9 \times 10^5}{c\sqrt{4\pi}},$$

showing a very close agreement with the value we have just calculated for p.

50. I must add, however, that the numerical agreement becomes somewhat less satisfactory, if, instead of Drude's formulae for the conductivities, one takes the equations to which I have been led by calculations that seem to me somewhat more rigorous than his. Taking into account that the electrons in a piece of metal have unequal velocities, and assuming **Maxwell's** law for the distribution of these among the particles, I find, instead of (114) and (115)[1]),

$$\sigma = \sqrt{\frac{2}{3\pi}}\,\frac{e^2 l N u}{\alpha T}, \tag{119}$$

and

$$k = \tfrac{8}{9}\sqrt{\frac{2}{3\pi}}\,\alpha N l u. \tag{120}$$

In these equations, u is a velocity of such a magnitude that its square is equal to the mean square of the velocities which the electrons have in their heat-motion, and l represents a certain mean length of free path.

The ratio of the two conductivities now becomes

$$\frac{k}{\sigma} = \tfrac{8}{9}\left(\frac{\alpha}{e}\right)^2 T;$$

it is still proportional to the absolute temperature, but it is only two thirds of the value given by **Drude**. On account of this we must replace (117) by the equation

$$p = \sqrt{\tfrac{1}{8}\frac{k}{\sigma}T},$$

whose right-hand side, in the example chosen in § 49, has the value

$$\frac{15{,}8\times 10^5}{c\sqrt{4\pi}}$$

This is rather different from (118).

If we prefer the formulae (119) and (120) to (114) and (115), as I think we are entitled to do, the agreement found in the preceding paragraph must be considered as produced by a fortuitous coincidence. Nevertheless, even the agreement we have now found, certainly warrants the conclusion that, in **Drude's** theory, a fair start has been made towards the understanding of the electric and thermal properties of metals.[2]) It is especially important to notice that our calculations rest on the assumption that the free electrons in a metal have charges equal to those of the ions of hydrogen.

---

1) Note **29**.

2) No more than a „start" however. The theory will have to be much further developed before we can explain the changes in the electric conductivity at low temperatures which **Kamerlingh Onnes** especially has shown to exist. Another important question is that of the part contributed by the free electrons to the specific heat of metals. [1915.]

CHAPTER II.

EMISSION AND ABSORPTION OF HEAT.

51. The subject of this and my next lecture will be the radiation and absorption of heat, especially the radiation by what is called a perfectly black body, considered with regard to the way in which these phenomena depend on the temperature and the wave-length. I shall first recall to your minds the important theoretical laws which Kirchhoff, Boltzmann and Wien have found by an application of thermodynamic principles. After that, we shall have to examine how far the theory of electrons can give us a clue to the mechanism of the phenomena.

We must begin by clearly defining what is meant by the absorbing power and the emissivity of a body. Let ω and ω' be two infinitely small planes perpendicular to the line r joining their centres, and let M be a body of the temperature T, placed so that it can receive a beam of rays going through ω' and ω. We shall suppose this beam to consist of homogeneous rays whose wave-length is λ, and to be plane-polarized, the electrical vibrations having a certain direction h, perpendicular to the line r. Part of the incident rays will be reflected at the front surface of the body, part of them will penetrate into its interior, and of these some will again leave the body, either directly or after one or more internal reflexions. However this may be, the body M, if it be not perfectly transparent, will retain a certain amount of energy, an amount that is converted into heat, because we shall exclude from our considerations all other changes that might be produced.

The *coefficient of absorption* A is defined as the fraction indicating what part of the incident energy is spent in heating the body M.

On the other hand, of the whole radiation emitted by M, a certain portion will travel outwards through the two elements ω and ω'. We shall decompose this radiation into rays of different wave-lengths, and we shall fix our attention on those whose wave-length lies between two limits infinitely near each other, λ and $\lambda + d\lambda$. We shall also decompose the electrical vibrations of these rays into a component along the line h of which I have just spoken, and a second component perpendicular both to it and to the direction of the beam itself. It can easily be shown that the amount of energy emitted by the body per unit of time through the two elements of surface, so far as it belongs to rays of the wave-lengths that have been specified, and to vibrations of the direction h, is proportional to ω, ω', $d\lambda$, and inversely proportional to the square of r. It can therefore be represented by

$$\frac{E\omega\omega' d\lambda}{r^2}. \tag{121}$$

The coefficient E is called the *emissivity* of the body M. It is a quantity depending on the nature of M, its position with respect to the line r, the wave-length λ, the temperature T and the direction h which we have chosen for the vibrations.

Starting from the thermodynamic principle that in a system of bodies having all the same temperature, the equilibrium is not disturbed by their mutual radiation, and using a train of reasoning which I shall not repeat, Kirchhoff[1]) finds that the ratio

$$\frac{E}{A}$$

between the emissivity and the absorbing power is independent, both of the direction we have chosen for h, and of the position and the peculiar properties of the body M. It will not be altered if we change the position of M, or replace it by an altogether different body of the same temperature. The ratio between the emissivity and the coefficient of absorption is a function of the temperature and the wave-length alone.

52. I shall now point out to you two other meanings that may be attached to this function. In the first place, following the example of Kirchhoff, we can conceive a *perfectly black* body, or, as we shall simply say, a *black* body, i. e. one that has the power of retaining for itself the total radiating energy which falls upon it. Its coefficient of absorption is therefore 1, and if we denote its emissivity by E_b, the symbols A and E relating to any other body, we shall have

$$\frac{E}{A} = E_b. \tag{122}$$

We may notice in passing that Kirchhoff's law requires all black bodies, whatever be their nature, to have exactly the same emissivity.

---

1) G. Kirchhoff, Über das Verhältnis zwischen dem Emissionsvermögen und dem Absorptionsvermögen der Körper für Wärme und Licht, Ann. Phys. Chem. **109** (1860), p. 275.

The equation (122) expresses one of the two meanings of $\frac{E}{A}$ to which I have alluded. The other will become apparent, if we fix our attention on the state existing in the ether in the neighborhood of radiating bodies.

We shall consider a space void of all ponderable matter and surrounded on all sides by a perfectly black envelop, which is kept at a fixed temperature T. The ether within this space is traversed in all directions by rays of heat. Let ω be an element of a plane situated at any point P of the space, and having any direction we like. We shall consider the quantity of energy by which this element is traversed per unit of time in the direction of its normal n, or rather in directions lying within an infinitely narrow cone, whose solid angle we shall denote by ε, and whose axis coincides with the normal n, always confining ourselves to wave-lengths between λ and $\lambda + d\lambda$, and to a particular direction h of the electrical vibrations. By this I mean that all vibrations of the rays within the cone are decomposed along lines h and k that are perpendicular as well to each other as to the axis of the cone, and that we shall only consider the components having the first named direction.

Let P' be a point on the normal n, at a distance r from the point P, and let us place at P an element of surface perpendicular to r, and whose magnitude is given by

$$\omega' = r^2 \varepsilon. \tag{123}$$

It is clear that, instead of speaking of the rays whose direction lies within the cone ε, we may as well speak of those that are propagated through the elements ω and ω'.

The quantity we wish to determine is therefore the flow of energy through the two small planes, issuing from the part of the enclosing wall behind ω. In virtue of the formula (121), it is given by

$$\frac{E_b \, \omega \, \omega' \, d\lambda}{r^2},$$

for which, on account of (123), we may write

$$E_b \, \omega \, \varepsilon \, d\lambda. \tag{124}$$

Having got thus far, we need no longer consider the element ω'; we have only to think of the element ω and the cone ε.

Now, what is most remarkable in our result, is the fact that it is wholly independent of the position of the point P, the direction of the element ω and the directions h and k, in which we have decomposed the vibrations. The radiation field within the ether is a truly isotropic one, i. e. the propagation takes place in exactly the same manner in all directions, and electrical vibrations of all different directions occur with the same intensity.

We shall now calculate the amount of energy in this radiation field per unit of volume. In the case of a beam of rays of a definite direction the quantity of energy that is carried per unit of time through a plane ω perpendicular to the rays, is equal to the amount existing at one and the same moment in a cylinder whose generating lines are parallel to the rays, and which has ω for its base and a height equal to the velocity of light c; it is $c\omega$ times the energy existing per unit of volume. Hence, the energy per unit of volume, belonging to the rays to which the expression (124) relates, is found if we divide that expression by $c\omega$; its value is

$$\frac{E_b}{c}\varepsilon d\lambda.$$

We must now keep in mind that we have all along considered only the rays whose direction lies within the cone ε, and only those components of their vibrations which have the direction h. If we wish to include all rays, whatever be their direction and that of their vibrations, we must make two changes. In the first place we must multiply by 2, because the vibrations of the direction k have the same intensity as those we have till now considered, and in the second place we must replace ε by 4π, because equal quantities of energy belong to rays whose directions lie within different cones of equal solid angles. The final result for the amount of energy present in unit volume of our radiation field, the „density" of the energy, so far as it is due to rays whose wave-lengths lie between the limits λ and $\lambda + d\lambda$, is

$$\frac{8\pi}{c}E_b d\lambda.$$

We shall write for this energy

$$F(\lambda, T)d\lambda,$$

so that, if we also take into account the relation (122), we have

$$F(\lambda, T) = \frac{8\pi}{c}E_b = \frac{8\pi}{c}\frac{E}{A}. \tag{125}$$

This equation, which expresses the relation between $\frac{E}{A}$ and the density of energy, shows us the other meaning that may be given to $\frac{E}{A}$.

53. One word more may be said about the state of radiation characterized by the function $F(\lambda, T)$. For the existence of this state it is not at all necessary that the walls of the enclosure should be perfectly black. We may just as well suppose that they are perfectly reflecting on the inside, and that the rays are produced by a body placed somewhere between them. Nor need this body be perfectly black. Whatever be its nature, if it is maintained at the temperature T we have chosen once for all, it can always be in equilibrium with a state of radiation in which each element of volume contains the energy we have been considering. We may add that not only will it be in equilibrium with this state, but that it will actually produce it, provided only the body have some emitting power, however small it may be, for all wave-lengths occurring in the radiation of a black body of the same temperature. If this condition is fulfilled, the radiation in the ether will be independent of the nature of the matter in which it originates; it will be determined by the temperature alone.

54. Kirchhoff has already laid stress on the importance of the function $F(\lambda, T)$, which must be independent of the peculiar properties of any body, and indeed the problem of determining this function is of paramount interest in modern theoretical physics. Boltzmann[1]) and Wien[2]) have gone as far towards the solution as can be done by thermodynamic principles, combined with general results of electromagnetic theory, if one leaves aside all speculations concerning the constitution of the radiating and absorbing matter.

Boltzmann's law shows us in what way the total energy existing per unit of volume in the radiation field we have spoken of, I mean the energy for the rays of all wave-lengths taken together, depends on the temperature. It is proportional to the fourth power of the *absolute* temperature, a result that had already been established as an empirical rule by Stefan.

In his demonstration, Boltzmann introduces the fact that there is a radiation pressure of the amount which we have formerly calculated.

Let us consider a closed envelop, perfectly reflecting on the inside, and containing a body M to which heat may be given or from which heat may be taken, in one way or another. The remaining part of the space contains only ether, and the walls are supposed to be movable, so that the enclosed volume can be altered.

---

1) L. Boltzmann, Ableitung des Stefan'schen Gesetzes, betreffend die Abhängigkeit der Wärmestrahlung von der Temperatur aus der elektromagnetischen Lichttheorie, Ann. Phys. Chem. **22** (1884), p. 291.

2) W. Wien, Eine neue Beziehung der Strahlung schwarzer Körper zum zweiten Hauptsatz der Wärmetheorie, Berlin. Sitzungsber. 1893, p. 55.

The system we have obtained in this manner is similar in many respects to a gas contained in a vessel of variable capacity. It is the seat of a certain energy, and like a gas it exerts a pressure on the bounding walls; only, we have now to do, not with the collisions of moving molecules, but with the pressure of radiation. If the walls move outwards, the system does a certain amount of work on them. Hence, a supply of heat is required, if we wish to maintain a constant temperature, and the temperature is lowered by the expansion, if the process is adiabatic. You will easily see that the system may be made to undergo a cycle of operations, two of which are isothermic and two adiabatic changes, and to which we may apply the well known law of Carnot.

Instead of imagining a cycle of this kind, I shall use a small calculation that will lead us to the same result. In all cases in which the state of a system is determined by the temperature T and the volume v, and in which the only force exerted by the system is a normal pressure p uniformly distributed over the surface, there is a simple thermodynamic relation by which we can learn something about the internal energy ε. If we choose v and T as independent variables, the equation has the form

$$\frac{\partial \varepsilon}{\partial v} = T \frac{\partial p}{\partial T} - p. \tag{126}$$

This may be applied to our envelop filled with rays, as well as to a gas; in a certain sense the case of the radiation is even the more simple of the two. The reason for this is, that the density of the energy depends solely on the temperature, so that, in an isothermic expansion, the new part that is added to the volume is immediately filled with an amount of energy proportional to its extent. The energy contained in the space that was already occupied by the radiation, remains unchanged, and the same may be said of the energy contained within the body M. In order to see this, we must keep in mind that, by what has been found in § 21, the pressure is equal to one third of the electromagnetic energy per unit of volume, so that the body remains exposed to the same pressure and, the temperature being likewise constant, will undergo no change at all.

Let us denote by K the electromagnetic energy per unit of volume, which, as we must take together all wave-lengths, may be represented by

$$K = \int_0^\infty F(\lambda, T)\, d\lambda.$$

Then we shall have

$$p = \tfrac{1}{3} K$$

and

$$\frac{\partial \varepsilon}{\partial v} = K,$$

because, if the volume is increased by dv, the energy augments by Kdv. Substituting in the formula (126), we find

$$K = \tfrac{1}{3} T \frac{dK}{dT} - \tfrac{1}{3} K,$$

$$4K = T \frac{dK}{dT},$$

$$\frac{dK}{K} = 4 \frac{dT}{T},$$

from which we deduce by integration

$$K = CT^4,$$

where C is a constant. The total energy per unit of volume, or as, in virtue of (125), we may also say, the total emissivity of a black body must be proportional to the fourth power of the temperature.

55. Passing on now to Wien's law, I shall first state the form in which it may be put if we avail ourselves of that of Boltzmann. Wien has not succeeded in determining the form of the function, which indeed cannot be done by thermodynamic reasoning and electromagnetic principles alone; he has however shown us how, as soon as the form of the function is known for one temperature, it may be found from this for any other temperature.

This may be expressed as follows. If T and T' are two different temperatures, λ and λ' two wave-lengths, such that

$$\lambda : \lambda' = T' : T, \tag{127}$$

we shall have

$$F(\lambda, T) : F(\lambda', T') = \lambda'^5 : \lambda^5. \tag{128}$$

If we put this in the form

$$F(\lambda', T') = \frac{T'^5}{T^5} F\left(\frac{T'}{T} \lambda', T\right),$$

we see that really $F(\lambda', T')$ can be determined for all values of λ', if we know $F(\lambda, T)$ for all values of λ.

We can also infer from (127) and (128) that if, while varying λ and T, we keep the product λT constant, the function $\lambda^5 F(\lambda, T)$ must also remain unchanged. Therefore, this last expression must be some function $f(\lambda T)$ of the product of wave-length and temperature, so that our original function must be of the form

$$F(\lambda, T) = \frac{1}{\lambda^5} f(\lambda T). \tag{129}$$

The relation between the forms of the function $F(\lambda, T)$ for different temperatures comes out very beautifully. If, for a definite temperature T, we plot the values of $F(\lambda, T)$. taking λ as abscissae and F as ordinates, we shall obtain a certain curve, which may be said to represent the distribution of energy in the spectrum of a black body of the temperature T From this we can get the corresponding curve for the temperature T' by changing all abscissae in the ratio of T' to T, and all ordinates in the ratio of T^5 to T'^5.

The form of the curve has been determined with considerable accuracy by the measurements of Lummer and Pringsheim.[1]) The accompanying figure will give an idea of it. It shows that, as could have been expected, the intensity is small for very short and very long waves, reaching a maximum for a definite wave-length which is represented by OA, and which I shall call λ_m. Now, if the curve undergoes the change of shape of which I have just spoken, this maximum will be shifted towards the right if T' is lower than T, and towards the left in the opposite case, the value of λ_m being in fact inversely proportional to the temperature. It is for this reason that Wien's law is often called the displacement-law (Verschiebungsgesetz).

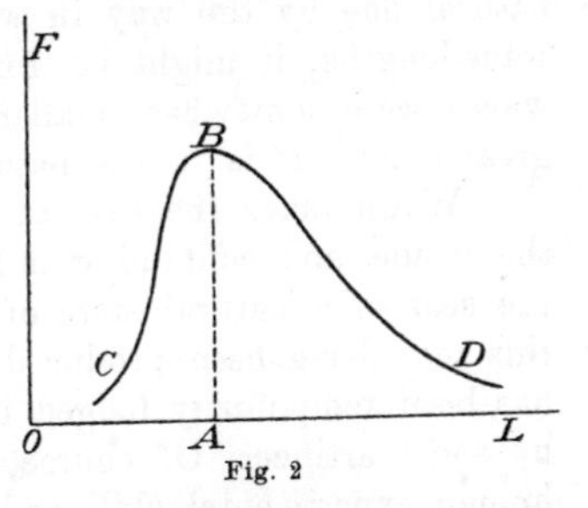

Fig. 2

The diagram may also be used for showing that Boltzmann's law is included in the formulae (127) and (128). The value of K is given by the total area included between the curve and the axis of abscissae, and this area changes in the ratio of T^4 to T'^4, when the abscissae and ordinates are changed as has been stated.

56. It would take too much of our time, if I were to give you a complete account of the theoretical deductions by which Wien found his law. Just as in Boltzmann's reasoning, we can distinguish two parts in it, one that is based on the equations of the electromagnetic field, and a second that is purely thermodynamic.

We have already seen that, for every temperature T, there is a perfectly definite state of radiation in the ether, which has the property that it can be in equilibrium with ponderable bodies of the temperature T. For the sake of brevity I shall call this the *natural*

1) O. Lummer u. E. Pringsheim, Die Strahlung eines schwarzen Körpers zwischen 100 und 1300° C, Ann. Phys. Chem. **63** (1897), p. 395; Die Verteilung der Energie im Spektrum des schwarzen Körpers, Verh. d. deutschen phys. Ges. **1** (1899), p. 23.

state of radiation for the temperature T. It is characterized by a definite amount K of energy per unit of volume, proportional to T^4, and which may therefore be used, instead of T itself, for defining the state of the ether. If we speak of a natural state of radiation with the energy-density K, we shall know perfectly what we mean.

In this natural state the total energy is distributed in a definite manner over the various wave-lengths, a distribution that is expressed by the function $F(\lambda, T)$. Now, we can of course imagine other states having the same density of energy K, but differing from the natural one by the way in which the energy is distributed over the wave-lengths; it might be, for example, that the energy of the long waves were somewhat smaller, and that of the short ones somewhat greater than it is in the natural state.

Wien takes the case of a closed envelop perfectly reflecting on the inside, and containing only ether. He supposes this ether to be the seat of a natural state of radiation A with the energy-density K; this may have been produced by a body of the temperature T that has been temporarily lodged in the enclosure, and has been removed by some artifice. Of course, this operation would require a superhuman experimental skill and especially great quickness, but we can suppose it to be succesfully performed. If then we leave the vessel to itself, the radiations that are imprisoned within it, will continue to exist for ever, the rays being over and over again reflected by the walls, without any change in their wave-lengths and their intensity.

At this point, Wien introduces an imaginary experiment by which the state of things can be altered. It consists in giving to the walls a slow motion by which the interior volume is increased or diminished. We have already seen (§ 46) that, if a mirror struck normally by a beam of rays is made to recede, this will have a twofold influence on the reflected rays; their frequency is lowered, so that the wave-length becomes larger, and their amplitude is diminished. The same will be true, though in a less degree, if the incidence of the rays is not normal but oblique, and in this case also the effect can be easily calculated.

In order to fix our ideas we shall suppose the walls of our vessel to expand. Then, every time a ray is reflected by them, it has its amplitude diminished and its wave-length increased, so that, after a certain time, we shall have got a new state of radiation B, differing from the original one by its energy per unit of volume and by the distribution of the energy over the wave-lengths. The density of energy will have a certain value K', smaller than the original value K, and the distribution over the wave-lengths will have been somewhat altered in favour of the larger wave-lengths.

Of course, K' can have different values, because the expansion by which the new state is produced may be a large or a small one. Since, however, the changes in the amplitudes and those in the wave-lengths are closely connected, it is clear that the distribution of the energy over the wave-lengths must be quite determinate if we know K', so that it was possible for Wien to calculate it. His result may be expressed as follows.[1]) If

$$\varphi(\lambda)d\lambda \tag{130}$$

is the part of the original energy per unit of volume that is due to the rays with wave-lengths between λ and $\lambda + d\lambda$, the amount of energy corresponding to the same interval in the new state B is given by

$$\sqrt[4]{\left(\frac{K'}{K}\right)^5} \cdot \varphi\left(\sqrt[4]{\frac{K}{K'}} \cdot \lambda\right) d\lambda. \tag{131}$$

57. I hope I have given you a sufficiently clear idea of one part of Wien's demonstration. As to the second part, the thermodynamic one, its object is to show that the new state B, in which there is a density of energy K', cannot be different from a *natural* state of radiation having the same K', that it must therefore itself be a natural state. If it were not, we could place our vessel containing the state B against a second vessel containing a natural state A' with the same value K', the two states being at first separated by the walls of the two vessels. Then we could make an opening in these walls, and close it immediately by means of a very thin plate of some transparent substance. Such a plate will transmit part of the rays by which it is struck, and, on account of the well-known phenomena of interference, the coefficient of transmission will not be the same for different kinds of rays. Let us suppose it to be somewhat greater for the long waves than for the short ones, and let us also assume that the state B contains more of the long waves than the state A', and less of the short waves. Then, it is easily seen that, in the first instants after communication has been established between the two vessels, more energy will pass from B towards A' than in the inverse direction, so that the energy of the two states will not remain equal. This can be shown to be in contradiction with the second law of thermodynamics.

Our conclusion must therefore be that, by means of the expression (131), we can calculate the distribution of energy in a *natural* state characterized by K', as soon as we know the distribution, represented by (130), for a natural state characterized by K. Now, both states being natural ones, we shall have, if we write T and T'

---

1) Note **30**.

for the temperatures to which they correspond,

$$K : K' = T^4 : T'^4$$

Therefore, (131) becomes

$$\frac{T'^5}{T^5}\varphi\left(\frac{T'}{T}\lambda\right)d\lambda,$$

by which we are led to Wien's law in the form in which I have stated it.

58. Though Boltzmann and Wien have gone far towards determining the function $F(\lambda, T)$, the precise form of the curve in Fig. 2 remains to be found, and since the means of thermodynamics are exhausted, we can only hope to attain this object, if we succeed in forming some adequate mental picture of the processes which manifest themselves in the phenomena of radiation and absorption.

The importance of the problem will be understood, if one takes into account that the curve in Fig. 2 requires for its determination at least two constants. Calling λ_m the abscissa OA for which the ordinate is a maximum, we have by Wien's law

$$\lambda_m = \frac{a}{T},$$

and if, as before, the total area included between the curve and the axis of abscissae is denoted by K, we shall have

$$K = bT^4.$$

Of the two constants a and b, the first determines, for a given temperature T, the position of the point A, and the second relates to the values of the ordinates, because the larger these are, the greater will be the area K. Now, if the state of radiation is produced by a ponderable body, the values of the two constants must be determined by something in the constitution of this body, and these values can only have the universal meaning of which we have spoken, if all ponderable bodies have something in common. If we wish completely to account for the form and dimensions of the curve, we shall have to discover these common features in the constitution of all ponderable matter.

59. I shall speak of three theories by which the problem has been at least partially solved, beginning with the one that goes farthest of all. This has been developed by Planck[1]), and leads to a definite formula for the function $f(\lambda T)$ in (129), viz. to

1) M. Planck, Über irreversible Strahlungsvorgänge, Ann. Phys. **1** (1900), p. 69; Über das Gesetz der Energieverteilung im Normalspektrum, Ann. Phys. **4** (1901), p. 553; Über die Elementarquanta der Materie und der Elektrizität, ibid., p. 564; see also his book: Vorlesungen über die Theorie der Wärmestrahlung, Leipzig, 1906.

$$F(\lambda, T) = \frac{8\pi ch}{\lambda^5} \cdot \frac{1}{\varepsilon^{\frac{ch}{k\lambda T}} - 1}, \tag{132}$$

in which ε is the basis of natural logarithms, whereas h and k are two universal physical constants.

Planck's theory is based on the assumption that every ponderable body contains an immense number of electromagnetic vibrators, or „resonators“ as he calls them, each of which has its own period. If a body is enclosed within the perfectly reflecting walls we have so often mentioned, there will be a state of equilibrium, on the one hand between the resonators and the radiation in the ether, and on the other hand between the resonators and the ordinary heat motion of the molecules and atoms constituting the ponderable matter. The first of these equilibria can be examined by means of the electromagnetic equations, and, in order to understand the second, one could try to trace the interchange of energy between the resonators and the ordinary particles. Planck, however, has not followed this course, which would lead us into very serious difficulties, but has found his formula by reasonings of a different kind.

In one of his papers he deduces it by examining what partition of the energy between the two sets of particles, the molecules and the resonators, is to be considered as the most probable one. Of course this is an expression, the precise meaning of which has to be fixed before we can make it the basis of the theory. I must abstain from explaining the sense in which it is understood by Planck. There is one point, however, in his theory to which I must refer for a moment. He is obliged to assume that the resonators can gain or lose energy, not quite gradually by infinitely small amounts, but only by certain portions of a definite finite magnitude. These portions are taken to be different for resonators of different frequencies. The portions of energy which we have to imagine when we speak of a resonator of the frequency n, have an amount that is given by the expression

$$\frac{hn}{2\pi}.$$

It is in this way that the constant h is introduced into the equations.

As to the constant k, it has a very simple physical meaning. According to the kinetic theory of gases, the mean kinetic energy of the progressive motion of a molecule is equal for all gases, when compared at the same temperature. This mean energy is proportional to T, and if we represent it by $\frac{3}{2}kT$, the quantity k will be the constant appearing in the formula (132).

Planck's law shows a most remarkable agreement with the experimental results of Lummer and Pringsheim, and it is of high value because it enables us to deduce from measurements on radiation the mean kinetic energy of a molecule, which, in its turn, leads us to the masses of the atoms in absolute measure. As the numbers obtained in this way[1]) are of the same order of magnitude as those that have been found by other means, there is undoubtedly much truth in the theory. Yet, we cannot say that the mechanism of the phenomena has been unveiled by it, and it must be admitted that it is difficult to see a reason for this partition of energy by finite portions, which are not even equal to each other, but vary from one resonator to the other.[2])

60. I shall dwell somewhat longer on the second theory[3]), because it is an application of the theory of electrons, and therefore properly belongs to my subject. In a certain sense, it may, I think, be considered as rather satisfactory, but it has the great defect of being confined to long waves. I may be permitted perhaps, by way of introduction, to tell you by what considerations I have been led to this theory. It is well known that, in general, the optical properties of ponderable bodies cannot be deduced quantitatively with any degree of accuracy from the electrical properties. For example, though Maxwell's theoretical inference, published long ago in his treatise, that good conductors for electricity must be but little transparent for light, is corroborated by the fact that metals are very opaque, yet, if we compare the optical constants of a metal, one of which is its coefficient of absorption, with the formulae of the electromagnetic theory of light, taking for the conductivity the ordinary value that is found by measurements on electric currents, there is a very wide disagreement. This shows, and so does the discrepancy between the refractive indices of dielectrics and the square root of their dielectric constants, that, in the case of the very rapid vibrations of light, circumstances come into play with which we are not concerned in our experiments on steady or slowly alternating electric currents.

If this idea be right, we may hope to find a better agreement, if we examine the „optical“ properties as we may continue to call them, not for rays of light, but for infra-red rays of the largest wave-lengths that are known to exist.

Now, in the case of the metals, this expectation has been verified in a splendid way by the measurements of the absorption that were

1) Note **31**.

2) Since this was written Planck's theory of „quanta“ has been largely developed. It now occupies a prominent place in several parts of theoretical physics. [1915.]

3) Lorentz, On the emission and absorption by metals of rays of heat of great wave-lengths, Amsterdam Proc., 1902—03, p. 666.

made some years ago by Hagen and Rubens.[1]) These physicists have shown that rays whose wave-length is between 8 and 25 microns, are absorbed to a degree that may be calculated with considerable accuracy from the known conductivity.[2]) We can conclude from this that, in order to obtain a theory of absorption in the case of these long waves, we only have to understand the nature of a common current of conduction. Moreover, if in this line of thought, we can form for ourselves a picture of the absorption, it must also be possible to get an insight into the way in which rays are emitted by a metal. Indeed, the universal validity of Kirchhoff's law clearly proves that the causes which produce the absorption by a body, and those which call forth its radiation, must be very closely related. Therefore, as soon as we have an adequate idea about a common current of conduction, we may hope to be able to explain the absorption and the emissivity of a metal, and to calculate the ratio between the two, i. e. our universal function $F(\lambda, T)$. However, we can only hope to succeed in this, if we confine ourselves to long waves.

Now, as we have already seen, a very satisfactory conception of the nature of a current of conduction has been worked out by Drude. We must therefore try to obtain a theory of the radiation and emission of metals that is based on his general principles, and in which we simply assume that the metal contains a large number of free electrons, moving with such speeds that their mean kinetic energy is equal to αT.

61. In doing so, we shall simplify as much as possible the circumstances of the case. We shall consider a metal plate, whose thickness Δ is so small that the absorption may be considered as proportional to it, and that, in examining the emission, we need not consider the absorption which the rays emitted by the back half of the plate undergo, while traversing the layers lying in front of it. We shall also confine ourselves to rays whose direction is perpendicular to the plate or makes an infinitely small angle with the normal. These assumptions will greatly facilitate our calculations without detracting from the generality of the final result. If we trust to Kirchhoff's law, the value which we shall find for the ratio between the emissivity and the coefficient of absorption may be expected to hold for all bodies and for all directions of the rays.

The calculation of the absorption is very easy. By the ordinary formulae of the electromagnetic field we find for the coefficient of absorption[3])

$$A = \frac{\sigma}{c}\Delta,$$

1) E. Hagen u. H. Rubens, Über Beziehungen des Reflexions- und Emissionsvermögens der Metalle zu ihrem elektrischen Leitvermögen, Ann. Phys. **11** 1903), p. 873.

2) Note **32**. 3) Note **33**

and here we have only to substitute the value of σ, given by Drude's theory. Using the formula (119), we find

$$A = \sqrt{\frac{2}{3\pi}} \cdot \frac{e^2 l N u}{\alpha c T} \Delta. \qquad (133)$$

62. The question now arises, in what manner a piece of metal in which free electrons are moving in all directions can be the source of a radiation. The answer is contained in what we have seen in a former lecture. We know that an electron can be the centre of an emission of energy only when its velocity changes. The cause of the emission must therefore be looked for in the impacts against the metallic atoms, by which the electron is made to rebound in a new direction, so that the radiation of heat, in the case we are now considering, very much resembles the production of Röntgen rays, as it is explained in Wiechert's and J. J. Thomson's theory.

The mathematical operations required for the determination of the effects of the impacts are rather complicated, the more so because we must decompose the total radiation into the parts corresponding to different wave-lengths. I shall therefore give only a general outline of the calculations.

I must mention in advance that the decomposition of which I have spoken just now will be performed by means of Fourier's theorem, and that the duration of an impact will be taken to be extremely small in comparison with the time of vibration of the rays considered. We shall even make the same assumption with regard to the time between two successive impacts of an electron. This is justified by the experiments of Hagen and Rubens. It is easily seen that the conductivity of a metal can be given by the formula (119), only if the electric force acts on the body either continually or at least for a time during which a large number of encounters of an electron take place. Therefore, the result found by Hagen and Rubens, viz. that the absorption corresponds to the coefficient of conductivity, proves that the time during which the electric force acts in one and the same direction, i. e. half a period, contains very many times the interval between two successive encounters.

63. In § 51 we have considered the radiation from the body M through two infinitely small planes ω and ω'. We shall now suppose the first of these to be situated in the front surface of the thin metallic plate, and we shall fix our attention on the radiation issuing from the corresponding part $\omega \Delta$ of the plate, and directed towards the element ω', parallel to ω, and situated at a point P of the line drawn normally to the plate from the centre O of the element ω.

We shall begin by taking into account only the component of the electric vibrations in a certain direction h perpendicular to OP.

Let us choose the point O as origin of coordinates, drawing the axis of z along OP, that of x in the direction h, and denoting the distance OP by r. According to what has been found in § 39, a single electron, moving with the velocity $\mathbf{v}$ in the part of the plate considered, will produce at P a dielectric displacement whose first component is given by

$$-\frac{e}{4\pi c^2 r}\frac{d\mathbf{v}_x}{dt},$$

if we take the value of the differential coefficient for the proper instant.

On account of our assumption as to the thickness of the plate, this instant may be represented for all the electrons in the portion $\omega\Delta$ by $t-\frac{r}{c}$, if t is the time for which we wish to determine the state of things at the point P. We may therefore write for the first component of the dielectric displacement at P

$$\mathbf{d}_x = -\frac{1}{4\pi c^2 r}\left(\Sigma e\frac{d\mathbf{v}_x}{dt}\right)_{t-\frac{r}{c}} \qquad (134)$$

The flow of energy through ω' per unit of time will be

$$c\mathbf{d}_x^2\omega'.$$

Since the motion of the electrons between the metallic atoms is highly irregular, we shall have, at rapidly succeeding instants, a large number of impacts in which the changes of the velocity are widely different. The state at P, which is due to all these impacts, will show the same irregularity. Nevertheless, we must try to deduce from the formulae relating to it, results concerning those quantities that can make themselves felt in actual experiments.

Results of this kind are obtained by considering the *mean* values of the variable quantities calculated for a sufficiently long lapse of time. We shall suppose this time to extend from $t=0$ to $t=\vartheta$. If the mean value of $\mathbf{d}_x^2$ is denoted by $\overline{\mathbf{d}_x^2}$, we shall have for the flow of energy through ω' that is accessible to our means of observation

$$c\overline{\mathbf{d}_x^2}\omega' = c\omega'\cdot\frac{1}{\vartheta}\int_0^\vartheta \mathbf{d}_x^2 dt. \qquad (135)$$

64. The introduction of this long time ϑ is also very useful for the application of Fourier's theorem. Whatever be the way in which $\mathbf{d}_x$ changes from one instant to the next, we can always expand it in a series by the formula

$$\mathbf{d}_x = \sum_{s=1}^{s=\infty} a_s \sin \frac{s\pi t}{\vartheta}, \tag{136}$$

where s is a positive whole number, each coefficient a_s being determined by

$$a_s = \frac{2}{\vartheta}\int_0^{\vartheta} \sin \frac{s\pi t}{\vartheta} \mathbf{d}_x dt. \tag{137}$$

It appears from (136) that the frequency of one of the terms is

$$n = \frac{s\pi}{\vartheta},$$

so that the corresponding wave-length is given by

$$\lambda = \frac{2\pi c}{n} = \frac{2c\vartheta}{s} \tag{138}$$

The interval ϑ being very large, the values of λ belonging to small values of s will be so too; we shall not, however, have to speak of these very long waves, because they may be expected to represent no appreciable part of the total radiation. The rays with which we are concerned, will have wave-lengths below a certain upper limit λ_0; therefore, provided the time ϑ (which we are free to choose as long as we like) be long enough, they will correspond to very high values of the number s. Now, if λ_s and λ_{s+1} are two successive wave-lengths, we shall have

$$\frac{\lambda_s - \lambda_{s+1}}{\lambda_s} = 1 - \frac{s}{s+1} = \frac{1}{s+1},$$

which is a very small number. The wave-lengths corresponding to the successive terms in our series are thus seen to diminish by exceedingly small steps. This means that, if we were to decompose the radiation represented by (136) into a spectrum, we should find a very large number of lines lying closely together. Their mutual distances may be indefinitely diminished by increasing the length of the time ϑ and the values of s corresponding to the part of the spectrum we wish to consider. This is the way in which we can deduce from our formulae the existence of a continuous spectrum and the laws relating to it.

Let λ and $\lambda + d\lambda$ be two wave-lengths, which, from a physical point of view, may be said to lie infinitely near each other. If ϑ is duly lengthened, the part of the spectrum corresponding to $d\lambda$ contains a large number of spectral lines, for which we find

$$\frac{2c\vartheta}{\lambda^2} d\lambda.$$

This is clear, if, after having written (138) in the form

$$s = \frac{2c\vartheta}{\lambda},$$

we observe that the number of lines is the same as the number of integers lying between the limits

$$\frac{2c\vartheta}{\lambda + d\lambda} \quad \text{and} \quad \frac{2c\vartheta}{\lambda},$$

for which we may take the difference

$$\frac{2c\vartheta}{\lambda^2}d\lambda,$$

because, in virtue of our supposition, this difference is much larger than 1.

We have now to substitute the value (136) in the equation (135). It is easily seen that the product of two terms of the series for $\mathbf{d}_x$ will give 0, if integrated with respect to time between the limits 0 and ϑ. Moreover

$$\int_0^\vartheta \sin^2 \frac{s\pi t}{\vartheta}\, dt = \tfrac{1}{2}\vartheta,$$

and (135) becomes

$$c\overline{\mathbf{d}_x^2}\omega' = \tfrac{1}{2}c\omega' \sum_{s=1}^{s=\infty} a_s^2. \tag{139}$$

This is the total flow of energy through ω'. In order to find the part of it, corresponding to wave-lengths between λ and $\lambda + d\lambda$, we have only to observe that the $\frac{2c\vartheta}{\lambda^2}d\lambda$ spectral lines lying within that interval, may be considered to have equal intensities.[1])

In other terms, the value of a_s may be regarded as equal for each of them, so that they contribute to the sum in (139) an amount

$$\frac{2c\vartheta}{\lambda^2}\, a_s^2 d\lambda$$

Consequently, the part of the flow of energy, belonging to the interval of wave-lengths $d\lambda$, is given by

$$\frac{c^2\vartheta\omega'}{\lambda^2}\, a_s^2 d\lambda, \tag{140}$$

and our problem will be solved, if we succeed in calculating a_s^2.

65. The following mathematical developments are somewhat more rigorous than those which I gave in my paper on the subject.

---

1) Note **34**.

In fact, I shall now introduce Maxwell's law for the distribution of the velocities among the electrons, and take into account that the free paths are not all of the same length. At the same time I shall introduce a simplification for which I am indebted to Langevin[1]), and by which it will be possible to give in a small space the essential part of the calculation.

By (134) and (137) we see that

$$a_s = -\frac{1}{2\pi\vartheta c^2 r}\sum\left\{e\int_0^\vartheta \sin\frac{s\pi t}{\vartheta}\frac{d[\mathsf{v}_x]}{dt}\,dt\right\}, \tag{141}$$

where the square brackets serve to indicate the value of v_x at the time $t-\frac{r}{c}$.

The meaning of this equation is, that we must first, for one definite electron, calculate the integral, taking into account all the values of the acceleration occurring during the interval of time between $-\frac{r}{c}$ and $\vartheta-\frac{r}{c}$. This having been done, we have to take the sum of the values that are found in this way for all the free electrons contained in the part $\omega\Delta$ of the plate.

Integrating by parts we find, because $\sin\frac{s\pi t}{\vartheta}$ vanishes at the limits,

$$a_s = \frac{se}{2\vartheta^2 c^2 r}\sum\left\{\int_0^\vartheta [\mathsf{v}_x]\cos\frac{s\pi t}{\vartheta}\,dt\right\}, \tag{142}$$

for which, understanding by v_x the value at the time t, we may also write

$$a_s = \frac{se}{2\vartheta^2 c^2 r}\sum\left\{\int_{-\frac{r}{c}}^{\vartheta-\frac{r}{c}} \mathsf{v}_x\cos\frac{s\pi}{\vartheta}\left(t+\frac{r}{c}\right)dt\right\}.$$

By this artifice of partial integration, the problem is reduced to a much simpler one. If we had directly to calculate the integral in (141), we should have to attend to the intervals of time during which an electron is subjected to the force which makes it rebound from an atom against which it strikes; indeed, it is only during these intervals that there is an acceleration. On the other hand, the integral in (142) is made up of parts, due, not only to the times of

1) See his translation of my paper in H. Abraham et P. Langevin, Les quantités élémentaires d'électricité, ions, électrons, corpuscules, Paris (1905), **1**, p. 507.

impact, but also to all intervening intervals. If we suppose the duration of an encounter to be very much smaller than the lapse of time between two successive collisions of an electron, we may even confine ourselves to the part that corresponds to the free paths between these collisions.

While an electron travels over one of these free paths, its velocity $\mathbf{v}_x$ is constant. We may also neglect the change in the factor $\cos \frac{s\pi}{\vartheta}\left(t + \frac{r}{c}\right)$, because the time between two encounters is supposed to be very much smaller than the time of vibration corresponding to s. The part of a_s which corresponds to one electron, and to the time during which it describes one of its free paths, is therefore given by

$$\frac{se}{2\vartheta^2 c^2 r} \tau \mathbf{v}_x \cos \frac{s\pi}{\vartheta}\left(t + \frac{r}{c}\right),$$

if we understand by τ the time during which the path is travelled over. In the last factor we may take for t the value corresponding to the middle of the time τ.

We shall now fix our attention on all the paths described by all the electrons during the time ϑ. If we use the symbol $\mathbf{S}$ for denoting a sum relating to all these free paths, we shall have

$$a_s = \frac{se}{2\vartheta^2 c^2 r} \mathbf{S}\left\{\tau \mathbf{v}_x \cos \frac{s\pi}{\vartheta}\left(t + \frac{r}{c}\right)\right\}. \tag{143}$$

66. We have to determine the square of the sum $\mathbf{S}$. This may be done rather easily, because the products of two terms

$$\tau \mathbf{v}_x \cos \frac{s\pi}{\vartheta}\left(t + \frac{r}{c}\right),$$

whether they correspond to two different free paths of one and the same electron, or to two paths described by different electrons will give 0, if all taken together. Indeed, the velocities of two electrons are wholly independent of each other, and the same may be said of the velocities of one definite electron at two instants between which it has undergone one or more impacts.[1]) Therefore, positive and negative values of $\mathbf{v}_x$ being distributed quite indiscriminately between the terms of (143), positive and negative signs will be equally probable for the products of two terms.

It is seen in this way that we have only to calculate the sum of the squares of the several terms, so that we find

$$a_s^2 = \frac{s^2 e^2}{4\vartheta^4 c^4 r^2} \mathbf{S}\left\{\tau^2 \mathbf{v}_x^2 \cos^2 \frac{s\pi}{\vartheta}\left(t + \frac{r}{c}\right)\right\}.$$

---

1) Note 35.

Now, since the irregular motion of the electrons takes place with the same intensity in all directions, we may replace $\mathbf{v}_x^2$ by $\frac{1}{3}\mathbf{v}^2$. Therefore, writing l for the length $\tau|\mathbf{v}|$ of the free path, we find

$$a_s^2 = \frac{s^2 e^2}{12\vartheta^4 c^4 r^2}\mathbf{S}\left\{l^2 \cos^2 \frac{s\pi}{\vartheta}\left(t+\frac{r}{c}\right)\right\}.$$

In the immense number of terms included in the sum, the length l is very different, and in order to effect the summation we may begin by considering only those terms for which it has a certain particular value. In these terms, which are still very numerous, the angle $\frac{s\pi}{\vartheta}\left(t+\frac{r}{c}\right)$ has values that are distributed at random over an interval ranging from 0 to $s\pi$. The square of the cosine may therefore be replaced by its mean value $\frac{1}{2}$, so that

$$a_s^2 = \frac{s^2 e^2}{24\vartheta^4 c^4 r^2}\mathbf{S}(l^2). \tag{144}$$

67. The metallic atoms being considered as immovable, the velocity of an electron is not altered by a collision. We can therefore fix our attention on a certain group of electrons which move along their zigzag-lines with a definite velocity u. During the time ϑ, one of these particles describes a large number of free paths, this number being given by

$$\frac{u\vartheta}{l_m},$$

if l_m is the mean length of the paths. It can be shown[1] that the number of paths whose length lies between l and $l+dl$, is

$$\frac{u\vartheta}{l_m^2}\varepsilon^{-\frac{l}{l_m}}dl,$$

so that

$$\frac{u\vartheta}{l_m^2}l^2\varepsilon^{-\frac{l}{l_m}}dl$$

is the part of the sum $\mathbf{S}(l^2)$ contributed by these paths. Integrating with respect to l from 0 to ∞, we find

$$2\vartheta u l_m \tag{145}$$

for the value of $\mathbf{S}(l^2)$ in so far as it is due to one electron.

The total number of electrons in the part of the metallic plate under consideration is $N\omega\Delta$ and, by Maxwell's law, among these

$$4\pi N\omega\Delta\sqrt{\frac{q^3}{\pi^3}}\varepsilon^{-qu^2}u^2du \tag{146}$$

1) Note **36**.

have velocities between u and $u + du$, the constant q being related to the velocity u_m whose square is equal to the mean value of u^2, by the formula

$$q = \frac{3}{2u_m^2}.$$

In order to find the total value of $\mathbf{S}(l^2)$ we must multiply (145) by (146), and integrate the product between the limits $u = 0$ and $u = \infty$. Supposing l_m to be the same for all values of u[1]), we find

$$\mathbf{S}(l^2) = \frac{4\vartheta}{\sqrt{\pi q}} l_m N \omega \varDelta = 4\sqrt{\frac{2}{3\pi}}\, \vartheta l_m N u_m \omega \varDelta.$$

Finally, the equation (144) becomes

$$a_s^2 = \sqrt{\frac{2}{3\pi}} \cdot \frac{s^2 e^2 l_m N u_m}{6\vartheta^3 c^4 r^2} \omega \varDelta,$$

and the expression (140) for the radiation through the element ω' takes the form

$$\sqrt{\frac{2}{3\pi}} \cdot \frac{s^2 e^2 l_m N u_m}{6\vartheta^2 c^2 r^2 \lambda^2} \omega \omega' \varDelta d\lambda,$$

or, in virtue of (138), if, instead of l_m, u_m, we simply write l, u,

$$\sqrt{\frac{2}{3\pi}} \cdot \frac{2}{3} \frac{e^2 l N u}{r^2 \lambda^4} \omega \omega' \varDelta d\lambda.$$

This is the energy radiated per unit of time, in so far as it belongs to wave-lengths between λ and $\lambda + d\lambda$, and to the components of the vibrations in one direction h. Thus, the quantity we have calculated is exactly what was represented by (121), and on comparing the two expressions we find

$$E = \sqrt{\frac{2}{3\pi}} \cdot \frac{2}{3} \frac{e^2 l N u}{\lambda^4} \varDelta \qquad (147)$$

for the emissivity of the plate.

68. We have now to combine this with the value (133), which we have found for the coefficient of absorption. If Kirchhoff's law is to hold, the ratio $\frac{E}{A}$ must be independent of those quantities by which one metallic plate differs from the other. This is really seen to be the case, since the number N of electrons per unit of volume, the mean length l of their free paths and the thickness $\varDelta$ of the plate all disappear from the ratio. We really get for $\frac{E}{A}$ and for $F(\lambda, T)$ values that are independent of the peculiar properties of

1) Note 37.

any ponderable body. I must repeat however that all our considerations only hold for large wave-lengths.

Using the formulae (125), (133) and (147), we find[1])

$$F(\lambda, T) = \frac{16\pi\alpha T}{3\lambda^4}. \tag{148}$$

It is very remarkable that this result is of the form (129) and that it agrees exactly with that of Planck. This may be seen, if in (132) we suppose the product λT to have a very large value, so that the exponent is very small. Then, we may put

$$\varepsilon^{\frac{ch}{k\lambda T}} = 1 + \frac{ch}{k\lambda T}$$

and (132) becomes

$$F(\lambda, T) = \frac{8\pi k T}{\lambda^4}.$$

This is equal to (148), because our coefficient α corresponds to $\frac{3}{2}k$ in Planck's notation. As has been stated, the mean kinetic energy of a molecule of a gas is $\frac{3}{2}kT$, and we have represented it by αT.[2])

69. A widely different theory of the radiation of a black body has been developed by Rayleigh and Jeans.[3]) It is based on the theorem of the so called equipartition of energy, which plays an important part in the kinetic theory of gases and in molecular theories in general. In its most simple form it was discovered by Maxwell in 1860; afterwards it was largely extended by Boltzmann, and Jeans has given an ample discussion of it in his book on the kinetic theory of gases.

Maxwell was led to the theorem by his theoretical investigations concerning the motion of systems consisting of a large number of molecules. If, from a mass of gas, we could select single molecules, we should find them to move with very different velocities, and to have very different kinetic energies. The mean kinetic energy of the progressive motion, taken for a sufficiently large number of molecules will however be the same in adjacent parts of the gas, if the temperature is the same everywhere, so that these parts can be said to be in equilibrium. This will even be true if the gas is subjected to external forces, such as the force of gravity, which make the density change from point to point. Also, if we have a mixture of two gases, the mean kinetic energy of a molecule can be shown to be equal for the two constituents, and we can safely assume that for

1) This formula is due to Lord Rayleigh [Phil. Mag. **49** (1900), p. 539]. See § 69. 2) Note **38**.

2) J. H. Jeans, On the partition of energy between matter and aether, Phil. Mag. (6) **10** (1905), p. 91.

two gases that are not mixed, but kept apart, this equality of the mean kinetic energy of a molecule is the condition for the existence of equilibrium of temperature. We can express this by saying that the kinetic energy of a gas, in so far as it is due to the progressive motion of the molecules, can be calculated by attributing to each molecule an amount of energy having the same definite value, whatever be the nature of the gas.

This amount of energy is proportional to the absolute temperature T, and may therefore be represented, as I have done already several times, by αT, α being a universal constant.

We can express the result in a somewhat different way. If the molecules of the gas are supposed to be perfectly elastic and rigid smooth spheres, the only motion with which we are concerned in these questions is their translation; the position of the particles can therefore be determined by the coordinates x, y, z of their centres. If N is the number of molecules, the configuration of the whole system requires for its determination $3N$ coordinates, or, as is often said, the system has $3N$ degrees of freedom. To each degree of freedom, or to each coordinate x, y or z, corresponds a certain velocity $\dot{x}$, $\dot{y}$ or $\dot{z}$, and also a certain kinetic energy $\frac{1}{2}m\dot{x}^2$, $\frac{1}{2}m\dot{y}^2$, $\frac{1}{2}m\dot{z}^2$. The total energy of the gas can be calculated by taking $\frac{1}{3}\alpha T$ for the kinetic energy corresponding to each degree of freedom. The factor $\frac{1}{3}$ is here introduced because the total kinetic energy of a molecule, whose mean value is αT, is the sum of the quantities $\frac{1}{2}m\dot{x}^2$, $\frac{1}{2}m\dot{y}^2$, $\frac{1}{2}m\dot{z}^2$, corresponding to its three degrees of freedom.

70. These remarks will suffice for the understanding of what is meant by the equipartition of energy in less simple cases. The configuration of a body of any kind, i. e. the position of the ultimate particles of which it is conceived to be made up, can always be determined, whatever be the connexions between these particles, by a certain number of coordinates p in the general sense in which the term has been used by Lagrange, and these coordinates can often be chosen in such a manner that the kinetic energy is equal to a sum of terms, each of which is proportional to the square of one of the velocities $\dot{p}$, so that it may be said to consist of a number of parts corresponding to the different degrees of freedom of the system The theorem of equipartition tells us that, if the temperature is T, the kinetic energy of a system having a very large number of degrees of freedom, as all bodies actually have, can be found by attributing to each degree of freedom a kinetic energy equal to $\frac{1}{3}\alpha T$.

It should be noticed that it is only the kinetic energy that can be calculated in this way. If we wish to determine the whole energy, we must add the potential part of it. Now, there is one case, and it is the very one that is most relevant to our purpose, in which the value of the potential energy is likewise determined by a very simple rule.

Let us consider a system capable of small vibrations about a position of stable equilibrium, and let the coordinates $p_1, p_2, \ldots, p_n$ be 0 in this position, so that they measure the displacement of the system from it. These coordinates can be chosen in such a way that not only, as we have already required, the kinetic energy is the sum of a number of terms each containing the square of a velocity $\dot{p}$, but that, besides this, the potential energy is expressed as a similar sum of terms of the form ap^2, where a is a constant.

The most general motion of the system is made up of what we may call fundamental or principal modes of vibration. These are characterized by the peculiarity that in the first mode only the coordinate p_1 is variable, in the second only p_2, and so on, the variable coordinate being in every case a simple harmonic function of the time t, with a frequency that is in general different for the different modes. It is a fundamental property of these principal vibrations, that, in each of them, the mean value of the potential energy for a full period, or for a lapse of time that is very long in comparison with the period, is equal to the mean value of the kinetic energy. Moreover, if the system vibrates in several fundamental modes at the same time, the total energy is found by adding together the values which the energy would have in each of these modes separately.[1])

71. We shall now suppose a system of this kind, having a very large number of degrees of freedom, to be connected with an ordinary system of molecules, with a gas for example, so that it can be put in motion by the forces which it experiences from the molecules, and can in its turn give off to these a part of its vibratory energy. Then, there can be a state of equilibrium between the heat motion of the molecules and the vibratory motion of the system. We may even speak of the vibrations of the system as of its heat motion, and say that the system has a definite temperature, the same as that of the system of molecules with which it is in equilibrium.

The theorem of the equipartition of energy requires that, whatever be the exact way in which the vibrating system loses or gains energy, it shall have for each of its coordinates a kinetic energy given by $\frac{1}{3}\alpha T$. The sum of the potential and kinetic energies must be $\frac{2}{3}\alpha T$ for each of its fundamental modes of vibration, and the problem of determining the total energy is, after all, a very simple matter. We need not even specify the coordinates by which the configuration of

---

1) Note **39**.

the system can be determined. All we want to know is the number of the fundamental modes of vibration; multiplying by this the quantity $\frac{2}{3}\alpha T$, we shall have the energy of the system corresponding to the temperature T.

72. It was a most happy thought to apply this method to the problem of radiation. It enables us to calculate the energy of radiation in the ether for a certain temperature T without having to trouble ourselves about the mechanism of emission and absorption, without even considering a ponderable body. The only question is, what is the number of degrees of freedom for a certain volume of ether. For the sake of convenience we shall enclose this volume by totally reflecting walls, and to begin with, we shall imagine two such walls, unlimited parallel planes at a distance q from each other. The ether between them can be the seat of standing waves, which we can compare to those existing in an organ-pipe, and which may be conceived to arise from the superposition of systems of progressive waves.

The condition at a perfectly reflecting surface is that Poynting's flow of energy be tangential to it. It will be so if, for example, the surface is a perfect conductor, the tangential components of the electric force being 0 in this case. Let us suppose the two boundary planes to be of this kind. If they are perpendicular to the axis of x, their equations being $x = 0$, and $x = q$, the condition for the electric force can be fulfilled by the superposition of two sets of progressive waves, such as are represented by the equations (7) and by those given in § 46. The total dielectric displacement

$$\mathbf{d}_y = a \cos n\left(t - \frac{x}{c}\right) - a \cos n\left(t + \frac{x}{c}\right)$$

$$= 2a \sin nt \sin \frac{nx}{c}$$

will be 0 for $x = 0$, and also for $x = q$, if $\frac{nq}{c}$ is a multiple of π, or, what amounts to the same thing, if the distance q is a multiple of half the wave-length. The possible modes of motion will therefore have wave-lengths equal to $2q$, q, $\frac{2}{3}q$, etc.

73. We shall next examine the vibrations that can take place in the ether contained within a box, whose walls are perfectly reflecting on the inside, and which has the form of a rectangular parallelepiped. Let the axes of coordinates be parallel to the edges, and let the lengths of these be q_1, q_2, q_3.

We can imagine *eight* lines such that their direction constants have equal absolute values, but all possible algebraic signs; indeed, denoting by μ_1, μ_2, μ_3 the absolute values of the constants, we shall have the eight combinations

$$\left.\begin{array}{c}(\mu_1, \mu_2, \mu_3), \quad (-\mu_1, \mu_2, \mu_3), \quad (\mu_1, -\mu_2, \mu_3), \quad (\mu_1, \mu_2, -\mu_3), \\ (\mu_1, -\mu_2, -\mu_3), \quad (-\mu_1, \mu_2, -\mu_3), \quad (-\mu_1, -\mu_2, \mu_3), \\ (-\mu_1, -\mu_2, -\mu_3).\end{array}\right\} \tag{149}$$

If a beam of parallel rays within the rectangular box has one of these lines for its direction of propagation, the reflexion at the walls will produce bundles parallel to the other seven lines, and if the values of μ_1, μ_2, μ_3 and the wave-length λ are properly chosen, the boundary conditions at the walls can be satisfied by the superposition of eight systems of progressive waves travelling in the eight directions. In order to express the condition to which μ_1, μ_2, μ_3, λ must be subjected, we shall imagine three lines P_1Q_1, P_2Q_2, and P_3Q_3 parallel to the sides of the box and joining points of two opposite faces, so that

$$P_1Q_1 = q_1, \quad P_2Q_2 = q_2, \quad P_3Q_3 = q_3.$$

In a system of progressive waves travelling in the direction determined by μ_1, μ_2, μ_3 the difference of phase between P_1 and Q_1 is measured by a distance $\mu_1 q_1$, that between P_2 and Q_2 by $\mu_2 q_2$, and that between P_3 and Q_3 by $\mu_3 q_3$. The condition for μ_1, μ_2, μ_3, λ amounts to this[1]) that each of these three lengths must be a multiple of $\frac{1}{2}\lambda$. Therefore, if we put

$$\frac{2\mu_1 q_1}{\lambda} = k_1, \quad \frac{2\mu_2 q_2}{\lambda} = k_2, \quad \frac{2\mu_3 q_3}{\lambda} = k_3, \tag{150}$$

k_1, k_2, k_3 must be whole positive numbers.

On account of the relation

$$\mu_1^2 + \mu_2^2 + \mu_3^2 = 1,$$

we have

$$\frac{k_1^2}{q_1^2} + \frac{k_2^2}{q_2^2} + \frac{k_3^2}{q_3^2} = \frac{4}{\lambda^2}, \tag{151}$$

and so we now see that for any three whole numbers k_1, k_2, k_3 there is a corresponding set of standing waves. The wave-length is given by (151) and the direction constants of the normals to the progressive waves which we have to combine, by (149) and (150). As these progressive waves can have two different states of polarization[2]), each set of numbers k_1, k_2, k_3 will lead us to *two* fundamental modes of vibration of the ether in the rectangular box, and the energy corresponding to each set (k_1, k_2, k_3) will be not $\frac{2}{3}\alpha T$, but $\frac{4}{3}\alpha T$.

---

1) Note **40**. 2) Note **41**.

Now, the object of our enquiry is the amount of energy of the ether in so far as it belongs to vibrations whose wave-length lies between given limits λ and $\lambda + d\lambda$. This amount is

$$\nu \cdot \tfrac{4}{3}\alpha T,$$

if ν is the number of sets of positive integers k_1, k_2, k_3 for which the value of λ given by (151) lies between λ and $\lambda + d\lambda$.

74. The number ν can easily be calculated if we confine ourselves, as we obviously may do, to wave-lengths that are very small in comparison with the dimensions q_1, q_2, q_3 of the box.

Let us consider k_1, k_2, k_3 as the rectangular coordinates of a point. Then (151) is the equation of an ellipsoid having for its semi-axes

$$\frac{2q_1}{\lambda}, \quad \frac{2q_2}{\lambda}, \quad \frac{2q_3}{\lambda}. \tag{152}$$

Changing λ into $\lambda + d\lambda$ we get a second ellipsoid, and ν will be the number of points (k_1, k_2, k_3) lying between these two surfaces, whose corresponding semi-axes differ by

$$\frac{2q_1}{\lambda} \cdot \frac{d\lambda}{\lambda}, \quad \frac{2q_2}{\lambda} \cdot \frac{d\lambda}{\lambda}, \quad \frac{2q_3}{\lambda} \cdot \frac{d\lambda}{\lambda}. \tag{153}$$

On account of our assumption concerning the wave-lengths, the expressions (152) are very high numbers, and we may even suppose that, notwithstanding the smallness of $d\lambda$, the numbers (153) are also very large. This means that all dimensions, the thickness included, of the ellipsoidal shell are very large in comparison with the unit of length.

The number of points with coordinates represented by whole numbers, which lie in a part of space whose dimensions are much larger than the unit of length, may be taken to be equal to the number representing the volume of that part. Remembering that we are only concerned with positive values of k_1, k_2, k_3, we find that ν is equal to the eighth part of the numerical value of the volume of the ellipsoidal shell. We have therefore

$$\nu = \frac{4\pi q_1 q_2 q_3}{\lambda^4}\, d\lambda,$$

and for the energy which we were to calculate

$$\nu \cdot \frac{4}{3}\alpha T = \frac{16\pi\alpha T q_1 q_2 q_3}{3\lambda^4}\, d\lambda.$$

This is the energy contained in the volume of our rectangular box. Dividing by $q_1 q_2 q_3$, one finds for the energy of radiation in the ether, per unit of volume, so far as it is due to vibrations whose wave-length lies between λ and $\lambda + d\lambda$,

$$\frac{16 \pi \alpha T}{3 \lambda^4} d\lambda,$$

a result agreeing exactly with (148).

75. The theory of radiation that was given in §§ 60—68 is restricted to systems containing free electrons and to the case of very long waves. It therefore requires a further development with regard to bodies, such as a piece of glass, in which we can hardly admit the existence of freely moving electrons, and with regard to the shorter waves. If we admit the laws of Boltzmann and Wien, and if we take for granted that a curve like that of Fig. 2 represents a state of radiation that can be in equilibrium with a ponderable body of a given temperature, we must try to account for the form of the curve and to discover the ground for the constancy of the product $\lambda_m T$. If we succeed in this, we may hope to find in what manner the value of this constant is determined by some numerical quantity that is the same for all ponderable bodies.

The theory of these phenomena takes a very different aspect if we regard the law of the equipartition of energy as a rule to which there is no exception, considering at the same time the ether as a continuous medium without molecular structure. Just like any other continuous distribution of matter, like a homogeneous string for example, a finite part of the ether must then be said to have an infinite number of degrees of freedom; there will be no upper limit to the frequency of the modes of vibration that can exist in the ether enclosed in the rectangular box of which we have spoken.

On the contrary, the number of degrees of freedom of a ponderable body is certainly finite if the ultimate particles of which it consists are considered as rigid. Consequently, as Jeans has observed, the theorem of equipartition requires that in a system composed of a ponderable body and ether, however large be the part of space that is occupied by the body, no appreciable part of the total energy shall be found in the latter when the equilibrium is reached. Indeed, according to Jeans's theory, the formula (148) must be true for *all* wave-lengths, so that, for a given temperature, we shall find an infinite value if, for the calculation of the total amount of energy, the expression is integrated as far down as $\lambda = 0$. This means that, if the ether receives any finite amount of energy, such as that which is stored up in a body of finite size, the temperature of the ether cannot perceptibly rise, the energy being wasted, so to say, for the production of extremely short electromagnetic ripples.

In order to reconcile these results with observed facts, Jeans points out that the emission of rays whose wave-lengths are below a certain limit may be a very slow process, so slow that a true equilibrium is never realized in our experiments. Under these circumstances it is conceivable that, though in length of time all energy of a body will be frittered away, yet a certain state may be reached in which there are no observable changes, and in which therefore there is a kind of spurious equilibrium.

76. Jeans's conclusions are certainly very important and deserve careful consideration. One can imagine three ways in which one might escape from them. In the first place, one could suppose the number of degrees of freedom of a ponderable body to be itself infinite, either on account of the deformability of the ultimate particles or on account of the ether the body contains; this, however, would lead us to a contradiction with experiments, because it would require a value of the specific heat, far surpassing that to which we are led if we attend only to the progressive motion of the molecules. In the second place, we could imagine a structure of the ether which would make a finite portion of it have only a finite number of degress of freedom. Lastly, we could altogether abandon the theorem of equipartition as a general law. Then, however, we shall be obliged to explain why it holds for the case of sufficiently long waves.

Questions of equal importance and no less difficulty arise when we adhere to Jeans's views. It is difficult to believe that, in establishing the laws of Boltzmann and Wien, which have been so beautifully confirmed by experiment, physicists have been on a wholly wrong track. It will therefore be necessary to show for what reason those spurious states of equilibrium of which I have spoken are subjected to the laws of thermodynamics, and we shall again have to find the physical meaning of the constant value of $\lambda_m T$.[1])

I shall conclude by observing that the law of equipartition which, for systems of molecules, can be deduced from the principles of statistical mechanics, cannot as yet be considered to have been proved for systems containing ether.[2])

1) Note **42**. 2) Note **42***.

CHAPTER III.

THEORY OF THE ZEEMAN-EFFECT.

77. The phenomenon of the magnetic rotation of the plane of polarization, discovered by Faraday in 1845, was the first proof of the intimate connexion between optical and electromagnetic phenomena. For a long time it remained the only instance of an optical effect brought about by a magnetic field. In 1877, however, Kerr showed that the state of polarization of the rays reflected by an iron mirror is altered by a magnetization of the metal, and in 1896 Zeeman[1]) detected an influence of a magnetic field on the emission of light. If a source of light, giving one or more sharp lines in the spectrum, is placed between the poles of a powerful electromagnet, each line is split into a certain number of components, whose distances are determined by the intensity of the external magnetic force.

In my discussion of these magneto-optical phenomena (in which, however, I shall not speak of the theory of the Kerr-effect), I shall first take the simplest of them all. This is the Zeeman-effect, as it showed itself in the first experiments, a division of the original spectral line into three or two components, the number depending on the direction in which the rays are emitted.

78. I shall first present to you the elementary explanation which this decomposition of the lines finds in the theory of electrons, and by which it has even been possible to predict certain peculiarities of the phenomenon.

We know already that, according to modern views, the emission of light is due to vibratory motions of electric charges contained in the atoms of ponderable bodies, of a sodium flame, for example, or the luminescent gas in a vacuum tube. The distribution of these

1) P. Zeeman, Over den invloed eener magnetisatie op den aard van het door een stof uitgezonden licht, Zittingsversl. Amsterdam **5** (1896), p. 181, 242 [translated in Phil. Mag (5) **43** (1897), p. 226]; Doublets and triplets in the spectrum produced by external magnetic forces, Phil. Mag. (5) **44** (1897), p. 55, 255; Measurements concerning radiation phenomena in the magnetic field, ibid. **45** (1898), p. 197. See also: Zeeman, Researches in magneto-optics, London, 1913.

charges and their vibrations may be very complicated, but, if we wish only to explain the production of a single spectral line, we can content ourselves with a very simple hypothesis. Let each atom (or molecule) contain one single electron, having a definite position of equilibrium, towards which it is drawn back by an "elastic" force, as we shall call it, as soon as it has been displaced by one cause or another. Let us further suppose this elastic force, which must be considered to be exerted by the other particles in the atom, but about whose nature we are very much in the dark, to be proportional to the displacement. According to this hypothesis, which is necessary in order to get simple harmonic vibrations, the components of the elastic force which is called into play by a displacement from the position of equilibrium, whose components are ξ, η, ζ, may be represented by

$$-f\xi, \quad -f\eta, \quad -f\zeta,$$

where f is a positive constant, determined by the properties of the atom.

If m is the mass of the movable electron, we shall have the equations of motion

$$m\frac{d^2\xi}{dt^2} = -f\xi, \quad m\frac{d^2\eta}{dt^2} = -f\eta, \quad m\frac{d^2\zeta}{dt^2} = -f\zeta,$$

whose general solution is

$$\xi = a\cos(n_0 t + p), \quad \eta = a'\cos(n_0 t + p'),$$
$$\zeta = a''\cos(n_0 t + p''), \tag{154}$$

a, a', a'', p, p', p'' being arbitrary constants, and the frequency n_0 of the vibrations being determined by

$$n_0 = \sqrt{\frac{f}{m}}. \tag{155}$$

Let us next consider the influence of an external magnetic field $\mathbf{H}$. This introduces a force given by

$$\frac{e}{c}[\mathbf{v}\cdot\mathbf{H}], \tag{156}$$

in which expression e denotes the charge of the electron and $\mathbf{v}$ its velocity. If the magnetic force $\mathbf{H}$ is parallel to the axis of z, the components of (156) are

$$\frac{e\mathbf{H}_z}{c}\frac{d\eta}{dt}, \quad -\frac{e\mathbf{H}_z}{c}\frac{d\xi}{dt}, \quad 0.$$

Hence the equations of motion become

$$m\frac{d^2\xi}{dt^2} = -f\xi + \frac{e\mathbf{H}_z}{c}\frac{d\eta}{dt}, \tag{157}$$

$$m\frac{d^2\eta}{dt^2} = -f\eta - \frac{e\mathbf{H}_z}{c}\frac{d\xi}{dt}, \tag{158}$$

$$m\frac{d^2\zeta}{dt^2} = -f\zeta. \tag{159}$$

79. The last equation shows that the vibrations in the direction of OZ are not affected by the magnetic field, a result that was to be expected, because the force (156) is 0, if the direction of $\mathbf{v}$ coincides with that of $\mathbf{H}$. The particular solution (154) therefore still holds. As to the pair of equations (157) and (158), these admit of two particular solutions, represented by the formulae

$$\xi = a_1 \cos(n_1 t + p_1), \quad \eta = -a_1 \sin(n_1 t + p_1) \tag{160}$$

and

$$\xi = a_2 \cos(n_2 t + p_2), \quad \eta = a_2 \sin(n_2 t + p_2), \tag{161}$$

in which the frequencies n_1 and n_2 are determined by

$$n_1^2 - \frac{e\mathbf{H}_z}{mc} n_1 = n_0^2 \tag{162}$$

and

$$n_2^2 + \frac{e\mathbf{H}_z}{mc} n_2 = n_0^2, \tag{163}$$

whereas a_1, a_2, p_1 and p_2 are arbitrary constants.

Combination of (154), (160) and (161) gives a solution that contains six constants and is therefore the general solution.

The two solutions (160) and (161) represent circular vibrations in a plane perpendicular to the magnetic field, and taking place in opposite directions. The frequency n_1 of one is higher (if $e\mathbf{H}_z$ is positive) and that of the other lower than the original frequency n_0. The possibility of these circular motions can also be understood by a very simple reasoning. If the electron describes a circle with radius r in a plane perpendicular to $\mathbf{H}_z$, and in a direction opposite to that which corresponds to this force, there will be, in addition to the elastic force fr, an electromagnetic force

$$\frac{e|\mathbf{v}|\mathbf{H}_z}{c}$$

directed towards the centre. Both forces being constant, the circular orbit can really be described, and we have, by the well known law of centripetal force,

$$fr + \frac{e|\mathbf{v}|\mathbf{H}_z}{c} = \frac{mv^2}{r},$$

or, since $|\mathbf{v}| = nr$,

$$f + \frac{en\mathbf{H}_z}{c} = mn^2,$$

from which (162) immediately follows. The equation (163) can be found in exactly the same way.

In all real cases the change in the frequency is found to be very small in comparison with the frequency itself. This shows that, even in the most powerful fields, $\frac{e\mathbf{H}_z}{mc}$ is very small in comparison with n_0. Consequently, (162) and (163) may be replaced by

$$n_1 = n_0 + \frac{e\mathbf{H}_z}{2mc}, \quad n_2 = n_0 - \frac{e\mathbf{H}_z}{2mc}. \tag{164}$$

The points in the spectrum corresponding to these frequencies lie at equal small distances to the right and to the left of the original spectral line n_0.

80. We have next to consider the nature of the light emitted by the vibrating electron. The total radiation is made up of several parts, corresponding to the particular solutions we have obtained, and which we shall examine separately.

Our former discussion (§§ 39—41) of the radiation by an electron shows that, if such a particle has a vibration about a point O, along a straight line L, the dielectric displacement at a distant point P has a direction perpendicular to OP, in the plane LOP, and that, for a given distance OP, its amplitude is proportional to the sine of the angle LOP. The radiation will be zero along the line of vibration L, and of greatest intensity in lines perpendicular to it; moreover, along each line drawn from O, the light will be plane polarized.

As to a circular vibration, such as is represented by the formulae (160), its effect is the resultant of those which are produced by the two rectilinear vibrations along OX and OY, into which it can be decomposed. We need only consider the state produced either in the plane of this motion, or along a line passing through the centre, at right angles to the plane. At a distant point P of the plane, the light received from the revolving electron is plane polarized, the electric vibrations being perpendicular to OP, in the plane of the circle; if, for example, P is situated on OY, the vibration along this line will have no effect, and we shall only have the field produced by the motion along OX.

Both components of (160) are, however, effective in producing a field at a point on the axis of the circle, i. e. on OZ, the first component giving rise to an electric vibration parallel to OX, and the second to one in the direction of OY. It is immediately seen that between these vibrations there is exactly the same difference of phase as between the two components of (160) themselves, i. e. a difference of a quarter period, and that their amplitudes are equal. The light emitted along OZ is therefore circularly polarized, the direction of the dielectric displacement rotating in the sense corresponding to the circular motion of the electron. The formulae (160) show that, for an observer placed on the positive axis of z, the rotation of the electron takes place in the same direction as that of the hands of a clock. From this it may be inferred that the rays emitted along the positive axis by the motion (160) have a right-handed circular polarization.

Similar considerations apply to the motion represented by (161). The radiation issuing from it in the direction just stated has a left-handed circular polarization. If it is further taken into account that the frequency of the rays is in every case equal to that of the motion originating them, one can draw the following conclusions, which have been fully verified by Zeeman's experiments.[1]

Let the source of light be placed in a magnetic field whose lines of force are horizontal, and let the light emitted in a horizontal direction at right angles to the lines of force be examined by means of a spectroscope or a grating. Then we shall see a triplet of lines, whose middle component occupies the place of the original line. Each component is produced by plane polarized light, the electric vibrations being horizontal for the middle line, and vertical for the two outer ones.

If, however, by using an electromagnet, one core of which has a suitable axial hole, we examine the light that is radiated along the lines of force, we shall observe only a doublet, corresponding in position to the outer lines of the triplet. Its components are both produced by circularly polarized light, the polarization being right-handed for one, and left-handed for the other.

81. After having verified all this, Zeeman was able to obtain two very remarkable results. In the first place, it was found that, for light emitted in a direction coinciding with that of the magnetic force, i. e., if $\mathbf{H}_z$ is positive, in that of OZ, the polarization of the component of the doublet for which the frequency is lowest, is right-handed This proves that, for a positive value of $\mathbf{H}_z$, the first of the two frequencies given by (164) is the smaller. Therefore, the charge e of the electron to whose motion the radiation has been ascribed must be negative. This agrees with the general result of other lines of research, that the negative charges have a greater mobility than the positive ones.

The other result relates to the ratio between the numerical values of the electric charge and the mass of the movable electrons. This ratio can be calculated by means of the formulae (164), as soon as the distance between the components, from which we can deduce

1) Note 43.

$n_1 - n_0$, and the strength of the magnetic field have been measured. The number deduced by Zeeman from the distance between the components of the D-lines, or rather from the broadening of these lines, whose components partly overlapped each other, was one of the first values of $\frac{e}{m}$ that have been published. In order of magnitude it agrees with the numbers that have been found for the negative electrons of the cathode-rays and the β-rays.

Unfortunately, the satisfaction caused by this success of the theory of electrons in explaining the new phenomenon, could not last long. It was soon found that many spectral lines are decomposed into more than three components, four, six or even more[1]), and till the present day, these more complicated forms of the Zeeman-effect cannot be said to have been satisfactorily accounted for.

All I can do, will therefore be to make some suggestions as to the direction in which an explanation may perhaps be looked for.

82. Before proceeding to do so, I may be permitted briefly to mention some of the important results that have been found in the examination of the distribution of spectral lines, such as they are in the absence of a magnetic field. In the spectra of many elements the lines arrange themselves in series, in such a manner that, for each series, the frequencies of all the lines belonging to it can be represented by a single mathematical formula. The first formula of this kind was given by Balmer[2]) for the spectrum of hydrogen. After him, equations for other spectra have been established by many physicists, especially by Rydberg[3]) and by Kayser and Runge.[4])

For our purpose it will be sufficient to mention some examples.

In the spectrum of sodium three series of double lines have been found, which are distinguished by the names of principal series, first subordinate or nebulous series, and second subordinate or sharp series. We may also say that each of the three is composed of two series of single lines, one containing the less refrangible, and the other the more refrangible lines of the doublets.

---

1) In later researches a decomposition into no less than 17 components has been observed.

2) J. J. Balmer, Notiz über die Spektrallinien des Wasserstoffs, Ann. Phys. Chem. **25** (1885), p. 80.

3) J. R. Rydberg, Recherches sur la constitution des spectres d'émission des éléments chimiques, Svenska Vetensk. Akad. Handl. **23** (1889), No. 11; La distribution des raies spectrales, Rapports prés. au Congrès de physique, 1900, **2**, p. 200.

4) H. Kayser u. C. Runge, Über die Spektren der Alkalien, Ann. Phys. Chem. **41** (1890), p. 302; Über die Spektra der Elemente der zweiten Mendelejeff'schen Gruppe, ibid. **43** (1891), p. 385.

The frequency in these six series, measured by the number n of wave-lengths in a centimetre, has been represented by Rydberg by means of the formulae contained in the following table.

Principal series I $$\frac{n}{N_0} = \frac{1}{(1+\sigma)^2} - \frac{1}{(m+\mu_1)^2}, \qquad (165)$$

" " II $$\frac{n}{N_0} = \frac{1}{(1+\sigma)^2} - \frac{1}{(m+\mu_2)^2}. \qquad (166)$$

First subordinate (nebulous) series I $$\frac{n}{N_0} = \frac{1}{(1+\mu_1)^2} - \frac{1}{(m+\delta)^2}, \qquad (167)$$

" " " " II $$\frac{n}{N_0} = \frac{1}{(1+\mu_2)^2} - \frac{1}{(m+\delta)^2}. \qquad (168)$$

Second subordinate (sharp) series I $$\frac{n}{N_0} = \frac{1}{(1+\mu_1)^2} - \frac{1}{(m+\sigma)^2}, \qquad (169)$$

" " " " II $$\frac{n}{N_0} = \frac{1}{(1+\mu_2)^2} - \frac{1}{(m+\sigma)^2}. \qquad (170)$$

In these equations, N_0, μ_1, μ_2, δ and σ are constants having the values

$$N_0 = 109675$$

$$\mu_1 = 1{,}1171, \qquad \mu_2 = 1{,}1163, \qquad \delta = 0{,}9884, \qquad \sigma = 0{,}6498$$

and we shall find the frequencies of the successive lines in each series by substituting for m successive positive whole numbers. If, in doing so, we get for n a negative value $-n'$, this is to mean that there is a line of the frequency n'.

83. I particularly wish to draw your attention to the following remarkable facts that are embodied in the above formulae.

1. If the value of m is made continually to increase, that of n increases at the same time, converging however towards a finite limit, corresponding to $m = \infty$, and given for the different series by $\frac{N_0}{(1+\sigma)^2}$, $\frac{N_0}{(1+\mu_1)^2}$, etc.

The lines of a series are not placed at equal distances from each other; as we proceed towards the side of the ultra-violet, the lines become crowded together, the series being unable, so to say, to pass the limiting position of the line given by one of the above numbers.

As to the number of lines that have been observed, this varies from one series to the other. If the above formulae (or equations of a similar kind) are the expression of the real state of things, the number of lines is to be considered as infinitely great.

2. The frequencies of a doublet of the first subordinate series (I, II) are obtained, if in (167) and (168) we substitute for m the same

number. These frequencies differ by

$$\frac{N_0}{(1+\mu_2)^2} - \frac{N_0}{(1+\mu_1)^2},$$

whatever be the value of m. The same difference is found, if we calculate the frequencies of a doublet of the second subordinate series (I, II). Therefore, if the distance between two lines is measured by the difference of their frequencies, the interval between the two components is the same for all the doublets of the first and of the second subordinate series.

It is otherwise with the doublets of the principal series (I, II). The distance between the two components is given by

$$\frac{N_0}{(m+\mu_2)^2} - \frac{N_0}{(m+\mu_1)^2},$$

a quantity, which diminishes when m increases, and approaches the limit 0 for $m = \infty$.

In connexion with this, it must be noticed that the convergence frequency has the same value $\frac{N_0}{(1+\sigma)^2}$ for the members I and II of the principal series.

3. This is not the only connexion between different series. The formulae show that the convergence frequencies are $\frac{N_0}{(1+\mu_1)^2}$ and $\frac{N_0}{(1+\mu_2)^2}$, both for the first and the second subordinate series (I, II). Finally, it is important to remark that, if in (165) and (166) we put $m = 1$, we get the same frequencies as from (169) and (170) for the same value of m. The doublet with these frequencies can therefore be considered to be at the same time the first of the principal, and the first of the second subordinate series.

We may further say that the entire principal series I and the entire sharp series I correspond to each other, being both characterized by the constants μ_1 and σ, and that there is a similar relation between the principal series II and the sharp series II. In this connexion it is proper to remark that the more refrangible lines of the principal doublets correspond to the less refrangible ones of the sharp doublets, and conversely. If, for example, μ_1 is greater than μ_2, the first constant will give the larger frequency in the principal series, and the lesser frequency in the second subordinate one.

4. Similar results have been obtained for the other alkali metals, which also show series of doublets in their spectrum, and for magnesium, calcium, strontium, zinc, cadmium and mercury. Only, in the spectra of these latter metals, one finds series, not of doublets but of triplets. To the scheme given in the formulae (165)—(170), we have

therefore to add in this case:

$$\text{Principal series III } \frac{n}{N_0} = \frac{1}{(1+\sigma)^2} - \frac{1}{(m+\mu_3)^2},$$

$$\text{First subordinate series III } \frac{n}{N_0} = \frac{1}{(1+\mu_3)^2} - \frac{1}{(m+\delta)^2}.$$

$$\text{Second ,, ,, III } \frac{n}{N_0} = \frac{1}{(1+\mu_3)^2} - \frac{1}{(m+\sigma)^2}.$$

However, even thus the scheme is not yet complete. In the spectrum of mercury, for example, there is a certain number of additional lines, which closely accompany those of which we have just spoken, and which are therefore often called satellites.

These again show certain remarkable regularities. They occur in the first subordinate series (I, II, III), but not in the second subordinate one. In each triplet of the first series, there are three satellites accompanying the first line of the triplet, two belonging to the second, and one for the third, so that the triplet is really a group of nine lines.

As to the principal series of the last named elements, I have added them only for the sake of analogy. Principal series of triplets have not yet been observed.

84. It is only for a comparatively small number of chemical elements, that one has been able to resolve the system of their spectral lines, or at least the larger part of them, into series of the kind we have been considering. In the spectra of such elements as gold, copper and iron, some isolated series have been discovered, but the majority of their lines have not yet been disentangled. Nevertheless, it cannot be denied that we have made a fair start towards the understanding of line spectra, which at first sight present a bewildering confusion. There can be no doubt that the lines of a series really belong together, originating in some common cause, and that even different series must be produced by motions between which there is a great resemblance.

The similarity of structure in the spectra of elements that resemble each other in their chemical properties, is also very striking. The metals in whose spectra the lines are combined in pairs are all monovalent, whereas the above series of triplets belong to divalent elements. Perhaps the most remarkable of all is the fact, that Rydberg was able to represent all series, whatever be the element to which they belong, by means of formulae containing the same number N_0. This equality, rigorous or approximate, of a constant occurring in the formulae of the different elements, must of course be due to some corresponding equality in the properties of the ultimate particles of which these elements consist, but at present we are wholly unable to form an idea of the nature of this similarity,[1]) or of the physical meaning of the length of time corresponding to $\frac{1}{N_0}$ [2]).

85. The investigation of the Zeeman-effect for a large number of spectral lines, to which many physicists have devoted themselves of late years, has fully confirmed the hypothesis of an intimate connexion between the different spectral lines of a substance; it has furnished rich material for future research, but which, in the present state of theory, we can understand only very imperfectly.

Before saying a few words of the results that have been obtained, I must revert once more to the elementary theory of the triplets and to the formulae (164) we deduced from it. These show that, if all spectral lines were split according to the elementary theory, and if, in all cases, the ratio $\frac{e}{m}$ had the same value, we should always observe triplets with the same difference of frequency between their components. This is what, for the sake of brevity, I shall call an *equal* splitting of the lines.

Now, the measurements of Runge and Paschen[3]) and other physicists have led to a very remarkable result. Though there are a large number of spectral lines which are split into more than three components, and though even the triplets that have been observed, are not equal to each other in the above sense, yet all lines forming a series, i. e. all lines that can be represented by one and the same formula, are divided in exactly the same way, and to exactly the same extent. There seems to be no doubt as to the validity of this general law.

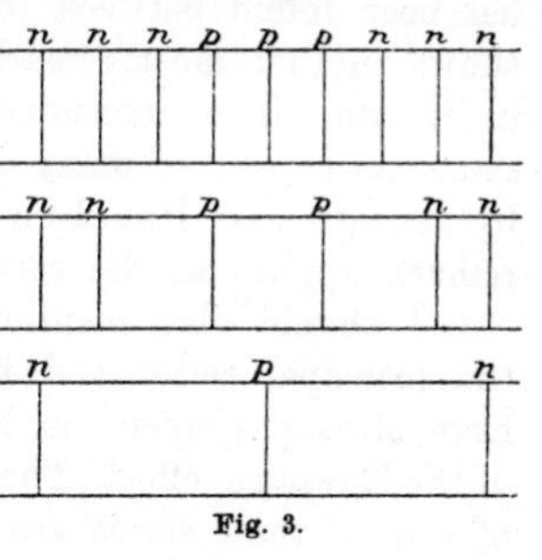

Fig. 3.

In those series which consist of triplets or doublets, the mode of division of the lines is in general different for the lines of one and the same triplet or pair, but, according to the law just mentioned, the same mode of division repeats itself in every triplet or every doublet. Thus, in each triplet belonging to the second subordinate

1) Several authors have tried to establish formulae by which the distribution of the lines of a series can be represented still more accurately than by those of Rydberg. See, for instance, W. Ritz, Ann. Phys. **12** (1903), p. 264, and E. E. Mogendorff, Amsterdam Proc. **9** (1906), p. 434.

2) See however: N. Bohr, Phil. Mag. **26** (1913), p. 1. [1915.]

3) C. Runge, Über den Zeeman-Effekt der Serienlinien, Phys. Zeitschr. **3** (1902), p. 441; C. Runge u. F. Paschen, Über die Strahlung des Quecksilbers im magnetischen Felde, Anhang z. d. Abhandl. Akad Berlin, 1902, p. 1.

series of mercury, the less refrangible line is split into nine components, the middle line into six, and the most refrangible line into three components. These divisions are shown in Fig. 3, in which the letters p and n mean that the electric vibrations of the line are parallel or perpendicular to the lines of force.

Equal modes of division are found not only in the different lines of one and the same series, but also in the corresponding series of different elements. For example, the lines D_1 and D_2 of sodium, which form the first member of the principal series, are changed into a quartet (Cornu's quartet) and a sextet (Fig. 4), and the first terms in the principal series of copper and silver present exactly the same division.

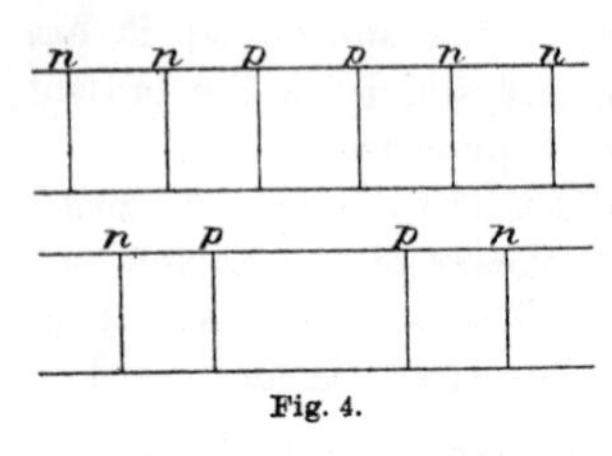

Fig. 4.

86. You see from all this that the phenomena are highly complicated, and that there would be a bewildering intricacy, were it not for the law which I have just pointed out to you, which reveals itself in the decomposition of the lines of the same series, or of corresponding series. Nor is this the only case in which a connexion has been found between the Zeeman-effect for different lines. Fig. 3 shows another most remarkable regularity. The distances represented in it can all be considered as multiples of one number, and the same can be said of many of the displacements that have been observed by Runge and Paschen in the spectrum of mercury. A similar remark applies to the case of Fig. 4.[1])

I should also mention that the interesting connexion between the principal series and the second subordinate series of which we have already spoken, is beautifully corroborated by the observations of the Zeeman-effect. The more refrangible components of the doublets of one of these series are split in the same way as the less refrangible components of the doublets of the other.

Finally, it must not be forgotten that, although a very large number of lines show a rather complicated Zeeman-effect, especially those which belong to the series of which we have spoken, yet there are also many lines which are changed into triplets by the action of a magnetic field. In the recent work of Purvis, for example, no less than fifty cases of this kind have been found in the spectrum of palladium. I must add that many more lines of this element are decomposed in a different way.

1) See on this question of the commensurability of the magnetic separations in different cases, C. Runge, Über die Zerlegung von Spektrallinien im magnetischen Felde, Phys. Zeitschr. **8** (1907), p. 232.

87. It has already been mentioned that Zeeman's first determination of the ratio $\frac{e}{m}$ led to a value of the same order of magnitude as that which has been found for the electrons of the cathode rays and the β-rays of radium. Later measurements have shown, however, that the distance between the components is not the same in different triplets, and that therefore different values of $\frac{e}{m}$ are found, if the formulae (164) are applied in all cases. Though some triplets give a value of $\frac{e}{m}$ equal to the number found for free negative electrons, the result is different in the majority of cases. This can be attributed, either to real differences between the values of $\frac{e}{m}$, or to the imperfectness of the elementary theory. I believe that there is much to be said in favour of the latter alternative. After all that has been said, we cannot have much confidence in the formulae (164), but there are strong reasons for believing in the identity of all negative electrons.

88. If time permitted it, it would be highly interesting to consider some of the hypotheses that have been put forward in order to explain the structure of spectra and the more complicated forms of the Zeeman-effect. There can be no difference of opinion as to the importance of the problem, nor, I believe, as to the direction in which we have to look for a solution. The liability of spectral lines to be changed by magnetic influences undoubtedly shows, what we had already assumed on other grounds, that the radiation of light is an electromagnetic phenomenon due to a motion of electricity in the luminous particles, and our aim must be to explain the observed phenomena by suitable assumptions concerning the distribution of the charges and the forces by which their vibrations are determined.

Unfortunately, though many ingenious hypotheses about the structure of radiating particles have been proposed, we are still very far from a satisfactory solution. I must therefore confine myself to some general considerations on the theory of the Zeeman-effect, and to the working out of a single example which may serve to illustrate them.

89. In the first place, we can leave our original hypothesis of a single movable electron for a more general assumption concerning the structure and properties of the radiating particles. Let each of these be a material system capable of very small vibrations about a position of stable equilibrium, and let its configuration be determined by a certain number of generalized coordinates $p_1, p_2, \ldots, p_\mu$. We shall suppose these to be chosen in such a manner, that they are 0 in the position of equilibrium, and that the potential energy and the kinetic energy are represented by expressions of the form

$$\tfrac{1}{2}(f_1 p_1^2 + f_2 p_2^2 + \cdots + f_\mu p_\mu^2),$$
$$\tfrac{1}{2}(m_1 \dot{p}_1^2 + m_2 \dot{p}_2^2 + \cdots + m_\mu \dot{p}_\mu^2).$$

Then, Lagrange's equations of motion become

$$m_1 \ddot{p}_1 = -f_1 p_1, \quad m_2 \ddot{p}_2 = -f_2 p_2, \quad \ldots, \quad m_\mu \ddot{p}_\mu = -f_\mu p_\mu. \quad (171)$$

Since each of these formulae contains but one coordinate, the changes of one coordinate are wholly independent of those of the other, so that each equation determines one of the fundamental modes of vibration of the system. The frequencies of these modes, and the positions of the corresponding spectral lines are given by

$$n_1 = \sqrt{\frac{f_1}{m_1}}, \quad n_2 = \sqrt{\frac{f_2}{m_2}}, \quad \ldots, \quad n_\mu = \sqrt{\frac{f_\mu}{m_\mu}}. \quad (172)$$

We shall now introduce an external magnetic force **H**, which of course may be considered to be the same in all parts of our small material system. In order to make this force have an influence on the vibrations, we shall suppose the parts of the system to carry electric charges, which are rigidly attached to them, so that the position of the charges is determined by the coordinates p.

As soon as the system is vibrating, the charges are subjected to forces due to the external magnetic field. These actions can be mathematically described by the introduction into the equations of motion of certain forces in the generalized sense of the word. Denoting these forces by $P_1, P_2, \ldots, P_\mu$, we shall have, instead of (171),

$$m_1 \ddot{p}_1 = -f_1 p_1 + P_1, \text{ etc.}$$

Without a knowledge of the structure of the vibrating system, and of the distribution of its charges, it is of course impossible, completely to determine $P_1, P_2, \ldots$. One can show, however, that the expressions for these quantities must be of the form

$$\left.\begin{aligned} P_1 &= c_{12}\dot{p}_2 + c_{13}\dot{p}_3 + \cdots + c_{1\mu}\dot{p}_\mu, \\ P_2 &= c_{21}\dot{p}_1 + c_{23}\dot{p}_3 + \cdots + c_{2\mu}\dot{p}_\mu, \\ &\text{etc.,} \end{aligned}\right\} \quad (173)$$

where the constants c are proportional to the intensity of the magnetic field.[1]) Between these coefficients there are the following relations

$$c_{21} = -c_{12}, \quad c_{32} = -c_{23}, \quad \text{etc.} \quad (174)$$

The proof of all this is very easy, if we remember the fundamental expression $\frac{1}{c}[\mathbf{v} \cdot \mathbf{h}]$ for the action of a field on a moving

1) Note **44**.

charge. The components of this action along the axes of coordinates are linear and homogeneous functions of the components of the velocity **v**. Consequently, all the rectangular components of the forces acting on the vibrating particle must be functions of this kind of $\dot{p}_1, \dot{p}_2, \ldots, \dot{p}_\mu$, because the velocity of any point of the system is a linear and homogeneous function of these quantities. The same must be true of the Lagrangian forces $P_1, P_2, \ldots, P_\mu$, because these are linear and homogeneous functions of the rectangular components of the forces.

In order to find the relations between the coefficients c, we have only to observe that the work of the additional forces P_1, P_2, etc. is 0, because the force exerted by the magnetic field on a moving charge is always perpendicular to the line of motion. The condition

$$P_1\dot{p}_1 + P_2\dot{p}_2 + \cdots + P_\mu\dot{p}_\mu = 0,$$

to which we are led in this way, is the ground for the relations (174) and for the absence of a term with $\dot{p}_1$ in the first of the equations (173), of one with $\dot{p}_2$ in the second, etc.

90. The equations of motion

$$m_1\ddot{p}_1 + f_1 p_1 = c_{12}\dot{p}_2 + c_{13}\dot{p}_3 + \cdots + c_{1\mu}\dot{p}_\mu,$$
$$m_2\ddot{p}_2 + f_2 p_2 = c_{21}\dot{p}_1 + c_{23}\dot{p}_3 + \cdots + c_{2\mu}\dot{p}_\mu,$$
$$\text{etc.}$$

can be treated by well known methods. Putting

$$p_1 = q_1\,\varepsilon^{int}, \quad p_2 = q_2\,\varepsilon^{int}, \quad \ldots, \quad p_\mu = q_\mu\,\varepsilon^{int}, \tag{175}$$

where $n, q_1, q_2, \ldots, q_\mu$ are constants, we find the μ equations

$$\left.\begin{aligned} (f_1 - m_1 n^2)\,q_1 - inc_{12}q_2 - inc_{13}q_3 - \cdots - inc_{1\mu}q_\mu &= 0, \\ -\,inc_{21}q_1 + (f_2 - m_2 n^2)\,q_2 - inc_{23}q_3 - \cdots - inc_{2\mu}q_\mu &= 0, \\ \text{etc.} \end{aligned}\right\} \tag{176}$$

If, from these, the quantities $q_1, q_2, \ldots, q_\mu$ are eliminated, the result is an equation which determines the coefficient n. On account of the relations (174), and the smallness of the terms with c_{12}, c_{13}, etc., it may be shown that the equation contains only n^2, and that it gives μ real positive values for this latter quantity. Hence, there are μ positive numbers $n_1', n_2', \ldots$ such that the resulting equation is satisfied by

$$n = \pm\, n_1', \quad n = \pm\, n_2', \quad \ldots, \quad n = \pm\, n_\mu'.$$

For each of these values of n, the ratios between $q_1, q_2, \ldots, q_\mu$ can be deduced from (176). Finally, if we take the real parts of the expressions (175), we find μ fundamental modes of vibration, whose frequencies are

$$n_1', n_2', \ldots, n_\mu'.$$

It is easily seen from this that, if we do not assume any special relations between the constants involved in our problem, there will be no trace at all of the Zeeman-effect. In the absence of the magnetic field we had μ spectral lines, corresponding to the frequencies $n_1, n_2, \ldots, n_\mu$. The effect of the field is, to replace these by the slightly different values $n_1', n_2', \ldots, n_\mu'$, so that the lines are shifted a little towards one side or another, without being split into three or more components.[1])

91. The assumption that is required for the explanation of the Zeeman-effect can be found without any calculation. Let us imagine, for this purpose, a source of light placed in a magnetic field, and giving in the spectrum a triplet instead of an original spectral line. The components of this triplet are undoubtedly due to three modes of motion going on in the interior of the radiating particles, and these modes must be different from each other, because otherwise their frequencies ought to be the same. Let us now diminish the strength of the field. By this the components are made to approach each other, perhaps so much, that we can no longer distinguish them, but the three modes of motion will certainly not cease to be there. Only, their frequencies are less different from each other than they were in the strong field. By continually weakening the field, we can finally obtain the case in which there is no field at all, but even then the three modes of motion must exist. They still differ from each other, but their frequencies have become equal.

The necessary condition for the appearance of a magnetic triplet is thus seen to be that, in the absence of a magnetic field, three of the frequencies $n_1, n_2, \ldots, n_\mu$, corresponding to three different degrees of freedom, are equal to each other, or, as I shall say for the sake of brevity, that there are three *equivalent* degrees of freedom. Then, the magnetic field, by which all the frequencies are changed a little, produces a slight inequality between the three that were originally equal. We can express the same thing by saying that only a spectral line which consists of three coinciding lines can be changed into a triplet, the magnetic field producing no new lines, but only altering the positions of already existing ones.

1) Note 45.

92. These conclusions, which one can easily extend to quartets, quintets etc., are fully corroborated by the mathematical theory. If originally

$$n_1 = n_2 = n_3,$$

we shall have, under the influence of a magnetic field, the three frequencies

$$n_1 \text{ and } n_1 \pm \frac{1}{2}\sqrt{\frac{c_{23}^2}{m_2 m_3} + \frac{c_{31}^2}{m_3 m_1} + \frac{c_{12}^2}{m_1 m_2}}, \tag{177}$$

indicating the existence of a symmetrical triplet, the middle line of which has the position of the original spectral line. In a similar manner it can be shown that we shall observe a quartet, a quintet, etc., whenever the system has four, five or more equivalent degrees of freedom. All these more complicated forms of division of a spectral line are found to be symmetrical to the right and to the left of the original position, so that, if the number of components is odd, the middle one always occupies the place of the primitive line.[1])

93. The existence of a certain number of equivalent degrees of freedom is not the only condition to which we must subject the radiating particles. The fact that the magnetic components of the spectral lines have the same degree of sharpness as the original lines themselves requires a further hypothesis. We can understand this by reverting for a moment to the expression (177). In it, the coefficients c_{23}, c_{31}, c_{12} are linear and homogeneous functions of the components $\mathbf{H}_x, \mathbf{H}_y, \mathbf{H}_z$ of the external magnetic force. Therefore, the distance between the outer components of the triplet and the middle one is given by an expression of the form

$$\sqrt{q_{11}\mathbf{H}_x^2 + q_{22}\mathbf{H}_y^2 + q_{33}\mathbf{H}_z^2 + 2q_{12}\mathbf{H}_x\mathbf{H}_y + 2q_{23}\mathbf{H}_y\mathbf{H}_z + 2q_{31}\mathbf{H}_z\mathbf{H}_x}, \tag{178}$$

in which $q_{11}, q_{22}, \ldots, q_{12}, \ldots$ are constants depending on the nature of the vibrating particle. If, without changing the direction of the field, its intensity is doubled, the distance between the lines will increase in the same ratio. So far our formula agrees with experimental results.[2])

Let us now consider the influence of a change in the *direction* of the magnetic field, the intensity $|\mathbf{H}|$ being kept constant. By turning the field we shall give other values to $\mathbf{H}_x, \mathbf{H}_y, \mathbf{H}_z$, and also to the expression (178). It is clear that the same change will be brought about if, leaving the field as it is, we turn the radiating particle itself. Hence, if the source of light contains a large number of particles having all possible orientations, the distance (178) will

1) Note **46**. 2) Note **47**.

vary between certain limits, so that the outer lines of the observed triplet, which is due to the radiation of all the particles together, must be more or less diffuse.

Since it is difficult to admit that the particles of a luminous gas, when subjected to a magnetic field, are kept in one definite position, the only way of explaining the triplet with sharp outer components seems to be[1]) the assumption that the coefficients in (178) are such that the quadratic function takes the form

$$q_{11}(\mathbf{H}_x^2 + \mathbf{H}_y^2 + \mathbf{H}_z^2) = q_{11}\mathbf{H}^2.$$

In this case, the influence of a magnetic field on the frequencies is independent of the direction of the force relatively to the particle. As regards this influence, the particle can then be termed isotropic.

The simple mechanism which we imagined in the elementary theory of the Zeeman-effect obviously fulfils the conditions to which we have been led in what precedes. Indeed, a single electron which can be displaced in all directions from its position of equilibrium, and which is pulled back towards this position by a force independent of the direction of the displacement, has the kind of isotropy we spoke of just now. It has also three degrees of freedom, corresponding to the displacements in three directions perpendicular to each other.

94. The question now arises, whether we can imagine other, more complicated systems fulfilling the conditions necessary for the production of magnetic quartets, quintets etc. In order to give an example of a system of this kind, I may mention the way in which A. A. Robb[2]) has explained a quintet. For this purpose he supposes that a radiating particle contains two movable electrons, whose positions of equilibrium coincide, and which are pulled towards this position by elastic forces proportional to the displacements, and determined by a coefficient that is the same for both electrons. The charges and the masses are also supposed to be equal. Robb does not speak of the mutual electric action of the electrons, but he introduces certain connexions between their positions and their motions. If $\mathbf{r}_1$ and $\mathbf{r}_2$ are vectors drawn from the position of equilibrium towards the two electrons, and $\mathbf{r}_{12}$ the vector drawn from the first electron towards the second, these connexions are expressed by the equations

---

1) See, however, Note **64.**

2) A. A. Robb, Beiträge zur Theorie des Zeeman-Effektes, Ann. Phys. **15** (1904), p. 107.

$$\mathbf{r}_{12}^2 = k(\mathbf{r}_1^2 + \mathbf{r}_2^2),$$
$$\dot{\mathbf{r}}_{12}^2 = k(\dot{\mathbf{r}}_1^2 + \dot{\mathbf{r}}_2^2),$$
$$\ddot{\mathbf{r}}_{12}^2 = k(\ddot{\mathbf{r}}_1^2 + \ddot{\mathbf{r}}_2^2),$$

where k is a constant. It is immediately seen that in all these assumptions there is nothing that relates to a particular direction in space. On account of this, the five different frequencies which are found to exist under the influence of a magnetic force, are independent of the direction of this force, and a large number of systems of the kind described would give rise to a quintet of sharp lines.

Robb has worked out his theory at a much greater length than appears from the few words I have said about it, and it certainly is very ingenious. Yet, his hypothesis about the connexions between the two electrons seems to me so artificial, that I fear he has given us but a poor picture of the real state of things.

95. The same must be said of an hypothesis which I tried many years ago. After having made clear to myself that the vibrating particles must be isotropic, I examined the motions of systems surely possessing this property, namely of uniformly charged spherical shells, having an elasticity of one kind or another, and vibrating in a magnetic field. By means of the theory of spherical harmonics, the different modes of motion corresponding to what we may call the different tones of the shell, can easily be determined, and it was found that each of the tones can originate in several modes of motion, so that we can truly say that each spectral line (if the vibrations can produce light) consists of a certain number of coinciding lines, this number increasing as we pass on to the higher tones of the shell. The calculation of the influence of an external magnetic force confirmed the inference drawn from the general theory; if a certain frequency can be produced in 3, 5 or 7 independent ways, the spectral line corresponding to it is split into 3, 5 or 7 components.

For more than one reason, however, this theory of vibrating spherical shells can hardly be considered as anything more than an illustration of the general dynamical theorem; it cannot be said to furnish us with a satisfactory conception of the process of radiation. In the first place, if the series of tones of the shell gave rise to the successive members of a series of spectral lines, the number of components into which these are divided in a magnetic field ought to increase as we proceed in the series towards the more refrangible side. This is in contradiction with the results of later experience, which has shown, as I already mentioned, that all the lines of a series are split in exactly the same way.

In the second place, I pointed out that the spherical shells, when vibrating in their higher modes, are very poor radiators. In these modes the surface of the shell is divided by nodal lines into parts, vibrating in different phases, so that the phases are opposite on both sides of a nodal line. The vibrations issuing from these several parts must necessarily destroy each other for the larger part by interference.

96. In the light of our present knowledge, a third objection, which is a very serious one, may be raised. Though in the Zeeman-effect the separation of the components is not exactly what it would be, if in the formulae (164) the ratio $\frac{e}{m}$ had the value that has been deduced from experiments on cathode-rays, yet it is at least of the same order of magnitude as the value which we should find in this case. Hence, if we write $\left(\frac{e}{m}\right)_c$ for the ratio deduced from the observations on cathode-rays, and if we use the symbol (=) to indicate that two quantities are of the same order of magnitude, we have for the distance between two magnetic components the general formula

$$\delta n \,(=)\, \left(\frac{e}{m}\right)_c \frac{|\mathbf{H}|}{c}. \tag{179}$$

On the other hand, the theory of the vibrating shells leads to an equation of the form

$$\delta n \,(=)\, \frac{e_s}{m_s} \frac{|\mathbf{H}|}{c}, \tag{180}$$

in which e_s is the charge and m_s the mass of the shell.

We may infer from (179) and (180) that

$$\frac{e_s}{m_s} \,(=)\, \left(\frac{e}{m}\right)_c,$$

an equation which shows that the properties of the charged sphere cannot be wholly different from those of a free electron. Therefore, as we know that the mass m_c of such an electron is purely electromagnetic, we are led to suppose that the mass m_s of the shell is of the same nature. This, however, leads us into a difficulty, when we come to consider the frequencies of the vibrations. The relative motions of the parts of the shell are in part determined by the electric interactions of these parts, and even if they were wholly so, i. e. if there were no „elasticity" of an other kind, the wave-lengths corresponding to the different tones as I have called them, would, on the above assumption concerning the mass, be extremely small; they would be of the same order of magnitude as the radius R_s. They would be still smaller if there were an additional elasticity. Therefore, as the radius R_s must certainly be very much smaller than the wave-length of light, we can never hope to explain the radiation of light by the distortional vibrations of spheres whose charge and radius are such as is required by the magnitude of the Zeeman-effect.

97. It is clear in what way we can escape from the difficulty I just now pointed out. We must ascribe the radiation, not to the distortional vibrations of electrons, but to vibrations in which they move as a whole over certain small distances. Motions of this kind can exist in an atom which contains a certain number of negative electrons, arranged in such a manner that they are in stable equilibrium under the influence of their mutual forces, and of those that are exerted by the positive charges in the atom. This conception is very like an assumption that has been developed to a considerable extent by J. J. Thomson[1]), and according to which an atom consists of a positive charge uniformly distributed over a spherical space, a certain number of negative electrons being embedded in this sphere, and arranging themselves in a definite geometrical configuration.

In what follows, it will be found convenient to restrict the name of electrons to these negative particles or, as Thomson calls them, „corpuscles".

If the atom as a whole is uncharged, the total positive charge of the sphere must be equal to the sum of the charges of the negative electrons; we can, however, also conceive cases in which this equality does not exist.

It is interesting to examine the dimensions that must be ascribed to a structure of the above kind. Let the mutual distances of the electrons be of the same order of magnitude as a certain line l, and let e be the charge of each electron. Then, the repulsion between two electrons is of the same order as $\frac{e^2}{4\pi l^2}$, and the change which this force undergoes by a very small displacement δ of one of the corpuscles, is of the order

$$\frac{e^2\delta}{4\pi l^3}.$$

This change may be considered as an additional force that is called into play by the displacement δ. Hence, if we exclude those cases in which a very large number of electrons produce additional forces of the same direction, and also those in which the additional force which is due to the negative electrons is compensated or far surpassed by that which is caused by the positive charge, the total force by

1) J. J. Thomson, The corpuscular theory of matter, London, 1907. chap. 6 and 7.

which an electron is pulled back towards its position of equilibrium is given, as to order of magnitude, by the above expression. I shall suppose the electrons to have the same radius R, charge e and mass m as the free negative electrons, and I shall write λ for the wave-length corresponding to their vibrations. Now, by what precedes, we have for the frequency

$$n^2 (=) \frac{e^2}{4\pi m l^3},$$

or, on account of (72),

$$n^2 (=) \frac{3}{2} \frac{R c^2}{l^3}.$$

But

$$n = \frac{2\pi c}{\lambda},$$

so that

$$l (=) \sqrt[3]{\frac{3 R \lambda^2}{8\pi^2}}.$$

Putting $\lambda = 0{,}5 \cdot 10^{-4}$ cm, and introducing the value of R (§ 35), one finds by this equation

$$l (=) 2{,}4 \cdot 10^{-8} \text{ cm } (=) 1{,}6 \cdot 10^5 R.$$

This means that the electrons must be placed at distances from each other that are very much larger than their dimensions, so that, compared with the separate electrons, the atom is of a very large size. Nevertheless, it is very small compared with the wave-length, for according to the above data we have

$$l (=) 5 \cdot 10^{-4} \lambda.$$

One consequence of the high value which we have found for $l : R$ is that the electromagnetic fields of the electrons do not appreciably overlap. This is an important circumstance, because, on account of it, we may ascribe to each electron the electromagnetic mass m which it would have if it were wholly free.

The value we have found for l is of about the same order of magnitude as the estimates that have been formed of molecular dimensions. We may therefore hope not to be on a wrong track if, in the above manner, we try to explain the production of light by the vibrations of electrons under the influence of *electric* forces.

98. It is easily seen that a number of negative electrons can never form a permanent system, if not held together by some external action. This action is provided for in J. J. Thomson's model by the positive sphere, which attracts all the electrons towards its centre O, and which must be supposed to extend *beyond* the electrons, because otherwise there could be no true static equilibrium. As already stated, I shall use the same assumption, but I shall so far depart from Thomson's ideas as to consider the density ϱ, not as constant throughout the sphere, but as some unknown function of the distance r from its centre. The greater generality that is obtained in this way will be seen to be of some interest. With a slight modification, our formulae might even be adapted to the case of electrons attracted towards the point O by some force $f(r)$ of unknown origin, for any field of force that is symmetrical around a centre O, can be imitated by the electric field within a sphere in which the density ϱ is a suitable function of r.

However, I shall suppose ϱ to be positive in all layers of the sphere, and to decrease from the centre outward.

As is well known, the general outcome of the researches on the α-rays of radio-active bodies and on the canal rays has been that the positive electricity is always attached to the mass of an atom.[1]) In accordance with this result, we shall consider the positive sphere as having nearly the whole mass of the atom, a mass that is so large in comparison with that of the negative electrons, that the sphere can be regarded as immovable, while the electrons can be displaced within it. The question as to whether the mass of the positive sphere is material or electromagnetic, can be left aside. Of course the latter alternative must be discarded, if we apply to the positive electricity a formula similar to the one we have formerly given for the electromagnetic mass of an electron; on account of the large radius of the sphere, the mass calculated by the formula would be an insignificant fraction of the mass of the negative electrons. It might however be that part of the charge is concentrated in a large number of small particles whose mutual distances are invariable; in this case the total electromagnetic mass of the positive charge could have a considerable value.

99. Before passing on to a special case, some other remarks may be introduced.

In the first place, an atom which contains N movable negative electrons, will have $3N$ degrees of freedom. Consequently, if its vibrations are to be made accountable for the production of one or more series of spectral lines, the number of electrons must be rather large. It ought even to be infinite, if a series really consisted of an infinite number of lines, as it would according to Rydberg's equations. Since, however, these formulae are only approximations, and since the lines that can actually be observed are in finite number, I believe this consideration need not withhold us from ascribing the

1) See, however, Note **64.**

radiation of light to atoms containing a finite, though perhaps a rather large number of negative electrons.

In the second place we shall introduce the condition that the vibrating system must be isotropic. True isotropy, i. e. perfect equality of properties in all directions, can never be attained by a finite number of separated particles. It is only when we are content with the explanation of triplets, that no difficulty arises from this circumstance, because in this case equality of properties with respect to *three* directions at right angles to each other will suffice for our purpose. Arrangements possessing this limited kind of isotropy, can easily be imagined for different numbers of corpuscles, provided there be at least four of them. The electrons may be placed at the angles of one of the regular polyhedra, or of a certain number of such polyhedra whose centres coincide with that of the positive sphere, and whose relative position presents a sufficient regularity.

Our final remark relates to the radiation emitted by the atom. When we examined the radiation from a single electron we found that it is determined by the acceleration. One can infer from this that the radiation produced at distant points by an atom which contains a number of equal vibrating electrons, and whose dimensions are very small in comparison with the wave-length, is equal to that which would take place if there were but one electron, moving with an acceleration that is found by compounding all the individual accelerations. In some cases, especially likely to occur in systems presenting a geometrical configuration of high regularity, this resultant acceleration is zero, so that there is no perceptible radiation at all, or at least only a very small residual one, due to the fact that the different electrons are not at exactly the same distance from the outer point considered, and that therefore we have to compound the accelerations, such as they are, not at one and the same instant, but at slightly different times. Vibrations presenting the peculiarity in question may properly be designated as ineffective ones.

100. We shall now occupy ourselves with a special case, the simplest imaginable, namely that of four equal electrons A, B, C, D, which, of course, are in equilibrium at the corners of a regular tetrahedron whose centre coincides with the centre O of the positive sphere.[1])

The fundamental modes of motion of this system can easily be determined.[2]) In order to obtain simple formulae for the frequencies,

1) The Zeeman-effect in a system of this kind has already been examined by J. J. Thomson, who, however, supposed the positive sphere to have a uniform volume-density.

2) Note **48**.

I shall imagine a spherical surface to pass through A, B, C, D; I shall denote by ϱ the value which the density of the positive charge presents at this surface, and by ϱ_0 the mean density in its interior.

I shall further introduce a certain coefficient ω, which, in those cases in which there is a Zeeman-effect, can be regarded as a measure of it. We shall be concerned only with triplets, and the meaning of ω is, that the actual separation of the components is found, if the separation required by the elementary theory, for the same value of $\frac{e}{m}$, is multiplied by ω.

In the first fundamental mode, the four electrons perform equal vibrations along the lines OA, OB, OC, OD, in such a way that, at every instant, they are at equal distances from the centre O. The frequency of this motion, which is inefficient, and not affected by a magnetic field, is determined by

$$n^2 = -\frac{\varrho e}{m},$$

a formula which gives a real value for n, because ϱ is positive and e negative.

Other modes of motion are best described by choosing as axes of coordinates the lines joining the middle points of opposite edges of the tetrahedron, and by fixing our attention on two such edges, for example on those which are perpendicular to OX. Let these edges be AB and CD, x being positive for the first, and negative for the second.

The corpuscles can vibrate in such a manner that, at every instant, the displacement of any one of them from its position of equilibrium can be considered as made up of a component p parallel to OX and a transverse component, which for A and B is along AB, and for C and D along CD. Calling the component p positive or negative according to its direction, which may be that of OX or the reverse, and giving to the transverse displacement the positive sign if it is away from OX, and the negative sign if it is directed towards this line, we have for all the electrons

$$p = a \cos nt,$$

for the transverse displacement of A and B

$$g = sp,$$

and for that of C and D

$$-g = -sp,$$

the constant s being determined by the equation

$$s = \nu\sqrt{2} \pm \sqrt{1 + 2\nu^2}, \tag{181}$$

where

$$\nu = \frac{2\varrho - \varrho_0}{8(\varrho - \varrho_0)}. \qquad (182)$$

The double sign in (181) shows that there are *two* modes of the kind considered. These have unequal frequencies, for which I find the formula

$$n^2 = -\frac{e}{12m}\{6\varrho - \varrho_0 \pm 4(\varrho - \varrho_0)\sqrt{2(1+2\nu^2)}\}, \qquad (183)$$

and are both effective for radiation, on account of the accelerations of the electrons in the direction OX. The system will therefore produce two lines L_1 and L_2 in the spectrum.

Now, it is immediately seen that, in addition to these two modes of vibrating, which are related, as we may say, to the direction OX, there are similar ones related in the same way to OY and OZ, so that L_1 and L_2 are triple lines, which can be split into three components by a magnetic field. For L_1, the separation between the outer components and the middle one is determined by

$$\omega = \frac{1}{4}\left[1 - \frac{6\nu}{\sqrt{2(1+2\nu^2)}}\right], \qquad (184)$$

and for L_2 by

$$\omega = \frac{1}{4}\left[1 + \frac{6\nu}{\sqrt{2(1+2\nu^2)}}\right]. \qquad (185)$$

Moreover, it can be shown that the state of polarization of the light producing the components of these triplets is the same which we have deduced from the elementary theory, the radiation along the lines of force again consisting of two circularly polarized beams of different frequencies, the one right-handed and the other left-handed.

The modes of motion to which I have next to call your attention may be described as a twisting of the system around one of the axes OX, OY, OZ. The first of these modes is characterized by small rotations of the lines AB and CD around the axis OX, the direction of the rotation changing periodically for each line and being at every instant opposite for the two lines. Since a twisting of this kind around OZ can be decomposed into a twisting around OX and one around OY, these motions constitute only two fundamental modes. They are ineffective, and their frequency, which is given by the formula

$$n^2 = -\frac{1}{4}\frac{\varrho_0 e}{m}, \qquad (186)$$

is not altered by a magnetic field.

We have now found nine fundamental modes of motion in all. The remaining ones are rotations around one of the axes OX,

OY, OZ; these are not controlled by the internal forces we have assumed, and cannot be called vibrations about the position of equilibrium.

101. It is worthy of notice, that (186) always gives a real value for n, and that the two frequencies determined by (183) are real too, provided the value of ϱ be greater than $\frac{4}{7}\varrho_0$. When this condition is fulfilled, the original state of the system is one of stable equilibrium.

If we adopt J. J. Thomson's hypothesis of a uniformly charged sphere, we have $\varrho = \varrho_0$. In this case we can write instead of (183), (184) and (185)[1])

$$n^2 = -\frac{1}{2}\frac{\varrho_0 e}{m} \quad \text{or} \quad -\frac{1}{3}\frac{\varrho_0 e}{m},$$

$$\omega = -\frac{1}{2} \qquad \text{or} \quad 1.$$

102. Other cases in which a certain number of electrons have a regular geometrical arrangement within the positive sphere, can be treated in a similar way, though for a larger number of particles the calculations become rather laborious. So far as I can see, the line of thought which we are now following promises no chance of finding the explanation of a quartet or a quintet, so that, after all, the progress we have made is not very important. The main interest of the preceding theory lies in the fact, that it shows the possibility of the explanation of magnetic triplets in which the separation of the components is different from that of the triplets of the elementary theory, as is shown by the value of ω differing from 1. According to our formulae, ω can even have a negative value. In the above example this means that, in the radiation along the lines of force, the circular polarization of the outer components of the doublet can be the inverse of what it would be according to the elementary theory.[2])

It is remarkable that negative electrons may in this way produce a Zeeman-effect which the elementary theory would ascribe to the existence of movable positive particles.

103. Shortly after Zeeman's discovery some physicists observed that, just like the magnetic rotation of the plane of polarization, the new phenomenon makes one think of some rotation around the lines of force, going on in the magnetic field. There is certainly much to be said in favour of this view. Only, if one means the hidden ro-

1) Note **49**. 2) Note **50**.

tations which some theories suppose to exist in the ether occupying a magnetic field (and to which those theories must ascribe every action of the field) a development of the idea lies outside the scope of the theory of electrons as I am now expounding it, because, in this theory, we take as our basis, without further discussion, the properties of the ether which are expressed in our fundamental equations. There is, however, a rotation of a different kind to which perhaps we may have recourse in our attempts to explain Zeeman's phenomenon.

Let us consider the interval of time during which a magnetic field is set up in a certain part of the ether. While the magnetic force $\mathbf{H}$ is changing, there are electric forces $\mathbf{d}$, whose distribution and magnitude are determined by our fundamental equations (2) and (5). These are the forces which cause the induction current produced in a metallic wire, and they may be said to be identical, though presented in a modern form, with the forces by which W. Weber explained the phenomena of diamagnetism, an explanation that can readily be reproduced in the language of the theory of electrons. I shall now consider the rotation they impart to a system of negative electrons such as we have been examining in the preceding paragraphs. In doing so, I shall suppose the positively charged sphere to have so large a mass that it may be regarded as unmovable, and I shall apply to the system of negative electrons the laws that hold for a rigid body; this will lead to no appreciable error, if the time during which the magnetic field is started, is very long in comparison with the periods of the vibrations of the electrons.

104. I shall again confine myself to arrangements of the electrons that are isotropic with respect to three directions at right angles to each other. Then, if the axes of coordinates are drawn through the centre O in any directions we like, and if the sums are extended to all the negative electrons of the system, we shall have

$$\sum x = \sum y = \sum z = 0.$$

Also, the moment of inertia will be the same with respect to any axis through O. We may write for it

$$Q = 2mK,$$

if

and we have

$$\left.\begin{aligned} K = \sum x^2 = \sum y^2 = \sum z^2, \\ \sum xy = \sum yz = \sum zx = 0. \end{aligned}\right\} \qquad (187)$$

The force acting on one of the electrons is given by

$$e\mathbf{d}_x, \quad e\mathbf{d}_y, \quad e\mathbf{d}_z,$$

and we find therefore for the components of the resultant couple with reference to the point O

$$e\sum(y\mathbf{d}_z - z\mathbf{d}_y), \quad e\sum(z\mathbf{d}_x - x\mathbf{d}_z), \quad e\sum(x\mathbf{d}_y - y\mathbf{d}_x). \tag{188}$$

By $\mathbf{d}$ we shall understand the electric force due to causes outside the system. On account of the small dimensions of the latter, this force will be nearly constant throughout its extent, so that, denoting by $\mathbf{d}_0$ the electric force at the centre, we may write

$$\mathbf{d}_x = \mathbf{d}_{0x} + x\frac{\partial \mathbf{d}_x}{\partial x} + y\frac{\partial \mathbf{d}_x}{\partial y} + z\frac{\partial \mathbf{d}_x}{\partial z},$$

$$\mathbf{d}_y = \mathbf{d}_{0y} + x\frac{\partial \mathbf{d}_y}{\partial x} + y\frac{\partial \mathbf{d}_y}{\partial y} + z\frac{\partial \mathbf{d}_y}{\partial z},$$

$$\mathbf{d}_z = \mathbf{d}_{0z} + x\frac{\partial \mathbf{d}_z}{\partial x} + y\frac{\partial \mathbf{d}_z}{\partial y} + z\frac{\partial \mathbf{d}_z}{\partial z}.$$

Substituting these values in the expressions (188), and bearing in mind the equations (187), one finds

$$eK\left(\frac{\partial \mathbf{d}_z}{\partial y} - \frac{\partial \mathbf{d}_y}{\partial z}\right), \quad eK\left(\frac{\partial \mathbf{d}_x}{\partial z} - \frac{\partial \mathbf{d}_z}{\partial x}\right), \quad eK\left(\frac{\partial \mathbf{d}_y}{\partial x} - \frac{\partial \mathbf{d}_x}{\partial y}\right),$$

or, in virtue of the fundamental equation (5),

$$-\frac{e}{c}K\dot{\mathbf{h}}_x, \quad -\frac{e}{c}K\dot{\mathbf{h}}_y, \quad -\frac{e}{c}K\dot{\mathbf{h}}_z.$$

In order to find the components of the angular acceleration, we must divide these expressions by $Q = 2mK$. The result is

$$-\frac{e}{2mc}\dot{\mathbf{h}}_x, \quad -\frac{e}{2mc}\dot{\mathbf{h}}_y, \quad -\frac{e}{2mc}\dot{\mathbf{h}}_z,$$

from which it at once appears that, after the establishment of a field $\mathbf{H}$, a system that was initially at rest, has acquired a velocity of rotation

$$\mathbf{k} = -\frac{e}{2mc}\mathbf{H}. \tag{189}$$

The axis of rotation has the direction of the magnetic field, and, if e is negative, the direction of the rotation corresponds to that of the field. It is interesting that the velocity of the rotation is independent of the particular arrangement of the electrons, and that its frequency, i. e. the number of revolutions in a time 2π, is equal to the change of frequency we have calculated in the elementary theory of the Zeeman-effect.

The same rotation would be produced if, after the setting up of the field, the system were, by a motion of translation, carried into it from an outside point. Once started, the rotation will go on for ever, as long as the field is kept constant, unless its velocity be slowly diminished by the radiation to which it gives rise.[1])

105. We shall now turn our attention to the small vibrations that can take place in the system while it rotates. For this purpose, we shall introduce axes of coordinates having a fixed position in the system, and distinguish between the motion with respect to these axes, the relative motion, and the motion with respect to axes fixed in space, which we may call the absolute one.

Let, for any one of the electrons, $\mathbf{v}$ be the absolute velocity, $\mathbf{q}$ the absolute acceleration, $\mathbf{q}_1$ the part of it that is due to the internal forces of the system, and $\mathbf{q}_2$ the part due to the magnetic field. Then, we shall have for the acceleration $\mathbf{q}'$ of the relative motion, if we neglect terms depending on the square of the angular velocity $\mathbf{k}$, and therefore on the square of the magnetic force $\mathbf{H}$,

$$\mathbf{q}' = \mathbf{q} - 2[\mathbf{k} \cdot \mathbf{v}] = \mathbf{q}_1 + \mathbf{q}_2 - 2[\mathbf{k} \cdot \mathbf{v}],$$

i. e. on account of (189),

$$\mathbf{q}' = \mathbf{q}_1 + \mathbf{q}_2 + \frac{e}{mc}[\mathbf{H} \cdot \mathbf{v}].$$

Since

$$\mathbf{q}_2 = \frac{e}{mc}[\mathbf{v} \cdot \mathbf{H}],$$

we find[2])

$$\mathbf{q}' = \mathbf{q}_1.$$

This shows that the relative motion is determined solely by the internal forces of the system; it is identical with the motion that could take place in a system without rotation and free from the influence of a magnetic field. I shall express this by saying that in the system rotating with the velocity which we calculated, there is no *internal* Zeeman-effect, the word „internal" being introduced, because, as we shall presently show, there remains a Zeeman-effect in the external radiation. This effect is brought about by the same cause that has made the internal effect disappear, namely by the rotation of the particles.

106. We have already observed (§ 99) that a particle which contains a certain number of equal vibrating electrons, and whose size is very small compared with the wave-length, will radiate in the same way as a single electron of the same kind, moving with the accelerations $\sum \ddot{x}$, $\sum \ddot{y}$, $\sum \ddot{z}$, the sums extending to all the separate electrons, and x, y, z being their coordinates with respect to axes

1) Note 51. 2) Note 52.

fixed in space. The accelerations will have these values if the coordinates of the equivalent electron, as it may properly be called, are given at every instant by $\sum x$, $\sum y$, $\sum z$.

In order to apply this theorem to the problem before us, I shall again choose the centre of the positive sphere as origin of coordinates, drawing the axis of z in the direction of the external magnetic force **H**. Let OX and OY be fixed in space, and let OX', OY' be axes rotating with the system; then, if k is the positive or negative velocity of rotation around OZ, we may put

$$\left.\begin{aligned} x &= x' \cos kt - y' \sin kt, \\ y &= x' \sin kt + y' \cos kt, \end{aligned}\right\} \qquad (190)$$

since we may take kt for the angle between OX and OX'. Now, if x_0', y_0', z_0' are the coordinates of one of the negative electrons in its position of equilibrium, and $\alpha \cos(nt+f)$, $\beta \cos(nt+g)$, $\gamma \cos(nt+h)$ the displacements from that position, due to the internal vibrations, and referred to the moving axes, we shall have for this particle

$$x' = x_0' + \alpha \cos(nt+f), \quad y' = y_0' + \beta \cos(nt+g). \qquad (191)$$

Whereas the constants α, β, f, g (and γ, h) have different values for the several electrons, the frequency n will have for all these corpuscles a common value, equal to the frequency of the radiation in the absence of a magnetic field.

Introducing the values (191) into the expressions (190) and taking the sum for all the corpuscles, we shall find the coordinates $\mathbf{x}$, $\mathbf{y}$ of the equivalent electron. Since $\sum x_0' = \sum y_0' = 0$, the result may be put in the form

$$\mathbf{x} = \mathbf{x}_1 + \mathbf{x}_2, \quad \mathbf{y} = \mathbf{y}_1 + \mathbf{y}_2,$$

where

$$\mathbf{x}_1 = A \cos\{(n+k)t + \varphi\}, \quad \mathbf{y}_1 = A \sin\{(n+k)t + \varphi\},$$
$$\mathbf{x}_2 = B \cos\{(n-k)t + \psi\}, \quad \mathbf{y}_2 = -B \sin\{(n-k)t + \psi\},$$

A, B, φ and ψ being constants. These formulae show that, leaving aside the vibration in the direction of OZ, which is entirely unaffected by the field and the rotation, we can decompose the motion of the equivalent electron into two circular motions in opposite directions, performed with the frequencies $n+k$ and $n-k$. Therefore, since in virtue of (189) k is given by the equation

$$k = -\frac{e}{2mc}|\mathbf{H}|,$$

the Zeeman-effect in the radiation issuing from the rotating particle exactly corresponds to that which we formerly derived from the elementary theory for a particle without rotation.

107. There are one or two points in this last form of the theory that are particularly to be noticed.

In the first place, we can suppose the system of electrons within the positive sphere to be capable of vibrating in different modes, thereby producing a series of spectral lines. In consequence of the rotation set up by the field, all these lines will be changed into equal triplets, so that we have now found a case, in which all the lines of a series are divided, as they really are, in the same way I may add that, according to the view of the phenomenon we are now discussing, the Zeeman-effect is due to a *combination* of the internal vibrations whose frequency is n, with the rotation of the frequency k.

This calls forth a more general remark. It is well known that in acoustic phenomena two tones with the frequencies n_1 and n_2 are often accompanied by the so called combination-tones whose frequencies are $n_1 + n_2$ and $n_1 - n_2$ respectively. Something of the same kind occurs in other cases in which a motion or any other phenomenon shows two different kinds of periodicity at the same time; indeed, on account of these, terms such as $\cos n_1 t$ and $\cos n_2 t$ will occur in the mathematical expressions, and as soon as the product of two quantities having the two periods shows itself in the formulae, the simple trigonometric formula

$$\cos n_1 t \cos n_2 t = \frac{1}{2} \cos (n_1 + n_2) t + \frac{1}{2} \cos (n_1 - n_2) t$$

leads us to recognize two new frequencies $n_1 + n_2$ and $n_1 - n_2$. Indeed, it is precisely in this way that, in the preceding paragraph, the frequencies $n + k$ and $n - k$ have made their appearance.

Many years ago, V. A. Julius observed that certain regularities in the spectra of elements may be understood, if we suppose the lines to be caused by combination-tones, the word being taken in the wide sense we can give it on the ground of what has just been said. If, for example, there are two fundamental modes of vibration with the frequencies n_1 and n_2 or, as we may say more concisely, two „tones“ n_1 and n_2, and if each of these combines with a series of tones, so that secondary tones with frequencies equal to the differences between those of their primaries are produced, we shall obtain a series of pairs, in which the components of each pair are at the distance $n_1 - n_2$ from each other.

In connection with this, it should also be noticed that, in Rydberg's formulae, every frequency is presented as the difference between two fundamental ones.

Of course it would be premature to attach much value to speculations of this kind. Yet, in view of the fact that all lines of a series undergo the same magnetic splitting, one can hardly help thinking that all the fundamental modes of motion belonging to the series are somehow combined with one or more periodic phenomena going on in the magnetic field, as, in the example we have worked out, they were combined with the rotation of the particles.

I may add that the form of Rydberg's equations, in which each frequency is represented as the difference of two terms, naturally suggests the idea that under the influence of a magnetic field one or both of these terms have their value changed, or rather, are replaced by a number of slightly different terms, to each of which corresponds a magnetic component. It is clear that if, for all lines of a series, the part of $\frac{n}{N_0}$ which they have in common, for instance the part $\frac{1}{(1+\mu_1)^2}$ in the second subordinate series I (§ 82), is altered in the same way, the other part $\left[\frac{1}{(m+\sigma)^2}\right]$ remaining unchanged, the equality of the Zeeman-effect for all the members of the series will be accounted for.

108. In the second place, it is important to remark that, for the entire prevention of an internal Zeeman-effect, the rotation of a particle as a whole must have exactly the velocity we have found for it in § 104.

For other values of $\mathbf{k}$, such as might occur if the rotating particle had a moment of inertia different from that which we formerly took into account, $\mathbf{q}'$ would come out different from $\mathbf{q}_1$, so that the relative motion of the electrons with respect to the rotating axes would still be affected by the magnetic force. In such a case, in order to find the Zeeman-effect as it becomes manifest in the radiation, we should have to combine the internal motions with the rotation, after the manner shown in § 106; the result would obviously be a decomposition of the original spectral lines into more than three components.

This seems rather promising at first sight, but it must be admitted that one can hardly assign a reason for the existence of a moment of inertia, different from the value used in § 104, and that it would be very difficult to reconcile the results with Runge's law for the multiple divisions of the lines.

109. The preceding theory of rotating radiating particles is open to some objections. Besides the two cases mentioned in § 104, a third must perhaps be considered as possible. In a Geissler tube or a flame combinations and decompositions of minute particles are no doubt continually going on; a radiating atom cannot therefore be supposed to have been in a free state ever since the magnetic field was set up. Now, in atoms combined with other particles, the mobility of the electrons might perhaps be so much diminished, that the production of the field cannot make them rotate; since there is no reason why they should begin to do so the moment the atoms are set free, we can imagine in this way the existence in the magnetic field of free atoms without a rotation.

Another difficulty, which one also encounters in some questions belonging to the theory of magnetism, arises from the fact that a rotating particle whose charge is not quite uniformly distributed, must necessarily, in the course of time, lose its energy by the radiation that is due to the rotation itself. It is probable that the time required for an appreciable diminution of the rotation would be very long. An exact determination of it would, however, require rather complicated calculations.

110. After all, you see by these considerations that we are rather at a loss as to the explanation of the complicated forms of the Zeeman-effect. In this state of things, it is interesting that some conclusions concerning the polarization of the radiation can be drawn from general principles, independently of any particular theory. For this purpose we shall avail ourselves of the consideration of what we may term the reflected image of an electromagnetic system.

Let S be a system composed of moving electrons and material particles, the motion of the former being accompanied by an electromagnetic field in the intervening ether. Then, a second system S', which may be called the image of S with respect to a plane V, may be defined as follows. To each particle or electron, and even to each charged element of volume in S, corresponds an equal particle, electron or element of volume in S', moving in such a way that the positions of the two are at every instant symmetrical with respect to the plane V; further, if P and P' are corresponding points, the vector representing the dielectric displacement at P' is the image of the corresponding one at P, whereas the magnetic forces in S and S' are represented by vectors, one of which is the *inverted* image of the other. On certain assumptions concerning the forces between the electrons and other particles, which seem general enough not to exclude any real case, the system S' can be shown to be a possible one, as soon as S has an objective existence.

We shall apply this to the ordinary experiment for the exhibition of the Zeeman-effect, fixing our attention on the rays that are emitted along the lines of force, and placing the plane V parallel to these lines. There are many positions of the plane fulfilling the latter condition, but it is clear that, whichever of them we choose, the image of the electromagnet will always have the same properties. The same may be said, so far as the properties are accessible to our observations, of the source of light itself; therefore, the radiation too must be exactly the same in all systems that can be got by taking the image of the experiment with respect to planes that are parallel to the lines of force. From this we can immediately infer that the light radiated along the lines of force can never show a trace of rectilinear or elliptic polarization; it must either be unpolarized, or have a circular polarization, partial or complete. This conclusion also holds for the part of the radiation that is characterized by a definite frequency, and is therefore found at a definite point of the spectrum.

By a similar mode of reasoning we can predict that, in the emission at right angles to the lines of force, there can never be any other polarization, either partial or complete, but a rectilinear one with the plane of polarization parallel or perpendicular to the lines of force.

Finally, since the image of a magnetic field with respect to the plane of which we have spoken, is a field of the opposite direction, the state of radiation must be changed into its image by an inversion of the magnetic force. At every point of the spectrum the direction of the circular polarization will be inverted at the same time.

CHAPTER IV.

PROPAGATION OF LIGHT IN A BODY COMPOSED OF MOLECULES.

THEORY OF THE INVERSE ZEEMAN-EFFECT.

111. In the preceding discussion we had in view the influence of a magnetic field on the light *emitted* by a source of light. There is a corresponding influence on the absorption, as was already shown by one of Zeeman's first experiments. He found that the dark lines which appear in the spectrum of a beam of white light, passed through a sodium flame, are changed in exactly the same way as the emission lines of the luminous vapour, when the flame is exposed to an external magnetic field. We can easily understand this inverse phenomenon if we bear in mind the intimate connexion between the emission and the absorption of light. According to the well known law of resonance, a body whose particles can execute free vibrations of certain definite periods, must be able to absorb light of the same periods which it receives from without. Therefore, if in a sodium flame under the influence of a magnetic field there are three periods of free vibrations instead of one, we may expect that the flame can produce in a continuous spectrum three absorption lines corresponding to these periods, and in general, if we want to know what kinds of light are emitted by a body under certain circumstances, we have only to examine the absorption in a beam of light sent across it.

A highly interesting theory based on this idea has been developed by Voigt.[1]) It has the advantage of being applicable to bodies whose density is so great that there is a certain mutual action between neighboring molecules, a case in which it is rather difficult directly to consider the emission of light.

Voigt's theory was not originally expounded in the language of the theory of electrons, his first method belonging to those which

---

1) W. Voigt, Ann. Phys. Chem. **67** (1899), p. 345; **68** (1899), p. 352, 604; **69** (1899), p. 290; Ann. Phys. **1** (1900), p. 376, 389; **6** (1901), p. 784; see also his book: Magneto- und Elektrooptik, Leipzig, 1908.

I have formerly alluded to, in which one tries to describe the observed phenomena by judiciously chosen differential equations, without troubling oneself about the mechanism underlying them. However, in order not to stray from the main subject of these lectures, I shall establish Voigt's equations, or rather a set of formulae equivalent to them, by applying the principles of the theory of electrons to the propagation of light in a ponderable body considered as a system of molecules.

These formulae are also interesting because by means of them we can treat a number of other questions, relating to the velocity of propagation and the absorption of light of different frequencies. It will be well to begin with some of these, deferring for some time the consideration of the action exerted by a magnetic field.

112. Let us imagine a body composed of innumerable molecules or atoms, of „particles" as I shall term them, each particle containing a certain number of electrons, all or some of which are set vibrating by an incident beam of light. Between the electrons and in their interior there will be a certain electromagnetic field, which we could determine by means of our fundamental equations, if the distribution and the motion of the charges were known; having calculated the field, we should also be able to find its action on the movable electrons, and to form the equations of motion for each of them. This method, in which the motion of the individual electrons and the field in their immediate neighborhood and even within them, would be the object of our investigation, is however wholly impracticable, when, as in gaseous bodies and liquids, the distribution of the particles is highly irregular. We cannot hope to follow in its course each electron, nor to determine in all its particulars the field in the intermolecular spaces. We must therefore have recourse to an other method. Fortunately, there is a simple way of treating the problem, which is sufficient for the discussion of what can really be observed, and is indeed suggested by the very nature of the phenomena.

It is not the motion of a single electron, nor the field produced by it, that can make itself felt in our experiments, in which we are always concerned with immense numbers of particles; only the resultant effects produced by them are perceptible to our senses. It is to be expected that the irregularities of which I have spoken, will disappear from the total effect, and that we shall be able to account for it, if, from the outset, we fix our attention, not on all these irregularities, but only on certain *mean* values. I shall now proceed to define these.

113. Let P be a point in the body, **S** a sphere described around it as centre, and φ one of the scalar or vector quantities occurring in our fundamental equations. Then the mean value of φ at the point P, which we shall denote by $\overline{\varphi}$, is given by the equation

$$\overline{\varphi} = \frac{1}{\mathbf{S}} \int \varphi \, dS,$$

in which **S** means the volume of the sphere, and the integration is to be extended to this volume. The elements dS are to be taken infinitely small in the mathematical sense of the words, so that even an electron is divided into many elements. As to the sphere **S**, it must be chosen neither too small nor too large. Since our purpose is to get rid of the irregularities in the distribution of φ, the sphere must contain a very large number of particles. On the other hand, we must be careful not to obliterate the changes from point to point that can really be observed. The radius of the sphere must therefore be so small that the state of the body, so far as it is accessible to our means of observation, may be considered as uniform throughout the sphere. In the problems we shall have to deal with, this means that the radius must be small compared with the wave-length. Fortunately, the molecular distances are so much smaller than the length of even the shortest light-waves, that both conditions can be satisfied at the same time.

114. The mean value φ, taken for a point P, is in general a function of the coordinates of this point, and if φ itself depends upon the time, $\overline{\varphi}$ will do so too. We can easily infer from our definition the relations

$$\overline{\frac{\partial \varphi}{\partial x}} = \frac{\partial \overline{\varphi}}{\partial x}, \quad \ldots, \quad \overline{\frac{\partial \varphi}{\partial t}} = \frac{\partial \overline{\varphi}}{\partial t},$$

by which the transition from our fundamental equations to the corresponding formulae for the mean values is made very easy. Of course, the mean values of the quantities on the right-and on the left-hand side of an equation must be equal to each other, so that all we have got to do, is to replace **d**, **h**, etc. by their mean values. The resultant formulae, viz.

$$\operatorname{rot} \overline{\mathbf{h}} = \frac{1}{c}(\dot{\overline{\mathbf{d}}} + \overline{\rho \mathbf{v}})$$

and

$$\operatorname{rot} \overline{\mathbf{d}} = -\frac{1}{c}\dot{\overline{\mathbf{h}}},$$

may be considered as the general electromagnetic equations for the ponderable body; they are comparable with those of which we spoke in § 4. In order to bring out the similarity, I shall put

$$\overline{\mathbf{d}} = \mathbf{E},$$

and

$$\overline{\mathbf{h}} = \mathbf{H}.$$

It only remains to examine the term $\overline{\varrho \mathbf{v}}$. According to our definition of mean values, we have for the components of this vector, if x, y, z are the coordinates of an element of the moving charges at the time t,

$$\overline{\varrho \mathbf{v}_x} = \frac{1}{\mathbf{S}} \int \varrho \mathbf{v}_x dS = \frac{1}{\mathbf{S}} \int \varrho \frac{dx}{dt} dS, \text{ etc.,}$$

or, if we suppose the surface of the sphere not to intersect any electrons,

$$\overline{\varrho \mathbf{v}_x} = \frac{d}{dt} \left[\frac{1}{\mathbf{S}} \int \varrho x dS \right], \text{ etc.}$$

We have formerly seen that $\int \varrho x dS$, $\int \varrho y dS$, $\int \varrho z dS$ are the components of the electric moment of the part of the body to which the integration is extended. Hence, $\frac{1}{\mathbf{S}} \int \varrho x dS$ and the two corresponding expressions with y and z are the components of the electric moment of the body per unit of volume.[1]) We shall represent this moment, or, as it may also be termed, the electric polarization of the body, by $\mathbf{P}$. Thus

$$\overline{\varrho \mathbf{v}} = \dot{\mathbf{P}},$$

and

$$\dot{\overline{\mathbf{d}}} + \overline{\varrho \mathbf{v}} = \dot{\mathbf{E}} + \dot{\mathbf{P}}.$$

Simplifying still further by putting

$$\mathbf{E} + \mathbf{P} = \mathbf{D}, \tag{192}$$

we are led to the equations

$$\text{rot}\, \mathbf{H} = \frac{1}{c} \dot{\mathbf{D}}, \tag{193}$$

$$\text{rot}\, \mathbf{E} = -\frac{1}{c} \dot{\mathbf{H}}, \tag{194}$$

which have exactly the form of those of which we spoke in § 4. If we like, we may now call $\mathbf{E}$ and $\mathbf{D}$ the electric force and the dielectric displacement, $\dot{\mathbf{D}}$ the displacement current. This exactly agrees with common usage; only, in our definition of these vectors, one clearly sees the traces of our fundamental assumption that the system is made up of ether and of particles with their electrons. Thus, $\mathbf{E}$ is the mean force acting on a charge that is at rest. The total dielectric displacement $\mathbf{D}$ consists of two parts, the one $\mathbf{E}$ having its seat in the ether, and the other $\mathbf{P}$ in the particles. Corresponding

1) Note 53.

to these, we distinguish two parts in the current $\dot{\mathbf{D}}$; the first, $\dot{\mathbf{E}}$ is the mean of the displacement current in the ether, and the second the mean of the convection current $\rho\mathbf{v}$.

115. To complete our system of equations we must now examine the relation between $\mathbf{D}$ and $\mathbf{E}$, or rather that between $\mathbf{P}$ and $\mathbf{E}$. This is found by considering the way in which the electric moment in a particle is produced or changed.

Let us suppose that each particle contains a single movable electron with charge e and mass m, and let us denote by ξ, η, ζ the distances over which it is displaced from its position of equilibrium in the directions of the axes of coordinates. The components of the electric moment of a single particle are

$$\mathbf{p}_x = e\xi, \quad \mathbf{p}_y = e\eta, \quad \mathbf{p}_z = e\zeta,$$

and, writing N for the number of particles per unit volume, we have

$$\mathbf{P}_x = Ne\xi, \quad \mathbf{P}_y = Ne\eta, \quad \mathbf{P}_z = Ne\zeta, \tag{195}$$

if the particles have a regular geometrical arrangement. If, on the contrary, they are irregularly distributed, so that the values of the displacements ξ, η, ζ change abruptly from one particle to the next, we may use the same equations, provided we understand by ξ, η, ζ mean values taken for all the particles situated in a space that is infinitely small in a physical sense. A similar remark applies to other quantities occurring in the equations we are going to establish for the motion of the electrons.

116. The values of ξ, η, ζ, and consequently those of $\mathbf{P}_x$, $\mathbf{P}_y$, $\mathbf{P}_z$, depend on the forces acting on the movable electrons. These are of four different kinds.

In the first place we shall conceive a certain elastic force by which an electron is pulled back towards its position of equilibrium after having been displaced from it. We shall suppose this force to be directed towards that position, and to be proportional to the displacement. Denoting by f a certain positive constant which depends on the structure and the properties of the particle, we write for the components of this elastic force

$$-f\xi, \quad -f\eta, \quad -f\zeta. \tag{196}$$

The second force is a resistance against the motion of the electron. We must introduce some action of this kind, because without it it would be impossible to account for the absorption which it is one of our principal objects to examine. Following the example given by Helmholtz in his theory of anomalous dispersion, with which the present investigation has many points in common, I shall take the resistance proportional to the velocity of the electron, and opposite to it. Thus, if g is a new positive constant, the components of the second force are

$$-g\frac{d\xi}{dt}, \quad -g\frac{d\eta}{dt}, \quad -g\frac{d\zeta}{dt}. \tag{197}$$

We shall later on return to this question.

117. We have next to consider the force acting on the electron on account of the electromagnetic field in the ether. At first sight it may be thought that this action is to be represented by $e\mathbf{E}$. On closer examination one finds however that a term of the form $ae\mathbf{P}$ is to be added, in which a is a constant whose value is little different from $\frac{1}{3}$. I shall not enter upon the somewhat lengthy calculations that are required for the determination of this additional force. In order to explain why it is introduced, I have only to remind you of the well known reasoning by which Kelvin long ago came to distinguish between the magnetic force and the magnetic induction. He defined these as forces exerted on a pole of unit strength, placed in differently shaped infinitely small cavities surrounding the point considered. The magnetically polarized parts of the body outside the cavity turn their poles more or less towards it, and thus produce on its walls a certain distribution of magnetism, whose action on an inside pole is found to depend on the form of the cavity.

In the problem before us we can proceed in an exactly similar manner. The general equations (33)—(36) show that the electromagnetic field is composed of parts that are due to the individual particles of the system, so that, if some of these were removed, the motion of the electrons in the remaining ones being left unchanged, a part of the field would be taken away. We must further take into account that each component of $\mathbf{d}$ or $\mathbf{h}$ belonging to the field that is produced by a certain number of particles, is obtained by an addition of the corresponding quantities for the fields due to each of the particles taken separately. The sum may be replaced by an integral in those cases in which the discontinuity of the molecular structure does not make itself felt. If we want to know the field produced at a point A by a part of the body whose shortest distance from A is very great compared with the mutual distance of adjacent particles, we may replace the real state of things by one in which the polarized matter is homogeneously distributed.

All this can also be said of the magnetized particles one has to consider in Kelvin's theory, though the cases are different, because the formulae (§ 42) for the field produced by a variable electric moment are less simple than those which determine the action of a constant molecular magnet. The formulae however much resemble each other if the point for which the field of a particle is to be determined, lies at a distance from it that is small compared with the wave-length. In this case the field can be approximately considered as an electrostatic one, such as would exist if the electric moment did not change in the course of time.

Around the particle A for which we wish to determine the action exerted on the electron it contains, we lay a closed surface σ, whose dimensions are infinitely small in a physical sense, and we conceive, for a moment, all other particles lying within this surface to be removed. The state of things is then exactly analogous to the case of a magnet in which a cavity has been formed. There will be a distribution of electricity on the surface, due to the polarization of the outside portion of the body, and the force $\mathbf{E}'$, exerted by this distribution on a unit charge at A must be added to the force $\mathbf{E}$ which appears in (194).

Now, if the particles we have just removed are restored to their places, their electric moments will produce a third force $\mathbf{E}''$ in the particle A, and the total electric force to which the movable electron of A is exposed, will be

$$\mathbf{E} + \mathbf{E}' + \mathbf{E}''.$$

It is clear that the result cannot depend on the form of the cavity σ, which has only been imagined for the purpose of performing the calculations. These take the simplest form if σ is a sphere. Then the calculation of the force $\mathbf{E}'$ leads to the result[1])

$$\mathbf{E}' = \tfrac{1}{3}\mathbf{P}.$$

The problem of determining the force $\mathbf{E}''$ is more difficult. I shall not dwell upon it here, and I shall only say that, for a system of particles having a regular cubical arrangement, one finds[2])

$$\mathbf{E}'' = 0,$$

a result that can be applied with a certain degree of approximation to isotropic bodies in general, such as glass, fluids and gases. It is not quite correct however for these, and ought to be replaced in general by

$$\mathbf{E}'' = s\mathbf{P},$$

where, for each body, s is a constant which it will be difficult exactly to determine.

---

1) Note **54**. 2) Note **55**.

Putting

$$a = \tfrac{1}{3} + s,$$

we find for the electric force acting on an electron

$$\mathbf{E} + a\mathbf{P}.$$

118. The last of the forces we are enumerating occurs in magneto-optical phenomena; it is due to the external magnetic field, which we shall denote by the symbol $\mathfrak{H}$, in order to distinguish it from the periodically changing magnetic force $\mathbf{H}$ that is due to the electric vibrations themselves[1]), and occurs in our equations (193) and (194).

In all that follows we shall suppose the external field $\mathfrak{H}$ to have the direction of the axis of z. Then its action on the vibrating electron, which in general is represented by

$$\frac{e}{c}[\mathbf{v} \cdot \mathfrak{H}],$$

has the components

$$\frac{e\mathfrak{H}}{c}\frac{d\eta}{dt}, \quad -\frac{e\mathfrak{H}}{c}\frac{d\xi}{dt}, \quad 0,$$

where $\mathfrak{H}$ is written instead of $\mathfrak{H}_z$.

Taking together all that has been said about the several forces, we find for the equations of motion of the movable electron contained in a particle

$$\left.\begin{aligned} m\frac{d^2\xi}{dt^2} &= e(\mathbf{E}_x + a\mathbf{P}_x) - f\xi - g\frac{d\xi}{dt} + \frac{e\mathfrak{H}}{c}\frac{d\eta}{dt}, \\ m\frac{d^2\eta}{dt^2} &= e(\mathbf{E}_y + a\mathbf{P}_y) - f\eta - g\frac{d\eta}{dt} - \frac{e\mathfrak{H}}{c}\frac{d\xi}{dt}, \\ m\frac{d^2\zeta}{dt^2} &= e(\mathbf{E}_z + a\mathbf{P}_z) - f\zeta - g\frac{d\zeta}{dt}. \end{aligned}\right\} \quad (198)$$

119. Another form of these equations will be found more convenient for our purpose.

In the first place, instead of the displacements of the movable electron, we shall introduce the components of the electric polarization $\mathbf{P}$. Taking into account the relations (195), dividing the formulae (198) by e, and putting

$$\frac{m}{Ne^2} = m', \quad \frac{f}{Ne^2} = f', \quad \frac{g}{Ne^2} = g', \quad (199)$$

---

1 Note 56.

one finds

$$\left.\begin{aligned} m'\frac{\partial^2 \mathbf{P}_x}{\partial t^2} &= \mathbf{E}_x + a\mathbf{P}_x - f'\mathbf{P}_x - g'\frac{\partial \mathbf{P}_x}{\partial t} + \frac{\mathfrak{H}}{cNe}\frac{\partial \mathbf{P}_y}{\partial t}, \\ m'\frac{\partial^2 \mathbf{P}_y}{\partial t^2} &= \mathbf{E}_y + a\mathbf{P}_y - f'\mathbf{P}_y - g'\frac{\partial \mathbf{P}_y}{\partial t} - \frac{\mathfrak{H}}{cNe}\frac{\partial \mathbf{P}_x}{\partial t}, \\ m'\frac{\partial^2 \mathbf{P}_z}{\partial t^2} &= \mathbf{E}_z + a\mathbf{P}_z - f'\mathbf{P}_z - g'\frac{\partial \mathbf{P}_z}{\partial t}. \end{aligned}\right\} \qquad (200)$$

These equations may be further transformed, if, in our investigation of the propagation of simple harmonic vibrations, we use the well known method in which the dependent variables in the system of equations are first represented by certain exponential expressions with imaginary exponents, the real parts of these expressions, to which one has ultimately to confine oneself, constituting a solution of the system.

Let ε be the basis of natural logarithms, and let all dependent variables contain the time only in the factor

$$\varepsilon^{int},$$

so that n is the frequency of the vibrations. Then, if we put

$$\alpha = f' - a - m'n^2, \qquad (201)$$

$$\beta = ng', \qquad (202)$$

$$\gamma = \frac{n\mathfrak{H}}{cNe}, \qquad (203)$$

all *real* quantities, the formulae (200) take the form

$$\left.\begin{aligned} \mathbf{E}_x &= (\alpha + i\beta)\mathbf{P}_x - i\gamma\mathbf{P}_y, \\ \mathbf{E}_y &= (\alpha + i\beta)\mathbf{P}_y + i\gamma\mathbf{P}_x, \\ \mathbf{E}_z &= (\alpha + i\beta)\mathbf{P}_z. \end{aligned}\right\} \qquad (204)$$

Since $\mathbf{P} = \mathbf{D} - \mathbf{E}$, these equations may be said to express the relation between $\mathbf{E}$ and $\mathbf{D}$ which we have to add to the general formulae (193) and (194).

120. Before coming to solutions of our system of equations, it will be well to go into some details concerning the cause by which the absorption is produced. We have provisionally admitted the existence of a resistance proportional to the velocity of an electron, which is represented by the terms $-g\frac{d\xi}{dt}$, $-g\frac{d\eta}{dt}$, $-g\frac{d\zeta}{dt}$ in (198), and by the terms $i\beta\mathbf{P}_x$, $i\beta\mathbf{P}_y$, $i\beta\mathbf{P}_z$ in (204). It must be observed, however, that in our fundamental equations there is no question of a resistance of this kind; as we have formerly seen, an electron can move for ever through the ether with undiminished velocity. In our considerations we have come across only one force that may be termed a resistance, namely the force

$$\frac{e^2}{6\pi c^3}\dot{\ddot{\mathbf{v}}}, \tag{205}$$

which is proportional to the rate of change of the acceleration. In the case of simple harmonic vibrations, its components can be represented in the form (197), with the following value of the coefficient

$$g = \frac{e^2 n^2}{6\pi c^3}. \tag{206}$$

Some numerical data which I shall mention later on, show however that this force (205) is much too small to account for the absorption that is really observed in many cases.[1]) We must therefore look for some other explanation.

It has occurred to me that this may be found in the assumption that the vibrations in the interior of a ponderable particle that are excited by incident waves of light, cannot go on undisturbed for ever. It is conceivable that the particles of a gaseous body are so profoundly shaken by their mutual impacts, that any regular vibration which has been set up in them, is transformed by the blow into the disorderly motion which we call heat. The rise in temperature produced in this way must be due to a part of the energy of the incident rays, so that there is a real absorption of light. It is also clear that the accumulation of vibratory energy in a particle, which otherwise, in the case of an exact agreement between the period of the vibrating electrons and that of the incident light, would never come to an end, will be kept within certain limits by this disturbing influence of the collisions, just as well as it could be by a resistance in the ordinary sense of the word.

In working out this idea, one finds that the formulae we have established in what precedes may still be used, provided only we understand by g the quantity[2])

$$g = \frac{2m}{\tau}, \tag{207}$$

in which τ is the mean length of time during which the vibrations in a particle can go on undisturbed. Since we can use the same formulae as if there were a real resistance, it is also convenient to adhere to the use of the latter term, and to speak of the resistance originating in the collisions, this resistance becoming greater when the interval τ is diminished.

According to the above idea, the interval τ ought, in gaseous bodies, to be equal to the mean length of time elapsing between two

---

1) Note **56***. 2) Note **57**.

successive encounters of a molecule. Unfortunately, it is found that the value of τ deduced from experimental data is smaller than the interval between two encounters. We must conclude from this that there are causes in the interior of a molecule by which the regularity of the vibrations is disturbed sooner than it would be by the molecular impacts. We cannot pretend therefore to have satisfactorily elucidated the phenomenon of absorption; its true cause remains yet to be discovered.

121. Leaving aside for some time the effects produced by a magnetic field, we shall now examine the propagation of light in the case $\mathfrak{H} = 0$, $\gamma = 0$. Let us first suppose that there is no resistance at all, so that β is likewise 0. Then the formulae (204) may be written

$$\mathbf{E} = \alpha \mathbf{P},$$

from which we deduce

$$\mathbf{D} = \left(1 + \frac{1}{\alpha}\right) \mathbf{E}. \tag{208}$$

Let the propagation take place in the direction of OZ, so that the components of $\mathbf{E}$, $\mathbf{D}$ and $\mathbf{H}$ are represented by expressions containing the factor

$$\varepsilon^{in(t - qz)}, \tag{209}$$

where q is a constant. Then, since all differential coefficients with respect to x and y vanish, we have by (193) and (194)

$$-\frac{\partial \mathbf{H}_y}{\partial z} = \frac{1}{c} \frac{\partial \mathbf{D}_x}{\partial t}$$

and

$$\frac{\partial \mathbf{E}_x}{\partial z} = -\frac{1}{c} \frac{\partial \mathbf{H}_y}{\partial t},$$

or

$$q \mathbf{H}_y = \frac{1}{c} \mathbf{D}_x, \quad q \mathbf{E}_x = \frac{1}{c} \mathbf{H}_y,$$

whence

$$\mathbf{D}_x = c^2 q^2 \mathbf{E}_x.$$

Combining this with (208), we get

$$c^2 q^2 = 1 + \frac{1}{\alpha}. \tag{210}$$

Supposing $1 + \frac{1}{\alpha}$ to be positive, we find a real value for q. The real part of (209) is

$$\cos n(t - qz),$$

from which it is seen that the velocity of propagation is

$$v = \frac{1}{q}.$$

It can therefore be calculated by means of the equation (210), for which we may write

$$\mu^2 = 1 + \frac{1}{\alpha},$$

if

$$\mu = \frac{c}{v}$$

is the index of refraction.

It is to be noticed that our result agrees with Maxwell's well known law, according to which the refractive index of a body is equal to the square root of its dielectric constant. Indeed, the equation (208) shows that the ratio between the dielectric displacement **D** and the electric force **E** is given by $1 + \frac{1}{\alpha}$; it is therefore this quantity which plays the part of the dielectric constant or the specific inductive capacity in Maxwell's equations.

122. In one respect, however, the theory of electrons has enabled us to go further than Maxwell. You see from the equation (201) that, for a given system, α is not a constant, but changes with the frequency n. Therefore, our formulae contain an explanation of the dispersion of light, i. e. of the fact that different kinds of light have not the same refractive index.

This explanation is very much like that which was proposed by several physicists who developed the undulatory theory of light in its original form in which the ether was considered as an elastic body. Sellmeyer, Ketteler, Boussinesq and Helmholtz showed that the velocity of light must depend on the period of the vibrations, as soon as a body contains small particles which are set vibrating by the forces in an incident beam of light, and which are subject to intramolecular forces of such a kind that they can perform free vibrations of a certain definite period. The amplitude of the forced vibrations of these particles, which is one of the quantities determining the velocity of propagation, will largely depend on the relative lengths of their own period of vibration and the period of the light falling on them. The theory of the propagation of light in a system of molecules which has been here set forth, is based on the same principles as those older explanations of dispersion, the only difference being that we have constantly expressed ourselves in the terms of the electromagnetic theory, and that the small particles imagined by Sellmeyer have now become our electrons.

If we conceive a single particle to be detached from the body, so that it is free from all external influence, and if we leave out of account the resistance which we have represented by means of the coefficient g, the equations of motion (198) simplify to

$$m\frac{d^2\xi}{dt^2} = -f\xi, \quad m\frac{d^2\eta}{dt^2} = -f\eta, \quad m\frac{d^2\zeta}{dt^2} = -f\zeta,$$

from which it appears that the electron can perform free vibrations with a frequency n_0 determined by

$$n_0 = \sqrt{\frac{f}{m}}.$$

Introducing this quantity, and using (199), we may write instead of (201), if we put $a = \frac{1}{3}$,

$$\alpha = m'(n_0^2 - n^2) - \frac{1}{3} = \frac{m}{Ne^2}(n_0^2 - n^2) - \frac{1}{3}. \tag{211}$$

The index of refraction is therefore determined by

$$\mu^2 - 1 = \frac{1}{\frac{m}{Ne^2}(n_0^2 - n^2) - \frac{1}{3}}. \tag{212}$$

The value of μ derived from this formula is greater than 1, if the frequency n is so far below that of the free vibrations n_0 that the denominator is positive; if this condition is satisfied, we can further conclude that μ increases with the frequency. This agrees with the dispersion as it is observed in transparent bodies, at least if we suppose that in these the frequency n_0 corresponds to rays in the ultra-violet part of the spectrum.

123. As a further application of our results we can take the old problem of the connexion between the index of refraction μ of a transparent body, and its density ϱ. As is well known, Laplace inferred from theoretical considerations, based on the form the undulatory theory had in his time, that, when the density of a body is changed, the expression

$$\frac{\mu^2 - 1}{\varrho} \tag{213}$$

should remain constant. In most cases the observed changes of the refractivity do not at all conform to this law, and it has been found that a better agreement is obtained if Laplace's rule is replaced by the empirical formula

$$\frac{\mu - 1}{\varrho} = \text{const.} \tag{214}$$

The electromagnetic theory of light leads to a new form of the relation. Indeed, by a slight modification, (212) becomes

$$\frac{m}{Ne^2}(n_0^2 - n^2) = \frac{\mu^2 + 2}{3(\mu^2 - 1)}.$$

For a given body and a given value of n, the expression

$$\frac{\mu^2 - 1}{\mu^2 + 2}$$

must therefore be proportional to the number of molecules per unit volume, and consequently to the density.

This result had been found by Lorenz[1]) of Copenhagen some time before I deduced it from the electromagnetic theory of light, which is certainly a curious case of coincidence.

124. In a certain sense the formula may be said to be much older. Putting in (201) $n = 0$ and, as before, $a = \frac{1}{3}$, we find for the case of extremely slow vibrations, or of a constant field

$$\alpha = f' - \frac{1}{3} = \frac{f}{Ne^2} - \frac{1}{3}.$$

The corresponding value of the ratio $1 + \frac{1}{\alpha}$ between **D** and **E** is

$$\varepsilon = 1 + \frac{1}{\frac{f}{Ne^2} - \frac{1}{3}}.$$

This, therefore, is the value of the dielectric constant for our system of molecules, a result which we could also have obtained by a direct calculation.

Now, the last formula shows that, when N is changed, the value of

$$\frac{\varepsilon - 1}{(\varepsilon + 2)N}$$

remains constant. Hence, the relation between the dielectric constant and the density ϱ is expressed by

$$\frac{\varepsilon - 1}{(\varepsilon + 2)\varrho} = \text{const.},$$

a formula corresponding to one that was given long ago by Clausius and Mossotti. Substituting in it Maxwell's value

$$\varepsilon = \mu^2, \tag{215}$$

we find the relation

$$\frac{\mu^2 - 1}{(\mu^2 + 2)\varrho} = \text{const.} \tag{216}$$

In this way, however, the formula is only proved for the case of very slow vibrations, to which Maxwell's law (215) may be applied, whereas our former deduction shows that it holds for any value of n, i. e. for any particular kind of light we wish to consider.

125. Let us now compare our formula with experimental results. Of course I can only mention a few of these. I shall first consider the changes in the refractivity of a gas produced by pressure, and

1) L. Lorenz, Über die Refraktionskonstante, Ann. Phys. Chem. **11** (1880), p. 70.

in the second place the change in the refractivity that is brought about by the passage of a liquid to the gaseous state. In both cases I shall compare the results of our formula with those that can be deduced from the empirical formula (214). As to Laplace's law, we need no longer speak of it, because in all cases it is much less satisfactory than either of the two other formulae.

The refractive index of air up to high densities has recently been measured with considerable accuracy by Magri.[1]) Some of his results are contained in the following table, together with the values of $\frac{2}{3}\frac{\mu-1}{\varrho}$ and $\frac{\mu^2-1}{(\mu^2+2)\varrho}$.

Temperature	Density	Refractive index	$\frac{2}{3}\frac{\mu-1}{\varrho}\cdot 10^7$	$\frac{\mu^2-1}{(\mu^2+2)\varrho}\cdot 10^7$
0°	1	1,0002929	1953	1953
14,6	14,84	1,004338	1949	1947
14,3	42,13	1,01241	1964	1959
14,4	69,24	1,02044	1968	1961
14,5	96,16	1,02842	1970	1961
14,5	123,04	1,03633	1969	1956
14,8	149,53	1,04421	1971	1956
14,9	176,27	1,05213	1972	1953

You see that with the formula (216) the agreement is somewhat better than with the empirical relation (214).

The difference between the two comes out still more markedly, if we compare the refractive index of a vapour with the value we can deduce from that of the liquid by means of (214) or of (216). In the following small table, which relates to sodium light, the index of the liquid is given for 15°, and that of the vapour for 0° and 760 mm. This means that the observed values of μ have been reduced to the density which the vapour would have at 0° and under atmospheric pressure, if it followed the laws of Boyle and Gay-Lussac. The reduction can be made either by (214) or by (216), the two formulae being equally applicable to the small changes in question.

	Liquid		Vapour			
				Index of refraction		
	Density	Index of refraction	Density	Obs.	Calculated by (214)	Calculated by (216)
Water	0,9991	1,3337	0,000809	1,000250	1,000270	1,000250
Bisulphide of carbon	1,2709	1,6320	0,00341	1,00148	1,00170	1,00144
Ethyl ether	0,7200	1,3558	0,00332	1,00152	1,00164	1,00151

1) L. Magri, Der Brechungsindex der Luft in seiner Beziehung zu ihrer Dichte, Phys. Zeitschr. 6 (1905), p. 629.

Other measurements which can be taken as a test for the two formulae are those of the indices of refraction of various bodies at different temperatures, or when submitted to different pressures. As a general rule, neither equation (214) nor (216) is found to represent these measurements quite correctly, the disagreement between the observed values and the calculated ones being of the same order of magnitude in the two cases, and generally having opposite directions. In most cases our formula leads to changes in the refractivity that are slightly greater than the observed ones; moreover, the deviations increase as one passes on to higher values of n.

As to the cause of this disagreement, it must undoubtedly be looked for, partly in the fact that the term a in equation (201) is not exactly equal to $\frac{1}{3}$, partly also in changes that take place in the interior of the particles when a body is heated or compressed. These changes can cause a variation in the value of the coefficients f and f'.

126. A problem closely connected with the preceding one is that of calculating the refractivity of a mixture from the refractivities of its constituents. Following the same line of thought that has led us to equation (212), but supposing the system to contain two or more sets of molecules mixed together, one finds the following formula[1]), in which $r_1, r_2, \ldots$ are the values of

$$\frac{\mu^2 - 1}{(\mu^2 + 2)\varrho} \tag{217}$$

for each of the mixed substances, taken separately, and $m_1, m_2, \ldots$ the masses of these substances contained in unit of mass of the mixture

$$\frac{\mu^2 - 1}{(\mu^2 + 2)\varrho} = m_1 r_1 + m_2 r_2 + \cdots. \tag{218}$$

This equation is found to hold as a rough approximation for various liquid mixtures. The same may be said of a similar equation that is often used for calculating the value of $\frac{\mu - 1}{\varrho}$.

127. It is very important that these formulae for mixtures can also serve in many cases for the purpose of calculating the refractivity of chemical compounds from that of the constituting elements. Let us consider a compound consisting of the elements $\varepsilon_1, \varepsilon_2, \ldots$, and let us denote by $p_1, p_2, \ldots$ their atomic weights, by $q_1, q_2, \ldots$ the numbers of the different kinds of atoms in a molecule, and by

$$P = q_1 p_1 + q_2 p_2 + \cdots$$

1) Note 58.

the molecular weight of the compound. Then, the amounts of ε_1, $\varepsilon_2, \ldots$ in unit of mass will be

$$m_1 = \frac{q_1 p_1}{P}, \quad m_2 = \frac{q_2 p_2}{P}, \ldots,$$

and (218) becomes

$$P \frac{\mu^2 - 1}{(\mu^2 + 2)\varrho} = q_1 p_1 r_1 + q_2 p_2 r_2 + \cdots. \tag{219}$$

Hence, if for each element we call the product of the constant (217) by its atomic weight p the refraction equivalent, and if we understand by the refraction equivalent of the compound the product of the value of (217) relating to it by the molecular weight P, we are led to the simple rule that, in order to find the refraction equivalent of the compound, we have only to multiply the refraction equivalent of each element by the number of its atoms in the molecule, and to add the results. A large number of physicists and chemists who have determined the refractivities of many compounds, especially of organic ones, have found the rule to be approximately correct.

128. The general meaning of this result will be obvious. When we find that some quantity which determines the refractivity of a compound is made up of a number of parts, each of which belongs to one of the elements, we may conclude that, in the propagation of light, each element exerts an influence of its own, which is not disturbed by the influence of the other elements. In the terms of our theory, this amounts to saying that the electric vibrations going on in a beam of light, in so far as they take place in the ponderable matter, have their seat in the separate atoms, the motions in one atom being more or less independent of those in the other atoms of the same molecule.

We may suppose, for example, that each atom contains one movable electron, which, after a displacement from its position of equilibrium, is pulled back towards it by an elastic force having its origin in the atom itself, and determined therefore by the properties of the atom. If we take this view, it is easy so to change the equations for the propagation of light that they can be applied to a system of polyatomic molecules.

129. Let us distinguish the quantities relating to the separate atoms of a molecule by the indices 1, 2, ..., k. Let $e_1, e_2, \ldots$ be the charges of the movable electrons contained in the first, the second atom etc., $m_1, m_2, \ldots$ their masses, $\xi_1, \eta_1, \zeta_1, \xi_2, \eta_2, \zeta_2, \ldots$ the components of their displacements from their positions of equilibrium, $f_1, f_2, \ldots$ the coefficients determining the intensities of the elastic forces. Then, if the resistances are left out of account, and if there is no external magnetic field, we shall have for each molecule, not one set of equations of motion of the form

$$m \frac{d^2 \xi}{dt^2} = e(\mathbf{E}_x + a\mathbf{P}_x) - f\xi,$$
etc.,

(which is got from (198) if we put $g = 0$, $\mathfrak{H} = 0$), but k sets of this form:

$$\left.\begin{aligned} m_1 \frac{d^2 \xi_1}{dt^2} &= e_1(\mathbf{E}_x + a\mathbf{P}_x) - f_1\xi_1, \text{ etc.} \\ m_2 \frac{d^2 \xi_2}{dt^2} &= e_2(\mathbf{E}_x + a\mathbf{P}_x) - f_2\xi_2, \text{ etc.} \\ &\text{etc.} \end{aligned}\right\} \quad (220)$$

The total electric polarization $\mathbf{P}$ of the body will now be the sum of the electric moments due to the separate atoms; its components are

$$\left.\begin{aligned} \mathbf{P}_x &= N(e_1\xi_1 + e_2\xi_2 + \cdots), \\ \mathbf{P}_y &= N(e_1\eta_1 + e_2\eta_2 + \cdots), \\ \mathbf{P}_z &= N(e_1\zeta_1 + e_2\zeta_2 + \cdots). \end{aligned}\right\} \quad (221)$$

For a determinate value of the frequency n we can deduce from (220), (221) and (192) the relation between $\mathbf{E}$ and $\mathbf{D}$. Combining it with the equations (193) and (194), one finds the following formula, corresponding to (212), but more general than it, for the index of refraction μ[1]),

$$\frac{\mu^2 - 1}{\mu^2 + 2} = \frac{Ne_1^2}{3(f_1 - m_1 n^2)} + \frac{Ne_2^2}{3(f_2 - m_2 n^2)} + \cdots. \quad (222)$$

It is thus seen that, according to our new assumptions, the value of $\frac{\mu^2 - 1}{\mu^2 + 2}$ remains proportional to N, and therefore to the density of the body. Moreover, if we denote by μ_1, μ_2, ... the refractive indices for the cases that unit volume of our system contains *only* N atoms of the group 1, or N atoms of the group 2, etc., we have

$$\frac{\mu_1^2 - 1}{\mu_1^2 + 2} = \frac{Ne_1^2}{3(f_1 - m_1 n^2)}, \quad \frac{\mu_2^2 - 1}{\mu_2^2 + 2} = \frac{Ne_2^2}{3(f_2 - m_2 n^2)}, \quad \cdots$$

Consequently, (222) may be written

$$\frac{\mu^2 - 1}{\mu^2 + 2} = \frac{\mu_1^2 - 1}{\mu_1^2 + 2} + \frac{\mu_2^2 - 1}{\mu_2^2 + 2} + \cdots,$$

which is but another form of the relation (219).

130. I need hardly observe that the assumptions we have made are at best rough approximations to the true state of things. We

1) Note 59.

have supposed the elastic force by which the movable electron of an atom is pulled towards its position of equilibrium, to arise from actions which are confined to the atom itself. Now, there is at all events an interaction of an electric nature between neighboring atoms, precisely on account of the displacements of their electrons; there may also be other interactions about whose nature we are as yet entirely in the dark. On these grounds we must expect greater or smaller deviations from the law of the refraction equivalent, deviations from which one may one day be able to draw some conclusions concerning the structure of a molecule.

One important result in this direction was already obtained by Brühl.[1]) He found that a double chemical binding between two atoms has a striking influence on the refractivity, which can be taken into account, if, in the formula (218), we add a term of proper magnitude for each double bond.

Like many other facts, this shows that our theory of the propagation of light in ponderable bodies is to be considered as rather tentative. I must repeat however that, undoubtedly, the actions going on in the separate atoms must be, to a large extent, mutually independent. If they were not, and if, on the contrary, the elastic force acting on an electron ought to be attributed, not to the atom to which it belongs, but to the molecule as a whole, the refractive index of a compound body would be principally determined by the connexions between the atoms, and not, at it is, by their individual properties.

131. At the point which we have now reached, it is interesting, once more to return to the theory of the dispersion of light, and to ask what the general formula (222) can teach us about it. To begin with, it may be observed that, if s is the value of $\frac{\mu^2-1}{\mu^2+2}$, we shall have

$$\mu^2 = \frac{1+2s}{1-s},$$

from which it is readily seen that, when s continually changes from $-\frac{1}{2}$ to 1, μ^2 increases from 0 to ∞. If s remains confined to this interval, as I shall for the moment suppose it to do, μ changes in the same direction as s, having the value 1 for $s=0$.

The latter case occurs for $N=0$, i. e. when there are no ponderable particles at all, so that the propagation takes place in the ether alone. This state of things is altered by the presence of the electrons, to

1) See, for instance, J. W. Brühl, The development of spectro-chemistry, Proc. Royal Institution, 18, 1 (1906), p. 122.

which the different terms on the right-hand side of (222) relate. Now, each of these electrons has a definite period of its own, in which it can perform its free vibrations. If the frequencies of these are n_1, n_2, etc., we shall have

$$n_1^2 = \frac{f_1}{m_1}, \quad n_2^2 = \frac{f_2}{m_2}, \ldots,$$

and

$$\frac{\mu^2 - 1}{\mu^2 + 2} = \frac{Ne_1^2}{3m_1(n_1^2 - n^2)} + \frac{Ne_2^2}{3m_2(n_2^2 - n^2)} + \cdots. \tag{223}$$

The influence of an atom is thus seen to depend on whether the frequency of the rays for which we wish to determine μ, lies below or above the frequency of the free vibrations. Each group of electrons tends to raise the value of $\frac{\mu^2 - 1}{\mu^2 + 2}$, and consequently that of μ, for all frequencies below its own, and to lower the refractive index for all higher frequencies.

As a function of n, each term of (223) can be graphically represented by a curve of the form shown in Fig. 5, in which OP corresponds to $n_1, n_2, \ldots$, as the case may be, and we shall obtain the curve for $\frac{\mu^2 - 1}{\mu^2 + 2}$ by taking the algebraic sum of the ordinates in the individual curves L_1, L_2, etc.

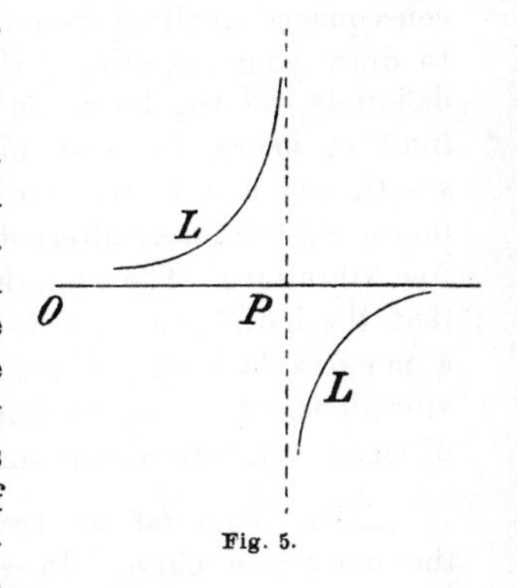

Fig. 5.

The form of the resultant line will be determined by the values of n_1, n_2, etc. or, as one may say, by the position in the spectrum of the lines that would be produced by the free vibrations of the electrons, and which we may provisionally call the spectral lines of the body. If, as we go from left to right, we pass one of these lines, the ordinate of the corresponding curve suddenly jumps from $+\infty$ to $-\infty$. Of course all these discontinuities are repeated in the resultant dispersion curve, and near each of the values $n_1, n_2, \ldots$ of the frequency there will be a portion of the curve, in which s first changes from $+1$ to $+\infty$, and then from $-\infty$ to $-\frac{1}{2}$. It may be assumed that these portions, which I shall call the discontinuous parts of the curve, have a breadth that is very small in comparison with the remaining parts, of which I shall speak as the continuous ones.

Since all the curves L_1, L_2, etc. rise from left to right, it is clear that each continuous portion of the resultant curve must present the same feature. This agrees with the dispersion as it exists in all transparent substances.

The question as to whether, for a definite value of the frequency, the index of refraction is greater or less than 1, depends on circumstances. If all the spectral lines of the body lie in the ultra-violet, the refractive index will be larger than 1 throughout the infra-red and the visible spectrum. It may remain so in the visible part, even if there are one or more infra-red lines, provided only there be also lines in the ultra-violet, whose influence in raising the refractive index predominates over the opposite influence of the lines in the infra-red. At all events, the dispersion of light observed in all transparent bodies requires for its explanation the existence of one or more lines in the ultra-violet.

132. We could now enter upon a comparison of our dispersion formula with the measurements of the indices of refraction, but I shall omit this, because we must not attach too much importance to the particular form which we have found for the equation. By slightly altering the assumptions on which it is based, it would be possible to find an equation of a somewhat different form, though agreeing with (223) in its main features. There is, however, one consequence resulting from the preceding theory, to which I should like to draw your attention. If the frequency n is made to increase indefinitely, all the terms on the right-hand side of (223) approach the limit 0; hence, for very high frequencies, we shall ultimately have $s = 0$, and $\mu = 1$, the reason being simply, that the electrons cannot follow electric forces alternating with a frequency far above that of their free vibrations. The remark is important, because it explains the fact that the Röntgen rays do not suffer any refraction when they enter a ponderable body. These rays, though not constituted by regular vibrations, are in all probability produced by a very rapid succession of electromagnetic disturbances of extremely short duration.[1])

133. Thus far we have only spoken of the continuous parts of the dispersion curve. In each of its discontinuous portions, as we have defined them, the right-hand side of (223) has values ranging from $+1$ to $+\infty$, and from $-\infty$ to $-\frac{1}{2}$. These values lead to negative values of μ^2, and to imaginary values of μ itself, indicating thereby that waves of the corresponding frequencies cannot be propagated by the body in the same way as those whose wave-length corresponds to a point in one of the continuous parts of the curve.

We need not however any further discuss the meaning of our formulae in this case, because, for frequencies very near $n_1, n_2, \ldots$ the resistance to the vibrations, and the absorption due to it may no longer be neglected. We must therefore now take up the subject

1) See Note 21*.

of the absorption of light. Not to complicate matters too much, I shall do so on the assumption, which we originally started from, that each particle contains a *single* movable electron.

If, in the equations (204), the resistance coefficient β has a certain value, and if there is no external magnetic field, we may write

$$\mathbf{E} = (\alpha + i\beta)\mathbf{P}.$$

This gives

$$\mathbf{D} = \mathbf{E} + \mathbf{P} = \left(1 + \frac{1}{\alpha + i\beta}\right)\mathbf{E}.$$

On the other hand, the equations deduced in § 121 from (193) and (194) remain unchanged, so that we find, instead of (210),

$$c^2 q^2 = 1 + \frac{1}{\alpha + i\beta}\cdot \tag{224}$$

The constant q in the expression (209) now becomes a complex quantity. It is convenient to put it in the form

$$q = \frac{1}{v} - i\frac{k}{n}, \tag{225}$$

v and k being real. Then, (209) becomes

$$\varepsilon^{-kz + in\left(t - \frac{z}{v}\right)},$$

and if, in order to find the expressions for the vibrations, we take the real parts of the complex quantities by which the dependent variables $\mathbf{E}_x$ etc. have first been represented, we are led to expressions of the form

$$\varepsilon^{-kz} \cos n\left(t - \frac{z}{v} + p\right), \tag{226}$$

where p is a constant. The meaning of the first factor is, that the amplitude of the vibrations is continually decreasing as we proceed in the direction of propagation. The light is absorbed to a degree depending on the coefficient k, which I shall call the index of absorption. On the other hand, the second factor in (226) shows that v is the velocity with which the phase of the vibrations is propagated; the ratio $\frac{c}{v}$, for which I shall write μ, is therefore properly called the refractive index.

Substituting (225) in (224), and separating the real and the imaginary parts, one finds the following equations for the determination of v (or μ) and k[1])

$$2\mu^2 = \sqrt{1 + \frac{2\alpha + 1}{\alpha^2 + \beta^2}} + \frac{\alpha}{\alpha^2 + \beta^2} + 1, \tag{227}$$

$$2\frac{c^2 k^2}{n^2} = \sqrt{1 + \frac{2\alpha + 1}{\alpha^2 + \beta^2}} - \frac{\alpha}{\alpha^2 + \beta^2} - 1. \tag{228}$$

1) Note **60**.

134. The discussion of these formulae, which in general would be rather complicated, can be considerably simplified by the assumption that β is much larger than 1.

This is true in the majority of cases, because in nearly all bodies the absorption in a layer whose thickness is equal to one wave-length in air, i. e. to $\frac{2\pi c}{n}$, is very feeble, even for those frequencies for which the absorption is strongest. According to (226) the amplitude diminishes in the ratio of 1 to

$$\varepsilon^{-\frac{2\pi c k}{n}},$$

while the beam travels over a distance $\frac{2\pi c}{n}$. Therefore, for the bodies in question,

$$\frac{ck}{n}$$

must be a very small number. Now, if we consider the particular frequency for which $\alpha = 0$, (228) becomes

$$2\frac{c^2 k^2}{n^2} = \sqrt{1 + \frac{1}{\beta^2}} - 1.$$

If this is to be very small, β must be a large number.

Availing ourselves of this circumstance, we find the following approximate equations[1])

$$\mu = 1 + \frac{\alpha}{2(\alpha^2 + \beta^2)}, \tag{229}$$

$$k = \frac{n}{2c} \cdot \frac{\beta}{\alpha^2 + \beta^2}. \tag{230}$$

For a given value of β the fraction

$$\frac{\beta}{\alpha^2 + \beta^2}$$

has its greatest value $\frac{1}{\beta}$ for $\alpha = 0$. For $\alpha = \pm \beta$ it has sunk to half this maximum value, and for $\alpha = \pm \nu\beta$ to $\frac{1}{(\nu^2 + 1)\beta}$. If we understand by ν a moderate number (say 3 or 6) the absorption can be said to be very feeble, in comparison with its maximum intensity, for values of α beyond the interval extending from $-\nu\beta$ to $+\nu\beta$.

135. These different cases succeed each other as we pass through the spectrum, and even, notwithstanding the high value we have ascribed to β, the transition from $-\nu\beta$ to $+\nu\beta$ can take place in a very narrow part of it. If we suppose this to be the

1) Note **61**.

case, the factor $\frac{n}{2c}$ in (230), and the factor n in (202) may be considered as constants. Moreover, in virtue of (201), if n_0' is the frequency for which $\alpha = 0$, we may write for any other value of α in the interval in question

$$\alpha = -2m'n_0'(n - n_0'). \tag{231}$$

I have written n_0' for the frequency corresponding to $\alpha = 0$, because its value

$$n_0' = \sqrt{\frac{f' - a}{m'}}$$

differs from the frequency

$$n_0 = \sqrt{\frac{f'}{m'}}$$

of the spectral line of a detached molecule of which we have formerly spoken. It is only when we may neglect the coefficient a, that the two may be considered as identical.

The phenomena which the system of molecules produces in the spectrum of a beam of white light which is sent across it, are as follows. There is an absorption band in which the place of greatest darkness corresponds to

$$n = n_0'.$$

The distribution of light is symmetrical on both sides of this point. As the band has no sharp borders, we cannot ascribe to it a definite breadth; we can, however, say that it is seen between the places where $\alpha = -\nu\beta$ and $\alpha = +\nu\beta$, ν being a number of moderate magnitude. Measured by a difference of frequencies, half the width can therefore be represented by

$$\frac{\nu\beta}{2m'n_0'},$$

as is seen from (231).

We may add an interesting remark about the intensity of the absorption. The maximum value of the index of absorption is found to be

$$\frac{n}{2c\beta},$$

and the formulae (202), (199) and (207) show therefore that the maximum is the larger, the smaller the resistance, or the longer the time τ during which the vibrations of the electrons remain undisturbed. This result, strange at first sight, can be understood, if we take into consideration that the vibrations which are set up in a particle by optical resonance, so to say, with the incident light, will be sooner or later converted into an irregular heat motion. It may very well be, that the total quantity of heat developed per unit of time is larger when vibratory energy is stored up during a long time, and then suddenly converted, than in a case in which the disturbances take place at shorter intervals.

In another sense, however, the absorption may be said to be intensified by an increase of the resistance g, or by a shortening of the time τ. Not only will a change of this kind enlarge the breadth of the absorption line; it will also heighten the total absorption, i. e. the amount of energy, all wave-lengths taken together, that is taken up from an incident beam.[1])

As a general rule, observation really shows that narrow absorption bands are more intense in the middle than broad ones.

136. In Fig. 6 the curve FGH represents the index of absorption as a function of the frequency. The other curve $ABCDE$ relates to the index of refraction; it corresponds to the formula (229). The index μ, which is 1 at large distances on either side of the point P, rises to a maximum QB, and then sinks to a minimum RD. The place of the maximum is determined by $\alpha = \beta$, or

$$n = n_0' - \frac{\beta}{2m'n_0'},$$

that of the minimum by $\alpha = -\beta$, or

$$n = n_0' + \frac{\beta}{2m'n_0'},$$

the corresponding values of μ being

$$1 + \frac{1}{4\beta} \quad \text{and} \quad 1 - \frac{1}{4\beta}.$$

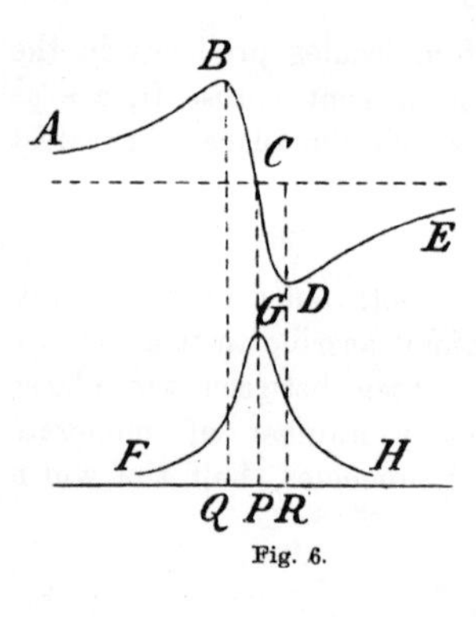

Fig. 6.

The maximum and the minimum are found at points of the spectrum where the index of absorption has half its maximum value.

In the line $ABCDE$ one will have recognized already the well known curve for the so-called anomalous dispersion. I must add that, if we had supposed, as we did in § 128, the particles of the system to be composed of a certain number of atoms, each containing a movable electron, and if we had assumed a resistance for every electron, we should finally have found a dispersion curve in which a part of the form $ABCDE$ repeats itself in the neighborhood of each free vibration. These parts would take the place of the discontinuous portions that would exist in the curve for the function (223).

---

1) Note 62.

137. The effect of an external magnetic field on the propagation of light in the direction of the lines of force can be examined by calculations much resembling the preceding ones. We have again to use the equations (192), (193) and (194), but we must now combine them with the formulae (204). Since, in these latter, the force $\mathfrak{H}$ has been supposed to have the direction of OZ, a beam of light travelling along the lines of force can be represented by expressions containing the factor (209). We are again led to the equation

$$\mathbf{D}_x = c^2 q^2 \mathbf{E}_x,$$

to which we must now add the corresponding formula

$$\mathbf{D}_y = c^2 q^2 \mathbf{E}_y,$$

which there was no occasion to consider in the preceding case. Using (192), we find

$$\mathbf{P}_x = (c^2 q^2 - 1)\mathbf{E}_x, \quad \mathbf{P}_y = (c^2 q^2 - 1)\mathbf{E}_y,$$

and the first and the second of the equations (204) become

$$\left.\begin{aligned} \left\{\frac{1}{c^2 q^2 - 1} - (\alpha + i\beta)\right\} \mathbf{P}_x = - i\gamma \mathbf{P}_y, \\ \left\{\frac{1}{c^2 q^2 - 1} - (\alpha + i\beta)\right\} \mathbf{P}_y = + i\gamma \mathbf{P}_x, \end{aligned}\right\} \tag{232}$$

showing that

$$\mathbf{P}_y = \pm i \mathbf{P}_x. \tag{233}$$

Thus, there are *two* solutions, corresponding to the double sign. In order to find out what they mean, we must remember that, if two variable quantities are given by the real parts of

$$a\varepsilon^{i(nt+p)} \quad \text{and} \quad ar\varepsilon^{i(nt+p+2\pi s)}, \tag{234}$$

i. e. if they are represented by

$$a \cos(nt + p) \quad \text{and} \quad ar \cos(nt + p + 2\pi s),$$

the number r determines the ratio between the maximum values or amplitudes, whereas s is the phase-difference expressed in periods. Since $r\varepsilon^{2\pi i s}$, the ratio between the expressions (234), becomes $\pm i$, when we take

$$r = 1, \quad s = \pm \tfrac{1}{4},$$

equation (233) shows that $\mathbf{P}_x$ and $\mathbf{P}_y$ have equal amplitudes and that, between their variations, there is a phase-difference of a quarter period. The same may be said of the displacements ξ and η of one of the movable electrons, these quantities being proportional to $\mathbf{P}_x$ and $\mathbf{P}_y$. We can conclude from this that each electron moves with constant velocity in a circle, whose plane is perpendicular to OZ, the motion having one direction in the solution corresponding to the upper sign, and the opposite direction in the other solution.

Similarly, the vector **P** has a uniform rotation in a plane at right angles to OZ, and the same is true of the vectors **E** and **D**. Each of our solutions therefore represents a beam of circularly polarized light, and it is easily seen that, when the real part of q has the positive sign (so that the propagation takes place in the direction of the positive z) the upper signs in our formulae relate to light whose circular polarization is right-handed, and the under signs to a left-handed polarization.

Now, if we substitute the value (233) in either of the formulae (232), we obtain the following condition for the coefficient q:

$$c^2 q^2 = 1 + \frac{1}{\alpha \pm \gamma + i\beta}, \tag{235}$$

from which, if we introduce the value (225), the index of absorption and the velocity v, or the index of refraction μ can be calculated.

138. It is not necessary to write down the expressions for these quantities. Comparing (235) with our former equation (224), we immediately see that the only difference between the two is, that α has been replaced by $\alpha \pm \gamma$. Now, in a narrow part of the spectrum, γ may be considered as a constant. Therefore, if we use right-handed circularly polarized light, the values of k and μ which correspond to a definite value of α must be the same as those which we had for the value $\alpha + \gamma$ in the absence of a magnetic field. On account of the relation (231), we can express the same thing by saying that, in the neighborhood of the frequency n_0', the values of μ and k for a frequency n are, under the influence of the magnetic force $\mathfrak{H}$, what they would be without this influence for the frequency

$$n - \frac{\gamma}{2\,m'\,n_0'}.$$

The absorption curve for a right-hand ray is therefore obtained by shifting the curve FGH of Fig. 6 over a distance

$$\frac{\gamma}{2\,m'\,n_0'}, \tag{236}$$

the displacement being in the direction of the increasing frequencies, when this expression is positive, and in the opposite direction, when it is negative. For the left-hand ray we find an equal displacement in the opposite direction.

It is clear that the inverse Zeeman effect is hereby explained. If a beam of unpolarized light, which we can decompose into a right and a left-handed beam, is sent through the flame, we shall get in its spectrum both the absorptions of which we have spoken. If the distance (236) is large enough in comparison with the breadth of the region of absorption, we shall see a division of the dark band into two components. It is especially interesting that the displacement (236), for which by (203) and (199) we may write

$$\frac{n_0' \mathfrak{H}}{cNe} : \frac{2mn_0'}{Ne^2} = \frac{e\mathfrak{H}}{2mc},$$

exactly agrees with the value we found in the elementary theory of the direct Zeeman effect. Our result also accords with our former one as to the direction of the effect. When we examined the emission in the direction of the magnetic lines of force, we found that the light of the component of highest frequency is left-handed, if e is negative. Our present investigation shows that for light of this kind, if e is again supposed to be negative, the absorption band is shifted towards the side of the greater frequencies.

139. The propagation of light in a direction perpendicular to the lines of force can be treated in a similar way. If the axis of x is laid in the direction of propagation, the axis of z being, as before, in the direction of the field, and if we assume that the expressions for the components of $\mathbf{E}$, $\mathbf{D}$, $\mathbf{P}$ and $\mathbf{H}$ contain the factor

$$\varepsilon^{-kx+in\left(t-\frac{x}{v}\right)},$$

k will again be the index of absorption, and v the velocity of propagation.

Now, it is immediately seen that these quantities are not in the least affected by the magnetic field, if the electric vibrations of the beam are parallel to the lines of force, for in this case we have only to combine the last of the equations (204) with the relations

$$\mathbf{D}_z = \mathbf{E}_z + \mathbf{P}_z,$$

$$\frac{\partial \mathbf{H}_y}{\partial x} = \frac{1}{c}\frac{\partial \mathbf{D}_z}{\partial t}, \quad \frac{\partial \mathbf{E}_z}{\partial x} = \frac{1}{c}\frac{\partial \mathbf{H}_y}{\partial t},$$

which are included in (192)—(194). Since none of these formulae contains the external force $\mathfrak{H}$, we may at once conclude that the magnetic field has no influence on the electric vibrations along the lines of force.

As to vibrations at right angles to these lines, I must point out a curious circumstance. The variable vectors being periodic functions of the time, and depending only on the one coordinate x, the condition

$$\operatorname{div} \dot{\mathbf{D}} = 0,$$

which follows from (193), requires that

$$\mathbf{D}_x = 0. \qquad (237)$$

We can express this by saying that the electric vibrations have no longitudinal component, meaning by „electric vibrations" the periodic changes of the vector $\mathbf{D}$. But our result by no means excludes values of $\mathbf{E}_x$ and $\mathbf{P}_x$ different from 0, so that, if the denomination of electric vibrations is applied to the fluctuations of the electric force $\mathbf{E}$, or of the polarization $\mathbf{P}$, the vibrations cannot be said to be transversal.

The formula (237) is very important for the solution of our problem. Writing it in the form

$$\mathbf{E}_x + \mathbf{P}_x = 0,$$

we can deduce from (204), combined with (192),

$$\mathbf{P}_x = \frac{i\gamma}{1+\alpha+i\beta}\mathbf{P}_y, \tag{238}$$

$$\mathbf{D}_y = \frac{(1+\alpha+i\beta)^2-\gamma^2}{(1+\alpha+i\beta)(\alpha+i\beta)-\gamma^2}\mathbf{E}_y.$$

The condition

$$\frac{1}{c^2}\frac{\partial^2 \mathbf{D}_y}{\partial t^2} = \frac{\partial^2 \mathbf{E}_y}{\partial x^2},$$

which follows from (193) and (194), will therefore be fulfilled if

$$\left(\frac{1}{v} - i\frac{k}{n}\right)^2 = \frac{1}{c^2}\cdot\frac{(1+\alpha+i\beta)^2-\gamma^2}{(1+\alpha+i\beta)(\alpha+i\beta)-\gamma^2}. \tag{239}$$

This is the equation by which the velocity of propagation and the index of absorption can be calculated. At the same time, the ratio between $\mathbf{P}_x$ and $\mathbf{P}_y$ may be taken from (238). If for this ratio we find the complex value $r\varepsilon^{2\pi is}$ (§ 137), so that

$$\mathbf{P}_x = r\varepsilon^{2\pi is}\mathbf{P}_y,$$

the amplitudes of $\mathbf{P}_x$ and $\mathbf{P}_y$ are as r to 1, and there is a phase-difference measured by s between the periodic changes of the two components. The quantities r and s also determine the ratio of the amplitudes and the difference of phase for the vibrations along OX and OY into which the motion of one of the movable electrons can be decomposed. Generally speaking, in the case now under consideration, the path described by each electron is an ellipse in a plane perpendicular to the lines of force. Since r and s vary with the frequency, the form and orientation of the ellipse will depend on the kind of light by which the flame is traversed.

140. In order to find the position of the absorption lines in the spectrum, we should have to determine k by means of the equation (239), and to seek the values of the frequency which make k a maximum. If the denominator of the last fraction in (239) is divested of imaginaries, the equation takes the form

$$\left(\frac{1}{v} - i\frac{k}{n}\right)^2 = \frac{1}{c^2} \cdot \frac{A - Bi}{Q},$$

and we get

$$k^2 = \frac{n^2}{2c^2} \cdot \frac{\sqrt{A^2 + B^2} - A}{Q}. \tag{240}$$

The general discussion of this result leads to formulae of such complexity that they can hardly be handled. Fortunately, in the cases we shall have to consider, the frequencies for which k is a maximum, may be found with sufficient accuracy by making the denominator Q a minimum. Moreover, in doing so, we may again consider α as the only variable quantity, the quantities β and γ not varying perceptibly in the narrow part of the spectrum with which we are concerned.

Now, the denominator may be written in the form[1])

$$Q = \{\alpha(1 + \alpha) + \beta^2 - \gamma^2\}^2 + \beta^2(1 + 4\gamma^2),$$

from which it immediately appears that the values in question are given by

$$\alpha(1 + \alpha) = \gamma^2 - \beta^2.$$

I shall suppose that

$$\gamma^2 - \beta^2 + \tfrac{1}{4} > 0,$$

so that the equation has two real roots

$$\alpha = -\tfrac{1}{2} \pm \sqrt{\gamma^2 - \beta^2 + \tfrac{1}{4}}. \tag{241}$$

Corresponding to these, one finds

$$A = 4\beta^2\gamma^2, \quad B = \tfrac{1}{2}\beta\left(1 + 4\gamma^2 \pm \sqrt{4\gamma^2 - 4\beta^2 + 1}\right), \quad Q = \beta^2(1 + 4\gamma^2),$$

$$r\,\varepsilon^{2\pi i s} = \frac{\mathsf{P}_x}{\mathsf{P}_y} = \frac{i\gamma}{\tfrac{1}{2} \pm \sqrt{\gamma^2 - \beta^2 + \tfrac{1}{4}} + i\beta}. \tag{242}$$

141. These results take a very simple form, when, as is generally the case (§ 134), β is great in comparison with 1, and the magnetic field is so strong that, for light travelling along the lines of force, the components of the original absorption line are separated to a distance greatly surpassing their breadth. This requires (§ 138) that γ be still many times greater than β. Instead of (241) we may therefore write approximately

$$\alpha = \pm\gamma, \tag{243}$$

which shows that there are two absorption lines, exactly at the points of the spectrum where we had lines when the light had the direction of the lines of force, i. e. in the positions which the elementary theory of the direct Zeeman-effect might lead us to expect.

---

1) Note **63**.

In calculating the index of absorption we may now replace B by $2\beta\gamma^2$ and Q by $4\beta^2\gamma^2$. Since

$$\sqrt{A^2+B^2}-A=\frac{B^2}{\sqrt{A^2+B^2}+A},$$

we find for both lines

$$k=\frac{n}{4\beta c}, \tag{244}$$

exactly one half of the index of absorption corresponding to $\alpha=0$ in the absence of a magnetic field.

Finally, the expression (242) has the value $\pm i$, so that we may conclude as follows.

If the absorbing body is traversed, in the direction of OX, by a beam of light whose electric vibrations were originally parallel to OY, the vibrations are absorbed to an amount determined by (244), when the frequency has either of the values given by (243). The electrons in the molecules will describe circles in planes parallel to OX and OY, the direction of their motion corresponding to that of the magnetic force when $\alpha=+\gamma$, and not corresponding to it when $\alpha=-\gamma$.

It should be noticed that, in the case treated in § 138, in accordance with our present result, we found the maximal absorption at the point $\alpha=+\gamma$, if the circular motion had the former, and at the place $\alpha=-\gamma$, if it had the latter of the directions just named.

142. Voigt has drawn from his equations another very remarkable conclusion. In general, for a beam of light travelling at right angles to the lines of force, and consisting of electric vibrations perpendicular to these lines, the two absorption bands which we get instead of the single original one, are neither equally distant from the position of the latter, nor equally strong, as the components of the doublet observed in the direction of the field invariably are. This follows immediately from the circumstance that the functions A, B and Q contain not only even, but also odd powers of α, so that the phenomena are not symmetrical on both sides of the point in the spectrum where $\alpha=0$.

In some experiments undertaken by Zeeman for the purpose of testing these predictions, a very slight want of symmetry was indeed detected. If this is really the dissymmetry to which Voigt was led by his calculations, the phenomenon is highly interesting, as we can deduce from it that the gaseous body in which it occurs exerts what we may call a *metallic* absorption in the middle of the band. Indeed, the peculiarity to which Voigt called attention, can make itself felt only in case the coefficient β is not much greater than unity, and this leads to an absorption which is very sensible even for a thickness equal to a wave-length (§ 134).[1])

143. I must now call your attention to the intimate connexion between the Zeeman-effect and the rotation of the plane of polarization that was discovered by Faraday. Reverting to the case of a propagation along the lines of force, we can start from our former result (§§ 137, 138), that the simplest solutions of our system of equations are those which represent either a right-handed or a left-handed circularly polarized beam, and that the formulae for these two cases are obtained, if, in the equations holding in the absence of a magnetic field, we replace α either by $\alpha + \gamma$ or by $\alpha - \gamma$. This is true, not only for the formulae giving the coefficient of absorption, but also for those which determine the velocity of propagation. Hence, if this velocity is denoted by v_1 for a left-handed, and by v_2 for a right-handed ray, we shall have (cf. equation (229)),

$$\frac{1}{v_1} = \frac{1}{c} + \frac{\alpha - \gamma}{2c[(\alpha - \gamma)^2 + \beta^2]},$$

$$\frac{1}{v_2} = \frac{1}{c} + \frac{\alpha + \gamma}{2c[(\alpha + \gamma)^2 + \beta^2]}.$$

For a definite frequency n, these values are unequal. So are also the corresponding values of the coefficient of absorption, so that, under the influence of a magnetic field, the system has a different degree of transparency for the two kinds of circularly polarized light. For the sake of simplicity, however, we shall now leave out of consideration this latter difference, and speak only of the phenomena that are caused by the difference in the velocities of propagation. You know that in every case in which these are unequal for the two kinds of circularly polarized light, a beam with a rectilinear polarization will have its plane of polarization turned as it travels onward. The angle of rotation per unit of length is given by

$$\omega = \frac{1}{2} n \left(\frac{1}{v_2} - \frac{1}{v_1}\right), \tag{245}$$

or in our case by

$$\omega = \frac{n}{4c}\left[\frac{\alpha + \gamma}{(\alpha + \gamma)^2 + \beta^2} - \frac{\alpha - \gamma}{(\alpha - \gamma)^2 + \beta^2}\right]. \tag{246}$$

The sense of the rotation depends on the algebraical sign of this expression. When $\mathfrak{H}$ is positive, i. e. when the magnetic force has the direction of the beam of light, a positive value of ω means a rotation whose direction corresponds to that of the magnetic force.

The general features of the phenomenon, as it depends on the frequency, come out most clearly if we avail ourselves of a graphical representation. In Fig. 6 we drew a curve giving the index of re-

1) See Note **64**.

fraction as a function of the frequency, and showing how it changes as we go through the spectrum from left to right. This curve, which relates to the body not subjected to a magnetic force, may also be taken to represent the values of $\frac{1}{v}$. Now, if there is a magnetic field, the curves for $\frac{1}{v_1}$ and $\frac{1}{v_2}$ are obtained by simply shifting that of Fig. 6 towards the left or towards the right over an interval equal to $\frac{e\mathfrak{H}}{2mc}$ (cf. § 138). In this way we get the two curves $A_1 B_1 D_1 E_1$ and $A_2 B_2 D_2 E_2$ of Fig. 7, and these immediately give us an idea of the angle of rotation ω, because, as (245) tells us, this angle is proportional to the algebraic difference between corresponding ordinates. It can therefore be represented by the line RR.

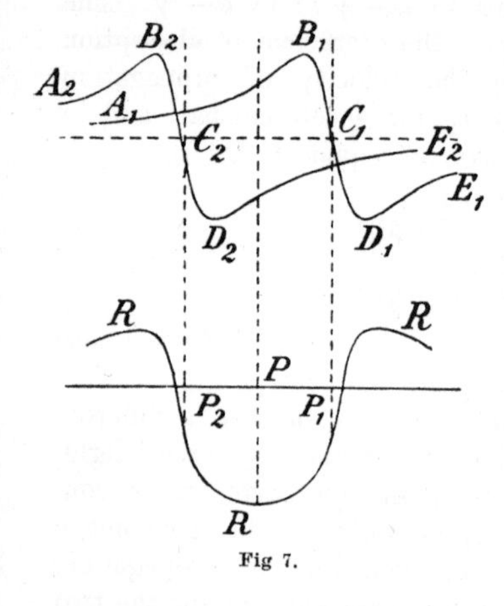

Fig 7.

Two interesting results become apparent by this construction. The first is, that in the narrow part of the spectrum close to the original absorption line, the rotation of the plane of polarization twice changes its sign; the second, that, on account of the high values of μ or $\frac{1}{v}$ which are found at some places, the angle of rotation can also attain a rather great value.

Macaluso and Corbino[1]), who were the first to examine this phenomenon in the case of a sodium flame, observed rotations as great as 270°. The results of their experiments could immediately be explained by the theory which Voigt had already developed. Some years later, Zeeman[2]) and Hallo[3]) made a very careful experimental study of the phenomenon, and again found a satisfactory agreement with Voigt's theory.

144. The Faraday-effect had been known for a long time, and the only thing in the above results apt to cause astonishment, was, that a rotation much greater than had ever been observed in transparent bodies, should be produced in a sodium flame. An other magneto-optic effect that was predicted by Voigt, is an entirely new

1) D. Macaluso and O. M. Corbino, Comptes rendus **127** (1898), p. 548.
2) P. Zeeman, Amsterdam Proc. **5** (1902), p. 41; Arch. néerl. (2) **7** (1902), p. 465.
3) J. J. Hallo, Arch. néerl. (2) **10** (1905), p. 148.

one. It consists in a double refraction that is observed when a body such as we have considered in this chapter, is traversed by a beam of light at right angles to the lines of force. For such a beam we have to distinguish between the electric vibrations perpendicular and parallel to the lines of force. For the former, the velocity of propagation is given by the equation (239), for the latter by (224) and (225), or as we may also say, by (239), if in this latter formula we put $\gamma = 0$. The difference between the two values is what was meant when I spoke just now of a double refraction. It can be calculated by our formulae as soon as α, β, γ are known, but I shall not lose time in these calculations. I shall only observe that the effect remains the same when the field is reversed; this follows at once from (239), because this equation contains only the square of γ, and therefore the square of $\mathfrak{H}$.

Voigt and Wiechert have experimentally verified these predictions, and Geest[1]) has carefully measured the magnetic double refraction in a sodium flame.

145. Availing ourselves of the theory that has been set forth in this chapter, we can draw from experimental data certain interesting conclusions concerning the absorbing (or radiating) particles. Some measurements enable us to calculate the relative values of the three quantities α, β, γ, whereas others can serve for the determination of their absolute values.

Thus, if we have measured the distance between the middle component of Zeeman's triplet and the outer ones, we know that for the frequency n belonging to one of these latter, α and γ have equal values. Replacing γ by its value (203), and α by (231), in which we shall now neglect the difference between n_0' and n_0 (§ 135), so that

$$\alpha = 2m'n_0(n_0 - n) = \frac{2mn_0(n_0 - n)}{Ne^2}, \tag{247}$$

the equality leads us back to our old equation

$$n_0 - n = \frac{e\mathfrak{H}}{2mc},$$

by means of which we can determine the ratio $\frac{e}{m}$.

The ratio between α and β could be found if quantitative determinations of the absorption, in the ordinary case in which there is no magnetic field, were at our disposal. If, for example, we knew that at a certain point in an absorption band the index of absorption k is $\varkappa$ times smaller than at the middle of the band, the ratio ν between α and β could be found (§ 134) by means of the formula

$$\varkappa = 1 + \nu^2. \tag{248}$$

---

1) J. Geest, Arch. néerl. (2) **10** (1905), p. 291.

The distribution of intensity has been determined by bolometric or similar measurements for the broad bands that are produced by such gases as carbonic acid, but we cannot tell what it is in the narrow bands observed in the case of a sodium flame for instance. All we can then do, is to form an estimate of the ratio ν between α and β for the border of the band. If we assume, for example, that here $\varkappa$ is equal to 10 or 20, we can calculate ν from the relation (248), and, substituting this value in the equation

$$\alpha = \nu\beta,$$

for which, on account of (247), (202) and (199), we may write

$$2m(n_0 - n) = \nu g,$$

we find

$$g = \frac{2m(n_0 - n)}{\nu}.$$

This formula takes an interesting form if we use the relation (207). It then becomes

$$\tau = \frac{\nu}{n_0 - n},$$

showing that the time during which the vibrations in a particle go on undisturbed may be deduced from the breadth of the band.

In Hallo's experiments the breadth of the D-lines was about one Angström unit, from which I infer that the value of τ lies between $12 \cdot 10^{-12}$ and $24 \cdot 10^{-12}$ sec. The first number is got by putting $\nu = 3$ $(\varkappa = 10)$, the second by taking $\nu = 6$ $(\varkappa = 37)$. As the interval between two successive encounters of a molecule is probably of the order 10^{-10} sec., we see that τ comes out somewhat smaller than this interval, as was already mentioned in § 120.

After having found the ratios between α, β, γ, we can try to evaluate the absolute values of these coefficients. For this purpose, we could use the absolute value of the coefficient of absorption, if it were but known. We can also avail ourselves, as Hallo and Geest have pointed out, of the rotation of the plane of polarization, or of the magnetic double refraction. If the ratios between α, β, γ are given, the three quantities may be deduced from the formula (246), or from the difference between the value of v given by (239), and the corresponding value for $\mathfrak{H} = 0$.

Now, when α is known for a certain point in the spectrum in the neighbourhood of the point n_0, i. e. when we know the value of (247), and if further we introduce the values of $\frac{e}{m}$ and e, we can draw a conclusion as to the number of absorbing (or radiating) particles per unit of volume. In this way one finds for the sodium flame used by Hallo

$$N = 4 \cdot 10^{14},$$

corresponding to a density of the sodium vapour of about 10^{-8}. In all probability this value is very much smaller than the density of the vapour actually present in the flame, a difference that must perhaps be explained by supposing that only those particles which are in a peculiar state, a small portion of the whole number, play a part in the phenomenon of absorption.

I need scarcely add that all these conclusions must be regarded with some diffidence. To say the truth, the theory of the absorption and emission of light by ponderable bodies is yet in its infancy. If we should feel inclined to think better of it, and to be satisfied with the results already obtained, our illusion will soon be dispelled, when we think a moment of Wood's investigations about the optical properties of sodium vapour, which show that a molecule of this substance must have a wonderful complexity, or of the shifting of the spectral lines by pressure that was discovered by Humphreys and Mohler, and which the theory in its present state is hardly able to account for.[1])

---

1) Note **64**.

CHAPTER V.

OPTICAL PHENOMENA IN MOVING BODIES.

146. The electromagnetic and optical phenomena in systems having a motion of translation, as all terrestrial bodies have by the annual motion of the earth, are of much interest, not only in themselves, but also because they furnish us with means of testing the different theories of electricity that have been proposed. The theory of electrons has even been developed partly with a view to these phenomena. For these reasons I shall devote the last part of my lectures to some questions relating to the propagation of light in moving bodies and, in the first place, to the astronomical aberration of light.

Before I go into some details concerning the attempts that have been made to explain this influence of the earth's motion on the apparent position of the stars, it will be well to set forth a general mode of reasoning that can be used in problems concerning the propagation of waves and rays of light. It consists in the application of Huygens's well known principle.

We shall consider a transparent medium of any kind we like, moving in one way or another, and we shall refer this motion and the propagation of light in the medium to three rectangular axes of coordinates, which we may conceive as likewise moving. We shall suppose our diagrams, which are to represent the successive positions of waves of light, to be rigidly fixed to the axes, so that these have an invariable position in the diagrams.

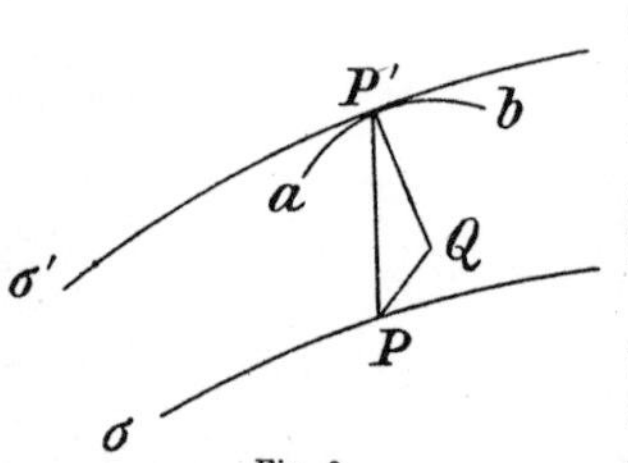

Fig. 8.

Let σ (Fig. 8) be a wave-front in the position it occupies at the time t, and let us seek to determine the position σ' which it will have reached after an infinitely short time dt. For this purpose we must regard each point P of σ as a centre of vibration, and construct around it the elementary wave that is formed in the time dt, i. e. the infinitely small surface that is reached at the instant $t + dt$ by a disturbance starting from P at the time t. The envelop of all these elementary waves will be the new position of the wave-front, and by continually repeating this construction we can follow the wave in its propagation step by step.

At the same time, the course of the rays of light becomes known. The line drawn from the centre of vibration P of an elementary wave to the point P' where it is touched by the envelop σ', is an element of a ray, and every new step in the construction will give us a new element of it.

The physical meaning of the lines so determined need scarcely be recalled here. The rays serve to indicate the manner in which beams of light can be laterally limited. If, for example, the light is made to pass through an opening in an opaque screen, the disturbance of the equilibrium behind the screen is confined to the part of space that can be reached by rays of light drawn through the points of the opening. It must be kept in mind, however, that this is true only if we neglect the effects of diffraction, as we may do when the dimensions of the opening are very large in comparison with the wave-length.

If we want to lay stress on the fact that, in the above construction, we had in view the *relative* motion of light with respect to the axes of coordinates or with respect to some system to which these are fixed, we can speak of the *relative* rays of light.

As to the elementary waves, on whose dimensions and form all is made to depend, these are determined in every case by the optical properties and the state of motion of the medium.

147. We are now prepared for examining the two theories of the aberration of light that have been proposed by Fresnel and Stokes. In doing so we shall confine ourselves to the annual aberration, so that the rotation of our planet around its axis will be left out of consideration. In order further to simplify the problem, we shall replace the motion of the earth in its annual course by a uniform translation along a straight line.

The theory of Stokes[1]) rests on the assumption that the ether surrounding the earth is set in motion by the translation of this body, and that, at every point of the surface of the globe, there is perfect equality of the velocities of the earth and the ether. According to this latter hypothesis, the instruments of an observatory are at rest relatively to the surrounding ether. It is clear that under these

1) G. G. Stokes, On the aberration of light, Phil. Mag. (3) **27** (1845), p. 9; Mathematical and physical papers **1**, p. 134.

circumstances the direction in which a heavenly body is observed, must depend on the direction of the waves, such as it is immediately before the light enters our instruments. Now, on account of the supposed motion of the ether, this direction may differ from the direction of the waves at some distance from the earth; this is the reason why the apparent position of a star will be different from the real one.

In order to determine the rotation of the waves we shall now apply the general method that has been sketched, using a system of coordinates that moves with the earth. We shall denote by $\mathfrak{g}$ the velocity with which the ether moves across our diagram, a velocity that is 0 at the surface of the earth, if there is no sliding, and equal and opposite to the velocity of the earth at a considerable distance. The state of motion being stationary, this relative velocity of the ether is independent of the time. We shall further neglect the influence of the air on the propagation of light, an influence that is known to be very feeble.

If the ether were at rest relatively to the axes, the light-waves would travel with the definite velocity c; every elementary wave would be a sphere whose radius is cdt, and whose centre lies at the point P from which the radiation goes forth. For the moving ether this has to be modified. The elementary wave still remains a sphere with radius cdt, because in the infinitely small space in which it is formed, the ether may be taken to have everywhere the same velocity, but while it expands, the sphere is carried along by the motion of the medium, in exactly the same manner in which waves of sound are carried along by the wind, or water waves by the current of a river. The elementary wave formed around a point P (Fig. 8) will therefore have its centre, not at P, but at another point Q, namely at the point that is reached at the time $t + dt$ by a particle of the ether which had the position P at the time t. There will be a rotation of the wave-front, if the velocity $\mathfrak{g}$ of the ether changes from one point of the wave to the next.

It will suffice for our purpose to consider so small a part of the wave as can be admitted into the instrument of observation. A part of this size can be considered as plane and the velocity of the ether at its different points can be regarded as a linear function of the coordinates. Consequently, the centres of the spheres lie in a plane and, since the spheres are equal, the part of the new wave-front σ' with which we are concerned is a plane of the same direction, so that the rotation of the wave is equal to the rotation of a plane σ that is carried along by the motion of the medium.

Let us lay the axis OX along the normal N to the wave-front σ, drawn in the direction of propagation. Then, the direction cosines of the normal N' to the new wave-front are easily found[1]) to be proportional to the expressions

$$1-\frac{\partial \mathbf{g}_x}{\partial x}dt,\quad -\frac{\partial \mathbf{g}_x}{\partial y}dt,\quad -\frac{\partial \mathbf{g}_x}{\partial z}dt.$$

We can express this result by saying that the direction of the normal N' is obtained if a vector of unit length in the direction of N is compounded with a vector whose components are

$$-\frac{\partial \mathbf{g}_x}{\partial x}dt,\quad -\frac{\partial \mathbf{g}_x}{\partial y}dt,\quad -\frac{\partial \mathbf{g}_x}{\partial z}dt. \qquad (249)$$

A vector which serves in this way to determine the change of a direction, by being compounded with a unit vector in the original direction, may be termed a *deviating vector*.

There is one assumption which plays a very important part in Stokes's theory and of which thus far no mention has been made. Stokes supposes the motion of the ether to be *irrotational*, or, in other terms, to have a velocity potential. In virtue of this we have

$$\frac{\partial \mathbf{g}_x}{\partial y}=\frac{\partial \mathbf{g}_y}{\partial x},\quad \frac{\partial \mathbf{g}_x}{\partial z}=\frac{\partial \mathbf{g}_z}{\partial x},$$

so that we can represent the components (249) of the deviating vector by

$$-\frac{\partial \mathbf{g}_x}{\partial x}dt,\quad -\frac{\partial \mathbf{g}_y}{\partial x}dt,\quad -\frac{\partial \mathbf{g}_z}{\partial x}dt,$$

and the vector itself by

$$-\frac{\partial \mathbf{g}}{\partial x}dt. \qquad (250)$$

148. The velocity $\mathbf{w}$ of the earth being only one ten-thousandth part of the speed of light, all the terms in our formulae which contain the factor $\frac{|\mathbf{w}|}{c}$, are very small. So are also the terms containing the factor $\frac{|\mathbf{g}|}{v}$, if $\mathbf{g}$ is one of the velocities of matter or ether, and v one of the velocities of light with which we are concerned. We shall call terms of this kind quantities of the first order of magnitude, and we shall neglect in the majority of cases the terms of the second order, i. e. those which are proportional to $\frac{\mathbf{w}^2}{c^2}$ or to $\frac{\mathbf{g}^2}{v^2}$.

If we do so, the calculation of the total rotation which the waves of light undergo while advancing towards the earth, and which is a quantity of the first order, is much simplified. We have only to form the sum of all the deviating vectors such as (250) which

1) Note 65.

belong to the successive elements of time; the resultant vector will be the total deviating vector, i. e. the vector which we must compound with a unit vector in the direction of the original normal to the waves, in order to get the final direction of the normal. Since (Fig. 8)

$$dt = \frac{QP'}{c},$$

(250) becomes

$$-\frac{1}{c}\frac{\partial \mathfrak{g}}{\partial x} \cdot QP',$$

and here we may replace QP' by the element $PP' = ds$ of the ray, because the ratio $\frac{PP'}{QP'}$ differs from 1 by a quantity of the order $\frac{|\mathfrak{g}|}{c}$, and the factor $\frac{1}{c}\frac{\partial \mathfrak{g}}{\partial x}$ is also of this order of magnitude. Finally, we may replace $\frac{\partial \mathfrak{g}}{\partial x}$ by $\frac{\partial \mathfrak{g}}{\partial s}$, because the angle between ds and the axis of x, which coincides with the wave-normal, is a quantity of the order $\frac{|\mathfrak{g}|}{c}$. The deviating vector corresponding to the element ds becomes by this

$$-\frac{1}{c}\frac{\partial \mathfrak{g}}{\partial s}ds,$$

an expression from which all reference to the axes of coordinates has disappeared, and, if the ray travels from a point A to a point B, we have for the total deviating vector

$$-\frac{1}{c}\int_A^B \frac{\partial \mathfrak{g}}{\partial s}ds = \frac{1}{c}(\mathfrak{g}_A - \mathfrak{g}_B),$$

where $\mathfrak{g}_A$ and $\mathfrak{g}_B$ are the relative velocities of the ether at the points A and B.

Now, let the point A be at a great distance from the earth, and let B lie in the immediate neighbourhood of its surface. Then, if there is no sliding, we have $\mathfrak{g}_B = 0$, whereas $\mathfrak{g}_A$ is equal and opposite to the velocity $\mathbf{w}$ of the earth. The deviating vector becomes

$$-\frac{\mathbf{w}}{c},$$

and we can draw the following conclusion:

In order to find the final direction of the wave-normal (in the direction of the propagation) we must draw a vector equal to the velocity c of light in the direction of the original normal to the waves at A, and compound it with a vector equal and opposite to the velocity of the earth. If one takes into account that the normal at A coincides with the real direction of the light coming from a star, it is clear that our result agrees with the ordinary explanation of aberration that is given in text-books of astronomy and that has been verified by observations.

149. Unfortunately, there is a very serious difficulty about this theory of Stokes: two assumptions which we have been obliged to make, namely that the motion of the ether is irrotational and that there is no sliding over the surface of the earth, can hardly be reconciled. It is wholly impossible to do so, if the ether is regarded as incompressible. Indeed, a well known hydrodynamical theorem teaches us that, when a sphere immersed in a boundless incompressible medium has a given translation, the motion of the medium will be completely determined if it is required that there shall be a velocity potential, and that, at every point of the surface, the velocity of the medium and that of the sphere shall have equal components in the direction of the normal. In the only state of motion which satisfies these two conditions there is a considerable sliding at the surface, the maximum value of the relative velocity being even one and a half times the velocity of translation of the sphere.[1]) This shows that an irrotational motion of the medium without sliding can never be realized if the medium is incompressible, and that we should have at once to dismiss Stokes's theory if we could be sure of the incompressibility of the ether.

The preceding reasoning fails however, if we admit the possibility of changes in the density of the ether, and Planck has observed[2]) that the two hypotheses of Stokes's theory no longer contradict each other, if one supposes the ether to be condensed around celestial bodies, as it would be if it were subjected to gravitation and had more or less the properties of a gas. We cannot wholly avoid a sliding at the surface, but we can make it as small as we please by supposing a sufficient degree of condensation. If we do not shrink from admitting an accumulation of the ether around the earth to a density ε^{11} times as great as the density in celestial space, we can imagine a state of things in which the maximum velocity of sliding is no more than one half percent of the velocity of the earth, and this would certainly be amply sufficient for an explanation of the aberration within the limits of experimental errors.[3])

In this department of physics, in which we can make no progress without some hypothesis that looks somewhat startling at first

1) Note **66**.

2) See Lorentz, Stokes's theory of aberration in the supposition of a variable density of the aether, Amsterdam Proceedings 1898—1899, p. 443 (Abhandlungen über theoretische Physik I, p. 454).

3) Note **67**.

sight, we must be careful not rashly to reject a new idea, and in making his suggestion Planck has certainly done a good thing. Yet I dare say that this assumption of an enormously condensed ether, combined, as it must be, with the hypothesis that the velocity of light is not in the least altered by it, is not very satisfactory. I am sure, Planck himself is inclined to prefer the unchangeable and immovable ether of Fresnel, if it can be shown that this conception can lead us to an understanding of the phenomena that have been observed.

150. The theory of Fresnel, the main principle of which has already been incorporated in the theory I have set forth in the preceding chapters, dates as far back as 1818. It was formulated for the first time in a letter to Arago[1]), in which it is expressly stated that we must imagine the ether not to receive the least part of the motion of the earth. To this Fresnel adds a most important hypothesis concerning the propagation of light in moving transparent ponderable matter.

I believe every one will be ready to admit that an optical phenomenon which can take place in a system that is at rest, can go on in exactly the same way after a uniform motion of translation has been imparted to this system, provided only that this translation be given to *all* that belongs to the system. If, therefore, all that is contained in a column of water or in a piece of glass shares a translatory motion which we communicate to these substances, the propagation of light in their interior will always go on in the same manner, whether there be a translation or not. The case will however be different, if the glass or the water contains something which we cannot set in motion.

Now, as I said, Fresnel supposed the ether not to follow the motion of the earth. The only way in which this can be understood, is to conceive the earth as impregnated throughout its bulk with ether and as perfectly permeable to it. When we have gone so far as to attribute this property to a body of the size of our planet, we must certainly likewise ascribe it to much smaller bodies, and we must expect that, if water flows through a tube, there is no current of ether, and that therefore, since a beam of light is propagated partly by the water and partly by the ether, the light waves, being held back as it were by the ether, will not acquire the full velocity of the water current. According to Fresnel's hypothesis, the velocity of the rays relative to the walls of the tube

1) Lettre de Fresnel à Arago, Sur l'influence du mouvement terrestre dans quelques phénomènes d'optique, Ann. de chim. et de phys. **9** (1818), p. 57 (Œuvres complètes de Fresnel **2**, p. 627).

(or, what amounts to the same thing, relative to the ether) is found by compounding the velocity with which the propagation would take place in standing water, with only a certain part of the velocity of the flow, this part being determined by the fraction $1-\frac{1}{\mu^2}$, where μ is the index of refraction of the water when at rest. The same coefficient $1-\frac{1}{\mu^2}$ is applied by him to all other isotropic transparent substances. If μ is little different from 1, as it is in gases, the coefficient is very small; light waves are scarcely dragged along by a current of air, because in air the propagation takes place almost exclusively in the ether it contains. If Fresnel's coefficient is to be nearly 1, i. e. if the light waves are to acquire almost the full velocity of the ponderable matter, we must use a highly refracting body.

151. I must add two remarks. In the first place, instead of the propagation relative to the ether, we can as well consider that relative to the ponderable matter. If water which is flowing through a tube towards the right-hand side with a velocity w, is traversed by a beam of light going in the same direction, the velocity of propagation relative to the ether is

$$v+\left(1-\frac{1}{\mu^2}\right)w,$$

where v means the velocity of light in standing water. The relative velocity of the light with respect to the water is got from this by subtracting w, so that it is given by

$$v-\frac{1}{\mu^2}w. \tag{251}$$

It may be considered as compounded of the velocity v and a part, determined by the fraction $\frac{1}{\mu^2}$, of the velocity with which the ether moves relatively to the ponderable matter, and which in our example is directed towards the left.

In the second place, the above statement of Fresnel's hypothesis requires to be completed for the case of media in which the velocity of light depends on the frequency. When a body is in motion, we must distinguish between the frequency of the vibrations at a fixed point of the ether and the frequency with which the electromagnetic state alternates at a point moving with the ponderable matter. If, using axes of coordinates fixed with respect to the ether, we represent the disturbances by means of formulae containing an expression of the form

$$\cos n\left(t-\frac{x}{u}+p\right), \tag{252}$$

n is the first of these frequencies, which may be termed the *true* or *absolute* one. We can pass to the other, the *relative* frequency, by introducing into this expression the coordinate with respect to an origin moving with the ponderable matter. If this coordinate is denoted by x', and if the motion of the matter takes place in the direction of OX with the velocity w, we have

$$x = x' + wt,$$

so that (252) becomes

$$\cos n\left(t - \frac{w}{u}t - \frac{x'}{u} + p\right).$$

The coefficient of t in this expression,

$$n' = n\left(1 - \frac{w}{u}\right)$$

is the relative frequency; that it differs from n agrees with Doppler's principle.

Fresnel's hypothesis may now be expressed more exactly as follows. If we want to know the velocity of propagation of light in moving ponderable matter, we must fix our attention on the *relative* frequency n' of the vibrations, and we must understand by v and μ in the expression (251) the values relating to light travelling in the body without a translation, and vibrating with a frequency equal to n'.

152. I have now to show that Fresnel's theory can account for the phenomena that have been observed. These may be briefly summarized as follows. First there is the aberration of light of which I have already spoken. Further it has been found that an astronomer, after having determined the apparent direction of a star's rays and their apparent frequency, can predict from these, by the ordinary laws of optics, and without attending any more to the motion of the earth, the result of all experiments on reflexion, refraction, diffraction and interference that can be made with these rays. Finally, all optical phenomena which are produced by using a terrestrial source of light are absolutely independent of the earth's motion. If, by a common rotation of the apparatus, the source of light included, we alter the direction of the rays with respect to that of the earth's translation, not the least change is ever observed.

It must be noticed that all this could be accounted for at a stroke and without any mathematical formula by Stokes's theory, if only we could reconcile with each other its two fundamental assumptions. In applying Fresnel's views, we need some calculations, but these will lead us to a very satisfactory explanation of all that has been mentioned, with the restriction however that we must confine ourselves to the effects of the first order.

153. We shall again begin by considering the propagation of the wave-front, this time in the interior of a ponderable transparent body, whose properties may change from point to point, but which we shall suppose to be everywhere isotropic. For a given frequency, the velocity of light in the body while it is at rest will have at every point a definite value v, connected with the index of refraction μ by the relation

$$\mu = \frac{c}{v}.$$

As before, we shall use axes of coordinates that are fixed to the earth; if we represent the progress of the waves in a diagram, this will likewise be supposed to move with the earth, so that the ether must be understood to flow across it, with a velocity which will again be denoted by $\mathfrak{g}$, but which now has the same direction and magnitude at all points, being everywhere equal and opposite to the velocity of the earth.

Let, as before, σ be the position of a wave-front (see Fig. 8, p. 168) at the time t, σ' the position at the time $t + dt$, the latter surface being the envelop of all the elementary waves that have been formed during the time dt. If the ether were at rest in our diagram, each elementary wave would be a sphere having a radius $v\,dt$, and whose geometric centre coincides with the centre of vibration. In reality, according to what has been said about Fresnel's hypothesis, the geometric centre of the sphere, whose radius is still $v\,dt$, is displaced from the centre of vibration over a certain distance, the displacement being given by the vector $\frac{1}{\mu^2}\mathfrak{g}\,dt$.

Let us consider the infinitely small triangle having its angles at the point P of the wave-front σ, which is the centre of disturbance for the elementary wave, the point Q which is its geometric centre, and the point P' where it is touched by the new wave-front σ'. As has just been said, the side PQ as a vector is given by $\frac{1}{\mu^2}\mathfrak{g}\,dt$. The side QP', being a radius of the sphere, is normal to σ', and, in the limit, to σ. Its length is $v\,dt$. As to the side PP', this is an element of a relative ray. According to general usage, we shall call $\frac{PP'}{dt}$ the velocity of the ray, so that, if this is denoted by v', we have

$$PP' = v'\,dt.$$

It appears from this that, if the angle between the relative ray and the velocity $\mathfrak{g}$ is represented by ϑ,

$$v^2 = v'^2 - 2\frac{|\mathfrak{g}|}{\mu^2}v'\cos\vartheta + \frac{\mathfrak{g}^2}{\mu^4},$$

from which one finds, omitting quantities of the third order, i. e. of the order $\frac{|\mathfrak{g}|^3}{v^3}$,

$$v' = v + \frac{|\mathfrak{g}|}{\mu^2} \cos \vartheta - \frac{\mathfrak{g}^2}{2 v \mu^4} \sin^2 \vartheta. \tag{253}$$

We shall have especially to consider the inverse of this quantity. To the same degree of approximation, it is given by

$$\frac{1}{v'} = \frac{1}{v} \left\{ 1 - \frac{|\mathfrak{g}|}{v \mu^2} \cos \vartheta + \frac{\mathfrak{g}^2}{2 v^2 \mu^4} (1 + \cos^2 \vartheta) \right\}. \tag{254}$$

There is further a simple rule by means of which we can pass from the direction of the wave-normal to that of the relative ray and conversely. The vector PP' is the sum of the vectors PQ and QP'. Hence, dividing the three by dt, we have the following proposition: If a vector having the direction of the normal to the wave and the magnitude v, is compounded with a vector $\frac{\mathfrak{g}}{\mu^2}$, the resultant vector will be in the direction of the relative ray. And, conversely, if a vector in the direction of the ray and having the magnitude v', is compounded with a vector $-\frac{\mathfrak{g}}{\mu^2}$, we shall find the direction of the normal to the wave.

In order fully to understand the meaning of these propositions, one must keep in mind that, at every point of the medium, the relative ray and the wave can have all possible directions. The above results apply to all cases.

154. These preliminaries enable us to prove the beautiful theorem that, if quantities of the second order are neglected, the course of the relative rays is not affected by the motion of the earth. We have seen in what manner Huygens's principle, while determining the successive positions σ, σ', σ'', ... of a wave-front, also gives us the succeeding elements PP', $P'P''$, $P''P'''$, ... of a relative ray. If the centre of vibration of an elementary wave and the point where it is touched by the envelop are called *conjugate* points, we may say that a ray passes through a series of conjugate points succeeding each other at infinitely small distances. Now, between any two consecutive positions of the wave-front, we can draw a large number of infinitely small straight lines, some joining conjugate points and others not, and for each of these lines ds we can calculate the value of

$$\frac{ds}{v'}, \tag{255}$$

taking for v' the value belonging to an element of a ray having the direction of ds. It is easily seen that this expression (255) has one and the same value for all lines joining conjugate points, and a greater value for all other lines. Indeed, by the definition of v', the value is for the first lines equal to the time dt in which the light advances from the first position of the wave-front to the second. As to a line ds which is drawn between a point P of the first wave-front and a point Q of the second, not conjugate with P, its end Q lies outside the elementary wave that is formed around P, because the new wave-front is less curved than the elementary wave and must lie outside it with the exception of the point of contact. Therefore, for the line PQ, the expression (255) must exceed the value it would have if Q lay on the surface of the elementary wave.

Now, let A and B be two points of a relative ray s, at a finite distance from each other, and let s' be any other line joining these points. If between A and B we construct a series of wave-fronts at infinitely small distances from each other, the line s is divided into elements each of which joins two conjugate points, whereas the elements of s' cannot be all of this kind. From this we can infer that the integral

$$\int \frac{ds}{v'} \tag{256}$$

taken for s will have a smaller value than the corresponding integral for the line s'. Thus, the course of the relative ray between two given points A and B is seen to be determined by the property that the integral (256) is smaller for it than for any other line between the same points.

Substituting in the integral the value (254) we find, if we neglect terms of the second order,

$$\int_A^B \frac{ds}{v'} = \int_A^B \frac{ds}{v} - \int_A^B \frac{|\mathbf{g}| \cos \vartheta}{\mu^2 v^2} ds. \tag{257}$$

Here, since $\mu v = c$, we may replace the last term by

$$\frac{1}{c^2} \int_A^B \mathbf{g}_s \, ds = \frac{1}{c^2} (AB)_g \, |\mathbf{g}|,$$

if we understand by $(AB)_g$ the projection of the path AB on the direction of the velocity $\mathbf{g}$, a projection that is entirely determined by the position of the extreme points A and B. The last term in (257) is therefore the same for all paths leading from A to B, and the condition for the minimum simply requires that the first term

$$\int_A^B \frac{ds}{v}$$

be a minimum. This term, however, contains nothing that depends on the velocity $\mathfrak{g}$; hence, the course of the ray, for which it is a minimum, is likewise independent of that velocity, by which our proposition is proved.

In the proof we have made no assumption concerning the way in which v and μ change from point to point. It applies to any distribution of isotropic transparent matter, and even to limiting cases in which there is a sudden change of properties at a certain surface. Consequently, for the relative rays, the law of refraction remains the same as it would be if the bodies were at rest (in which case the word „relative" might as well be dropped). I must add that this proposition can easily be proved by itself, by directly applying Huygens's principle to the refraction at a surface, and that the reflexion of rays can be treated in the same manner and with the same result.

155. In order to account for the phenomenon of aberration, one has only to combine the above results. Let P be a distant point, which we imagine to be rigidly connected with the earth, and to lie just outside the atmosphere in the free ether. At this point, the light coming from some star will have waves whose normal has a definite direction N, opposite to the direction in which the star is really situated. It has also a definite relative frequency, which in general differs from the true or absolute one according to Doppler's principle.

At the point P we have $v = c$, $\mu = 1$. Hence, if we want to find the direction of the relative ray s at this place, we must compound a vector c in the direction of the wave-normal N with a vector $\mathfrak{g}$, which represents the velocity of the ether relative to the earth, and which is therefore equal and opposite to the velocity of the earth itself. This construction evidently leads to a direction of the relative ray identical with the apparent direction of the rays as determined in the elementary theory of aberration. We shall therefore have explained this latter phenomenon if we can show that the result of observations made at the surface of our planet is such that an astronomer (who does not think of the earth's motion), reckoning so far as necessary with the frequency n which shows itself to him, would conclude from them that the rays reach the atmosphere in the direction s. This is really so, because, as we have seen, the progress of the relative rays from P onward is exactly what would be the progress of the absolute rays if the earth did not move and the true frequency were equal to n.

We may mention in particular that, if, in this latter case, the path of a ray were mapped out by means of suitably arranged screens with small openings, a ray can still pass through these openings, if the screens move with the earth. Further that if, on the immovable earth, the absolute rays were brought to a focus in a telescope, the relative rays will likewise converge towards this point, producing in it a real concentration of light. The truth of this is at once seen if, by means of the theorem of § 153, we determine the shape of the wave-fronts in the neighbourhood of the focus. It is found that the convergence of the relative rays towards a point necessarily implies a contraction of the waves around this point.[1])

The explanation of the fact that all optical phenomena which are produced by means of terrestrial sources of light are uninfluenced by the earth's motion, is so simple that few words are needed for it. It will suffice to observe that in experiments on interference the differences of phase remain unaltered. This follows at once from our formula (257) for the time in which a relative ray travels over a certain path. If two relative rays, starting from a point A, come together at a point B, the lengths of time required by them are given by the expressions

$$\int_A^B \frac{ds_1}{v} + \frac{1}{c^2}(AB)_g\,|\mathfrak{g}|$$

and

$$\int_A^B \frac{ds_2}{v} + \frac{1}{c^2}(AB)_g\,|\mathfrak{g}|,$$

where the integrals relate to the two paths. Since the last terms are identical, we find for the difference between the two times

$$\int_A^B \frac{ds_1}{v} - \int_A^B \frac{ds_2}{v}.$$

This being independent of the motion of the earth, the result of the interference must be so likewise, a conclusion that may be extended to *all* optical phenomena, because, in the light of Huygens's principle, we may regard them all as cases of interference.

It should be noticed, however, that the position of the bright and the dark interference bands is determined by the differences of phase *expressed in times of vibration*, so that the above conclusions are legitimate only if the motion of the earth does not affect the periods themselves in which the particles in the source of light are vibrating. This condition will be fulfilled if neither the elastic forces acting on them, nor their masses are changed. Then, in all experiments performed on the moving earth, the relative frequency at any

1) Note **68**.

point of our apparatus will be equal to the frequency that would exist if we could experiment in the same manner on a planet having no translation.

156. Fresnel's coefficient $1 - \frac{1}{\mu^2}$, the importance of which we have now learned to understand, can be deduced from the theory that in a beam of light in a ponderable body there is an oscillatory motion of electric charges. Unfortunately, if these latter are supposed to be concentrated in separate electrons, the deduction suffers from the difficulties that are inherent in most molecular theories, and the true cause of the partial convection of light-waves by matter in motion does not become clearly apparent. For this reason I shall first consider an ideal case, namely that of a body in which the charges are continuously distributed. In this preliminary treatment I shall make light of the difficulty that we are now obliged to imagine four different things, thoroughly penetrating each other, so that they can exist in the same space, viz. 1. the ether, 2. the positive and the negative electricity and 3. the ponderable matter.

For the sake of simplicity, I shall suppose that only one of the two electricities can be shifted from its position of equilibrium in the ponderable body, the other being rigidly fixed to this latter, and having no other motion than the common translation of the entire system. I shall denote by ϱ the volume-density of the movable, and by ϱ' that of the fixed charge. The body as a whole being uncharged, we shall have in the state of equilibrium

$$\varrho + \varrho' = 0, \tag{258}$$

and this will remain true while the one charge is vibrating, unless it be condensed or rarefied by doing so.

The question as to whether it be the positive or the negative electricity that can be displaced in the body may be left open in this theory.

157. We shall suppose the movable charge to have a certain mass, and to be driven back towards its position of equilibrium by an elastic force opposite to the displacement and proportional to it; let $\mathbf{q}$ be the displacement, $-f\mathbf{q}$ the elastic force, and m the mass, both reckoned per unit of volume.

The equations that must be applied to the problem before us were already mentioned in § 11. Introducing axes of coordinates that have a fixed position in the ether, we have

$$\operatorname{div} \mathbf{d} = \varrho + \varrho', \tag{259}$$

$$\operatorname{div} \mathbf{h} = 0, \tag{260}$$

$$\text{rot } \mathbf{d} = -\frac{1}{c}\dot{\mathbf{h}}, \tag{261}$$

$$\text{rot } \mathbf{h} = \frac{1}{c}(\dot{\mathbf{d}} + \varrho\mathbf{v} + \varrho'\mathbf{v}'), \tag{262}$$

where $\mathbf{v}$ and $\mathbf{v}'$ are the velocities of the two electricities, so that $\varrho\mathbf{v} + \varrho'\mathbf{v}'$ represents the convection current.

To these formulae we must add the equation of motion of the vibrating electricity. If its acceleration is denoted by $\mathbf{j}$, we have

$$m\mathbf{j} = -f\mathbf{q} + \varrho\mathbf{d} + \frac{1}{c}\varrho[\mathbf{v}\cdot\mathbf{h}]. \tag{263}$$

158. Let us first briefly examine the propagation of electric vibrations in the body when kept at rest. We may limit ourselves to the case that there is a displacement $\mathbf{q}_y$ of the movable charge in the direction of OY, combined with a dielectric displacement $\mathbf{d}_y$ of the same direction in the ether, and a magnetic force $\mathbf{h}_z$ parallel to OZ, all these quantities being functions of x and t only. As the relation (258) is not violated, the equations (259) and (260) are fulfilled by these assumptions, and (261) and (262) reduce to

$$\frac{\partial \mathbf{d}_y}{\partial x} = -\frac{1}{c}\frac{\partial \mathbf{h}_z}{\partial t}, \tag{264}$$

$$-\frac{\partial \mathbf{h}_z}{\partial x} = \frac{1}{c}\left(\varrho\frac{\partial \mathbf{q}_y}{\partial t} + \frac{\partial \mathbf{d}_y}{\partial t}\right). \tag{265}$$

Finally the equation of motion becomes

$$m\frac{\partial^2 \mathbf{q}_y}{\partial t^2} = -f\mathbf{q}_y + \varrho\mathbf{d}_y. \tag{266}$$

A solution of these equations is obtained by putting

$$\mathbf{d}_y = a\cos n\left(t - \frac{x}{v}\right),$$

from which we find, by means of (264) and (266),

$$\mathbf{h}_z = \frac{c}{v}\mathbf{d}_y, \quad \mathbf{q}_y = \frac{\varrho}{f - mn^2}\mathbf{d}_y. \tag{267}$$

Substituting these values in (265), we find the following formula for the determination of the velocity of propagation v:

$$\frac{c^2}{v^2} = \frac{\varrho^2}{f - mn^2} + 1. \tag{268}$$

159. When the body has a uniform translation with the velocity w in the direction of OX, we can still satisfy the equations by suitable values of $\mathbf{d}_y$, $\mathbf{h}_z$, $\mathbf{q}_y$, but some alterations are necessary. The first of these relates to the convection current. Its component in the direction of OX remains 0, since both the positive and the negative electricity are carried along with the translation of the body, but, if we continue to use axes of coordinates fixed in the ether, the convection current parallel to OY can no longer be represented by $\varrho \frac{\partial \mathbf{q}_y}{\partial t}$. The right expression for it is found as follows. If a definite point of the vibrating charge has the coordinate x at the time t, its coordinate at the instant $t + dt$ will be $x + w\,dt$, so that the increment of its displacement $\mathbf{q}_y$ is given by

$$\frac{\partial \mathbf{q}_y}{\partial t} dt + w \frac{\partial \mathbf{q}_y}{\partial x} dt,$$

and its velocity in the direction of OY by

$$\frac{\partial \mathbf{q}_y}{\partial t} + w \frac{\partial \mathbf{q}_y}{\partial x},$$

for which we may also write

$$\left(\frac{\partial \mathbf{q}_y}{\partial t}\right),$$

if we use the brackets for indicating the differential coefficient for a point moving with the body. The convection current may therefore be represented by

$$\varrho \left(\frac{\partial \mathbf{q}_y}{\partial t}\right).$$

It is clear that the acceleration is

$$\left(\frac{\partial^2 \mathbf{q}_y}{\partial t^2}\right),$$

and that, for any quantity φ which depends on the coordinates and the time, we may distinguish two differential coefficients $\frac{\partial \varphi}{\partial t}$ and $\left(\frac{\partial \varphi}{\partial t}\right)$, just as we have done for $\mathbf{q}_y$. The first is the partial derivative when φ is considered as a function of t and the „absolute" coordinates, i. e. the coordinates with respect to axes fixed in the ether, and we have to use the second symbol when the time and the „relative" coordinates, i. e. the coordinates with respect to axes moving with the body, are taken as independent variables. The relation between the two quantities is always expressed by the formula

$$\left(\frac{\partial \varphi}{\partial t}\right) = \frac{\partial \varphi}{\partial t} + w \frac{\partial \varphi}{\partial x}. \tag{269}$$

As to the differential coefficients with respect to x, y, z, each of these has the same value, whether we understand by x, y, z the absolute or the relative coordinates.

The second alteration which we have to make is due to the last term in (23). On account of its velocity w in the direction of OX, the charge ϱ will be acted on by a force

$$-\frac{\varrho}{c} w \mathbf{h}_z,$$

parallel to OY, and this force must be added on the right-hand side of the equation of motion.

In virtue of the assumptions now made, $\varrho + \varrho'$ again remains 0 during the vibrations, and (259) and (260) are satisfied. The equation (264) can be left unchanged, but (265) and (266) must be replaced by

$$-\frac{\partial \mathbf{h}_z}{\partial x} = \frac{1}{c}\left\{\varrho\left(\frac{\partial \mathbf{q}_y}{\partial t}\right) + \frac{\partial \mathbf{d}_y}{\partial t}\right\},$$

and

$$m\left(\frac{\partial^2 \mathbf{q}_y}{\partial t^2}\right) = -f\mathbf{q}_y + \varrho\,\mathbf{d}_y - \frac{w}{c}\varrho\,\mathbf{h}_z.$$

The three formulae are somewhat simplified if we choose as independent variables the time and the relative coordinates and if, at the same time, we put

$$\mathbf{d}_y - \frac{w}{c}\mathbf{h}_z = \mathbf{d}_y'.$$

Applying the relation (269) to $\mathbf{d}_y$ and $\mathbf{h}_z$, we find

$$\frac{\partial \mathbf{d}_y'}{\partial x} = -\frac{1}{c}\left(\frac{\partial \mathbf{h}_z}{\partial t}\right),$$

$$-\frac{\partial \mathbf{h}_z}{\partial x} = \frac{1}{c}\left\{\varrho\left(\frac{\partial \mathbf{q}_y}{\partial t}\right) + \left(\frac{\partial \mathbf{d}_y'}{\partial t}\right) - w\frac{\partial \mathbf{d}_y'}{\partial x} + \frac{w}{c}\left(\frac{\partial \mathbf{h}_z}{\partial t}\right)\right\},$$

$$m\left(\frac{\partial^2 \mathbf{q}_y}{\partial t^2}\right) = -f\mathbf{q}_y + \varrho\,\mathbf{d}_y'.$$

The first and the third of these equations have the same form as (264) and (266). Hence, if we put

$$\mathbf{d}_y' = a\cos n\left(t - \frac{x}{v'}\right), \tag{270}$$

understanding by x the relative coordinate, we have, corresponding to (267),

$$\mathbf{h}_z = \frac{c}{v'}\mathbf{d}_y', \quad \mathbf{q}_y = \frac{\varrho}{f - mn^2}\mathbf{d}_y',$$

by which the second equation becomes

$$\frac{c^2}{v'^2} = \frac{\varrho^2}{f - mn^2} + 1 + 2\frac{w}{v'}.$$

Comparing this with (268) we see that, for a definite value of the frequency n, we may write

$$\frac{c^2}{v'^2} = \frac{c^2}{v^2} + 2\frac{w}{v'}.$$

As we continually neglect quantities of the second order, we may, in the last term, replace v' by v. By this we get

$$\frac{c}{v'} = \frac{c}{v} + \frac{w}{c},$$

$$v' = v - \frac{w v^2}{c^2} = v - \frac{w}{\mu^2},$$

if μ is the index of refraction for the stationary body.

It must be kept in mind that in (270) x means the relative coordinate. Therefore, n is the relative frequency, and v' the speed of propagation relative to the ponderable matter. The velocity of light with respect to the ether is

$$v' + w = v + \left(1 - \frac{1}{\mu^2}\right) w,$$

in accordance with Fresnel's hypothesis.

160. I have now to show you in what manner the same result may be derived from the theory of electrons. For this purpose we might repeat for a moving system all that has been said in Chap. IV about the propagation of light in a system of molecules. We shall however sooner reach our aim by following another course, consisting in a comparison of the phenomena in a moving system with those that can occur in the same system when at rest.

In this comparison we shall avail ourselves of the assumptions that have been made in Chap. IV.

In the absence of the translatory motion, the problem may be stated as follows. In the molecules of the body there are electric moments $\mathbf{p}$ changing from one molecule to the next, and variable with the time. On account of its moment, each molecule is surrounded by an electromagnetic field, which is determined (§ 42) by the potentials

$$\varphi = -\frac{1}{4\pi}\left\{\frac{\partial}{\partial x}\frac{[\mathbf{p}_x]}{r} + \frac{\partial}{\partial y}\frac{[\mathbf{p}_y]}{r} + \frac{\partial}{\partial z}\frac{[\mathbf{p}_z]}{r}\right\},$$

$$\mathbf{a} = \frac{[\dot{\mathbf{p}}]}{4\pi c r},$$

x, y, z being the coordinates of the point considered, r its distance from the molecule, and the square brackets reminding us that we have to do with retarded potentials. The electric force $\mathbf{d}$ and the magnetic force $\mathbf{h}$ are given by the following formulae, to be deduced from (33) and (34),

$$\mathbf{d} = -\frac{1}{4\pi c^2 r}[\ddot{\mathbf{p}}] + \frac{1}{4\pi}\operatorname{grad}\left\{\frac{\partial}{\partial x}\frac{[\mathbf{p}_x]}{r} + \frac{\partial}{\partial y}\frac{[\mathbf{p}_y]}{r} + \frac{\partial}{\partial z}\frac{[\mathbf{p}_z]}{r}\right\}, \quad (271)$$

$$\mathbf{h} = \frac{1}{4\pi c}\operatorname{rot}\left\{\frac{1}{r}[\dot{\mathbf{p}}]\right\}. \quad (272)$$

After having compounded with each other the fields produced by all the molecules of the body, we must add one field more, namely that which is due to external causes, and which I shall represent by $\mathbf{d}_0$, $\mathbf{h}_0$. It satisfies the equations

$$\left.\begin{aligned} \operatorname{div} \mathbf{d}_0 &= 0, \\ \operatorname{div} \mathbf{h}_0 &= 0, \\ \operatorname{rot} \mathbf{h}_0 &= \frac{1}{c} \dot{\mathbf{d}}_0, \\ \operatorname{rot} \mathbf{d}_0 &= -\frac{1}{c} \dot{\mathbf{h}}_0. \end{aligned}\right\} \quad (273)$$

Lastly, we have to consider the equations of motion of the electrons which, by their displacement, bring about the electric moments $\mathbf{p}$. Let each molecule contain a single movable electron e, whose displacement $\mathbf{q}$ gives rise to an electric moment

$$\mathbf{p} = e\mathbf{q}. \quad (274)$$

If the symbol Σ relates to the superposition of the fields of all the surrounding particles, and if $-f\mathbf{q}$ is the elastic force, $-g\dot{\mathbf{q}}$ a resistance to the motion, the equation of motion is

$$m\ddot{\mathbf{q}} = e\Sigma\mathbf{d} + e\mathbf{d}_0 - f\mathbf{q} - g\dot{\mathbf{q}}. \quad (275)$$

161. In the theory of the system moving with a velocity $\mathbf{w}$ we may avail ourselves with great advantage of the transformation that has already been used in § 44.

Taking as independent variables the coordinates x', y', z' with respect to axes moving with the system, and the „local" time

$$t' = t - \frac{1}{c^2}(\mathbf{w}_x x' + \mathbf{w}_y y' + \mathbf{w}_z z'), \quad (276)$$

we find the equations (104)—(107) for the vectors $\mathbf{d}'$ and $\mathbf{h}'$, which now take the place of $\mathbf{d}$ and $\mathbf{h}$. It is true that the new formulae have not quite the same form as (33)—(36), and that the term $\frac{1}{c} \operatorname{grad}(\mathbf{w} \cdot \mathbf{a}')$, which makes the difference, must not be omitted[1]), being of the first order of magnitude with respect to $\frac{|\mathbf{w}|}{c}$, but notwithstanding this it is found that the field caused by an electric moment is determined by the formulae[2])

$$\mathbf{d}' = -\frac{1}{4\pi c^2 r}[\ddot{\mathbf{p}}] + \frac{1}{4\pi} \operatorname{grad} \left\{ \frac{\partial}{\partial x'} \frac{[\mathbf{p}_x]}{r} + \frac{\partial}{\partial y'} \frac{[\mathbf{p}_y]}{r} + \frac{\partial}{\partial z'} \frac{[\mathbf{p}_z]}{r} \right\},$$

1) See however Note **72***. 2) See Note **26**.

$$\mathbf{h}' = \frac{1}{4\pi c} \operatorname{rot} \left\{ \frac{1}{r} [\dot{\mathbf{p}}] \right\},$$

exactly corresponding to (271) and (272).

It is scarcely necessary to repeat that the symbols grad and rot have the meaning that has been specified in § 44, and that, if we want to calculate $\mathbf{d}'$ and $\mathbf{h}'$ for a point (x', y', z') at a distance r from the polarized particle, and for the instant at which the local time of this point has a definite value t', we must take for $\mathbf{p}$, $\dot{\mathbf{p}}$, $\ddot{\mathbf{p}}$ the values existing at the moment when the local time of the particle is $t' - \frac{r}{c}$.

The field produced by causes outside the body is again subjected to the fundamental equations for the free ether. Expressed in terms of our new variables, these are

$$\operatorname{div} \mathbf{d}_0' = 0,$$

$$\operatorname{div} \mathbf{h}_0' = 0,$$

$$\operatorname{rot} \mathbf{h}_0' = \frac{1}{c} \dot{\mathbf{d}}_0',$$

$$\operatorname{rot} \mathbf{d}_0' = -\frac{1}{c} \dot{\mathbf{h}}_0',$$

as is found by making $\varrho = 0$ in (100)—(103). The form of these equations is identical with that of (273).

The equation of motion of an electron must now contain the electromagnetic force $\frac{1}{c}[\mathbf{w} \cdot \mathbf{h}]$, which is due to the translation $\mathbf{w}$, so that we must write for the total force acting on unit charge

$$\mathbf{d} + \frac{1}{c}[\mathbf{w} \cdot \mathbf{h}].$$

This, however, is precisely the vector which we have called $\mathbf{d}'$. Consequently, if we suppose that the elastic force determined by the coefficient f, and the resistance measured by g, are not modified by the translation, we may write for the equation of motion

$$m\ddot{\mathbf{q}} = e\Sigma\mathbf{d}' + e\mathbf{d}_0' - f\mathbf{q} - g\dot{\mathbf{q}},$$

where the sign Σ has the same meaning as in (275).

It should be noticed that the relation (274) remains true, and that at a definite point of the moving system, the differential coefficients with respect to t are equal to those with respect to t'. On account of this we may attach to the dots in the above equation the meaning of partial differentiations with respect to t'. They must be understood in the same sense in the preceding formulae.

162. It appears from what has been said that, by the introduction of the new variables, all the equations of the problem have again taken the form which they have when there is no translation. This at once leads to the following conclusion:

If, in the system at rest, there can exist a state of things in which $\mathbf{d}$, $\mathbf{h}$ and $\mathbf{p}$ are certain functions of x, y, z and t, the moving system can be the seat of phenomena in which the vectors $\mathbf{d}'$, $\mathbf{h}'$, $\mathbf{p}$ are the same functions of the relative coordinates x', y', z' and the local time t'.

The theorem may be extended to the mean values of $\mathbf{d}$, $\mathbf{h}$ or $\mathbf{d}'$, $\mathbf{h}'$, the electric moment $\mathbf{P}$ per unit of volume, and also to the vector $\mathbf{D}$ which we have introduced in § 114, compared with a similar one that may be defined for the moving system. If, for the one system, we put

$$\bar{\mathbf{d}} = \mathbf{E}, \quad \bar{\mathbf{h}} = \mathbf{H}, \quad \mathbf{D} = \mathbf{E} + \mathbf{P},$$

and for the other

$$\bar{\mathbf{d}}' = \mathbf{E}', \quad \bar{\mathbf{h}}' = \mathbf{H}', \quad \mathbf{D}' = \mathbf{E}' + \mathbf{P},$$

the result is, that for each state in which $\mathbf{E}$, $\mathbf{H}$, $\mathbf{D}$ are certain functions of x, y, z, t, there is a corresponding state in the moving system, characterized by values of $\mathbf{E}'$, $\mathbf{H}'$, $\mathbf{D}'$ which depend in the same way on x', y', z', t'.

163. The value of Fresnel's coefficient follows as an immediate consequence from this general theorem. Let us suppose that in a transparent ponderable body without translation, there is a propagation of light waves, in which the components of $\mathbf{E}$ and $\mathbf{H}$ are represented by expressions of the form

$$a \cos n\left(t - \frac{\alpha x + \beta y + \gamma z}{v} + p\right),$$

where α, β, γ are the direction cosines of the normal to the wave, and v the velocity of propagation. Then, corresponding to this, we may have in the same body while in motion phenomena that may likewise be described as a propagation of light waves, and which are represented by expressions of the form

$$a \cos n\left(t' - \frac{\alpha x' + \beta y' + \gamma z'}{v} + p\right),$$

i. e., on account of (276),

$$a \cos n\left(t - \frac{\mathbf{w}_x x' + \mathbf{w}_y y' + \mathbf{w}_z z'}{c^2} - \frac{\alpha x' + \beta y' + \gamma z'}{v} + p\right).$$

If we put here

$$\frac{\alpha}{v} + \frac{\mathbf{w}_x}{c^2} = \frac{\alpha'}{v'}, \quad \frac{\beta}{v} + \frac{\mathbf{w}_y}{c^2} = \frac{\beta'}{v'}, \quad \frac{\gamma}{v} + \frac{\mathbf{w}_z}{c^2} = \frac{\gamma'}{v'} \qquad (277)$$

with the condition

$$\alpha'^2 + \beta'^2 + \gamma'^2 = 1, \tag{278}$$

the formula becomes

$$a \cos n \left(t - \frac{\alpha' x' + \beta' y' + \gamma' z'}{v'} + p\right),$$

showing in the first place that v' is the velocity of propagation relative to the moving body, and in the second place that n is the frequency at a point moving with it. Hence, if we take v and v' for the same value of n, we are sure to compare the speed of propagation in the two cases for equal relative frequencies.

Neglecting the square of $\mathbf{w}$, we easily find from (277) and (278)

$$\frac{1}{v'^2} = \frac{1}{v^2} + 2\frac{\alpha \mathbf{w}_x + \beta \mathbf{w}_y + \gamma \mathbf{w}_z}{c^2 v} = \frac{1}{v^2} + 2\frac{\mathbf{w}_n}{c^2 v},$$

where $\mathbf{w}_n$ is the component of the velocity of translation along the wave-normal. It may be observed that, since α', β', γ' differ from α, β, γ only by quantities of the order $\frac{\mathbf{w}}{c}$, we may take the normal such as it is in the moving system.

Further:

$$\frac{1}{v'} = \frac{1}{v} + \frac{\mathbf{w}_n}{c^2},$$

$$v' = v - \frac{v^2}{c^2}\mathbf{w}_n = v - \frac{\mathbf{w}_n}{\mu^2},$$

so that we have been led back to our former result.

164. The hypothesis advanced by Fresnel has been confirmed by Fizeau's observations on the propagation of light in flowing water[1]), and, still more conclusively, by the elaborate researches of Michelson and Morley on the same subject.[2]) In these experiments the water was made to flow in opposite directions through two parallel tubes placed side by side and closed at both ends by glass plates; the two interfering beams of light were passed through these tubes in such a manner that, throughout their course, one went with the water, and the other against it.

In order to calculate the change in the differences of phase caused by the motion of the fluid, it is necessary to know the velocity of propagation of the light relative to the fixed parts of the appa-

1) H. Fizeau, Sur les hypothèses relatives à l'éther lumineux, et sur une expérience qui paraît démontrer que le mouvement des corps change la vitesse avec laquelle la lumière se propage dans leur intérieur, Comptes rendus **33** (1851), p. 349; Ann. d. Phys. u. Chem., Erg. **3** (1853), p. 457.

2) A. A. Michelson and E. W. Morley, Influence of motion of the medium on the velocity of light, Amer. Journ. of Science (3) **31** (1886), p. 377.

ratus.[1]) If T is the period of vibration of the source of light, the preceding theory gives the following expression for the velocity in question

$$\frac{c}{\mu} \pm w\left(1 - \frac{1}{\mu^2}\right) \mp \frac{w}{\mu} T \frac{d\mu}{dT}.$$

Here the velocity of the flow of water is represented by w, and we must take the upper or the under signs, according as the light goes with or against the stream. I must add that the last term, which depends on the dispersive power of the fluid, has been omitted by Michelson and Morley in the comparison of their experiments with the theory. If it is taken into account, the agreement becomes somewhat worse; it remains however fairly satisfactory, since the influence of the term is but small.[2])

165. After having found Fresnel's coefficient, we may apply it to various phenomena, as has already been shown in §§ 152—155. The discussion of many a question may, however, also be based directly on the theorem of corresponding states without the intervention of the coefficient.

If, for instance, the state of things in the system that is kept at rest, is such that in some parts of space both the electric and the magnetic force are continually zero, the corresponding state in the moving system will be characterized by the absence, in the same regions, of $\mathbf{d}'$ and $\mathbf{h}'$, and this involves the absence of $\mathbf{d}$ and $\mathbf{h}$. Therefore, the geometrical distribution of light and darkness must be the same in the two systems, always provided that the comparison be made for equal relative frequencies.

An interesting example is afforded by a cylindrical beam of light. The generating lines of its bounding surface, i. e. the relative rays, may have the same course in the two systems, even when the beams are reflected or refracted, so that the translation has no influence on the laws of reflexion and refraction for the relative rays. Nor can it change the position of the point where the rays are brought to a focus by a mirror[3]) or a lens, and the principle also shows that the place of the dark fringes in experiments on interference must remain unaltered.

The condition that is necessary for these conclusions, namely that the relative frequencies be equal in the two cases, will always be fulfilled if the source of light has a fixed position with respect to the rest of the apparatus, sharing its translation or its immobility.

166. It is important to notice that the foregoing results are by no means limited to isotropic bodies. The case of crystals may

1) Note **69**. 2) Note **69***. 3) Note **70**.

easily be included by conceiving either some appropriate regular arrangement of the particles, or a want of isotropy in the structure of the individual molecules, revealing itself in the elastic forces being unequal for different directions of the displacement of an electron. The latter assumption would require us to represent the components of the elastic force by expressions of the form

$$-(f_{11}\mathbf{q}_x + f_{12}\mathbf{q}_y + f_{13}\mathbf{q}_z),$$
$$-(f_{21}\mathbf{q}_x + f_{22}\mathbf{q}_y + f_{23}\mathbf{q}_z),$$
$$-(f_{31}\mathbf{q}_x + f_{32}\mathbf{q}_y + f_{33}\mathbf{q}_z),$$

with $f_{21} = f_{12}$, $f_{32} = f_{23}$, $f_{13} = f_{31}$, and for the proof of the theorem of corresponding states it would be necessary to consider the coefficients f as unaffected by a translation of the system.

After having shown that, in the phenomena of double refraction, the course of the relative rays is not altered by the motion of the earth, one can also examine what becomes of Fresnel's coefficient in the case of crystalline bodies. The result may be expressed as follows:

If, for a definite direction s of the relative ray, u and u' are the velocities of this ray in a crystal that is kept at rest and in the same body when moving, then

$$u' = u - \frac{u^2}{c^2}\mathbf{w}_s,$$

where $\mathbf{w}_s$ is the component of the velocity of translation in the direction of the ray.[1])

167. Thus far we have constantly neglected terms of the second order with respect to $\frac{|\mathbf{w}|}{c}$, and in fact in nearly all the experiments that have been made in the hope of discovering an influence of the earth's motion on optical phenomena, it would have been impossible to detect effects proportional to $\frac{\mathbf{w}^2}{c^2}$. There are, however, some exceptions, and these are of great importance, because they give rise to difficult and delicate problems, of which one has not, as yet, been able to give an entirely satisfactory solution.[2])

We have in the first place to speak of a celebrated experiment made by Michelson[3]) in 1881, and repeated by him on a larger scale with the cooperation of Morley[4]) in 1887. It was a very bold one,

1) Note **71**. 2) See however Note **72***.

3) A. A. Michelson, The relative motion of the earth and the luminiferous ether, Amer. Journ. of Science (3) **22** (1881), p. 20.

4) A. A. Michelson and E. W. Morley, Amer. Journ. of Science (3) **34** (1887), p. 333.

two rays of light having been made to interfere after having travelled over paths of considerable length in directions at right angles to each other. Fig. 9 shows the general arrangement of the apparatus. The rays of light coming from the source L are divided by the glass plate P, which is placed at an angle of 45°, into a transmitted part PA and a reflected one PB. After having been reflected by the mirrors A and B, these beams return to the plate P, and now the part of the first that is reflected and the transmitted part of the second produce by their interference a system of bright and dark fringes that is observed in a telescope placed on the line PC.

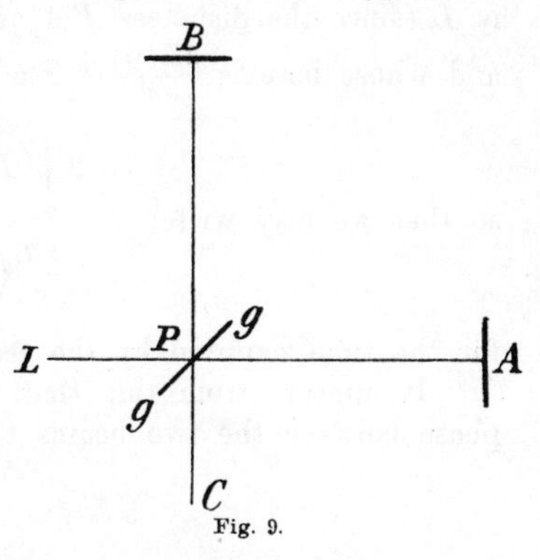

Fig. 9.

The fundamental idea of the experiment is, that, if the ether remains at rest, a translation given to the apparatus must of necessity produce a change in the differences of phase, though one of the second order. Thus, if the translation takes place in the direction of PA or AP, and if the length of PA is denoted by L, a ray of light will take a time $\frac{L}{c+|\mathbf{w}|}$ for travelling along this path in one direction, and a time $\frac{L}{c-|\mathbf{w}|}$ for going in the inverse direction. The total time is

$$\frac{2Lc}{c^2-\mathbf{w}^2},$$

or, up to quantities of the second order,

$$\frac{2L}{c}\left(1+\frac{\mathbf{w}^2}{c^2}\right), \tag{279}$$

so that for the rays that have gone forward and back along PA there will be a retardation of phase measured by

$$\frac{2L\mathbf{w}^2}{c^3}.$$

There is a similar retardation, though of smaller amount, for the other beam. In order to see this by an elementary reasoning, one has only to consider that a ray of this beam, even if it returns, as I shall suppose it to do, to exactly the same point of the plate P, does not come back to the same point of the ether, the point of the glass having moved, with the velocity $\mathbf{w}$ of the earth's translation, over a certain distance, say from P to P', while the light went from P

to B and back. If Q is the point in the ether where the ray reaches the mirror B, we may say with sufficient approximation that the points P, Q, P' are the angles of an isoscele triangle, whose height is L (since the distances PA and PB in the apparatus were equal) and whose base is $\frac{2L|\mathbf{w}|}{c}$. The sum of the sides PQ and QP' is

$$2\sqrt{L^2 + \frac{L^2\mathbf{w}^2}{c^2}},$$

so that we may write

$$\frac{2L}{c}\left(1 + \frac{\mathbf{w}^2}{2c^2}\right) \tag{280}$$

for the time required by the second beam.

It appears from this that the motion produces a difference of phase between the two beams to the extent of

$$\frac{L\mathbf{w}^2}{c^3},$$

and this may be a sensible fraction of the period of vibration, if L has the length of some metres.

The same conclusion may be drawn somewhat more rigorously from the general formula (254). The time during which a relative ray travels along a certain path s is found to be

$$\int\frac{ds}{v} - |\mathfrak{g}|\int\frac{\cos\vartheta}{v^2\mu^2}\,ds + \frac{1}{2}\,\mathfrak{g}^2\int\frac{1+\cos^2\vartheta}{v^3\mu^4}\,ds.$$

Here the first term represents the time that would be required if there were no translation, and in the problem now before us the second has equal values for two paths beginning and ending at the same points, so that we have only to consider the last term, for which, using our present notation and putting $\mu = 1$, we shall write

$$\frac{\mathbf{w}^2}{2c^3}\int(1 + \cos^2\vartheta)\,ds. \tag{281}$$

The paths for which this integral must be calculated may be taken to be the straight lines indicated in Fig. 9.[1]) According to what has been said, $\cos^2\vartheta$ has the value 1 all along PAP, and the value 0 at every point of PBP. Therefore our last expression really takes the two values given by (279) and (280).

Now the difference of phase that is due to the motion of the earth must be reversed if, by a rotation of the apparatus, the path of the first ray is made to become perpendicular to the translation, and that of the second to be parallel to it. Hence, if the phenomena

1) Note 72.

follow the above theory, such a rotation must produce a change determined by

$$\frac{2 L \mathbf{w}^2}{c^3} \tag{282}$$

in the differences of phase, and a corresponding shifting of the interference bands.

In the original apparatus of Michelson the length L was rather too small to bring out the effect that was sought for, but in the later experiments made with Morley the course of the rays was lengthened considerably. They were repeatedly thrown forwards and back by mirrors having suitable positions on different sides of the plate P, and which, together with the other parts of the apparatus, the source of light and the telescope included, were mounted on a slab of stone floating on mercury. For each of the rays the lines along which it had to travel successively nearly coincided, so that $\cos^2 \vartheta$ may be regarded as constant for the entire course of a ray. If the values of this constant for the two beams are first 1 and 0, and afterwards, after a rotation of 90°, 0 and 1, the change undergone by the differences of phase can be found from (281); it may still be represented by (282), if we understand by $2L$ the whole length of one of the rays. As this length amounted to about 22 metres, the value of (282) is equal to 0,4 times the time of vibration of yellow light, and a sensible shift of the bands could therefore be looked for. In no case, however, the least displacement of such a kind that it could be attributed to the cause above explained was observed. A similar result was subsequently obtained by Morley and Miller[1]), who came to the conclusion that, if there is any effect of the nature expected, it is less than one hundredth part of the computed value.

168. In order to explain this absence of any effect of the earth's translation, I have ventured the hypothesis, which has also been proposed by Fitz Gerald, that the dimensions of a solid body undergo slight changes, of the order $\frac{\mathbf{w}^2}{c^2}$, when it moves through the ether. If we assume that the lengths of two lines L_1 and L_2 in a ponderable body, the one parallel and the other perpendicular to the translation, which would be equal to each other if the body were at rest, are to each other in the ratio

$$\frac{L_2}{L_1} = 1 + \frac{\mathbf{w}^2}{2 c^2} \tag{283}$$

during the motion, the negative result of the experiments is easily accounted for. Indeed, these changes in length will produce an

1) E. W. Morley and D. C. Miller, Report of an experiment to detect the Fitz Gerald-Lorentz effect, Phil. Mag. (6) 9 (1905), p. 680.

alteration in the phases of the interfering rays, amounting to a relative acceleration

$$\frac{Lw^2}{c^3}$$

for the ray that is passed along the line having the direction of the earth's motion, and this acceleration will exactly counterbalance the changes in phase which we have considered in the preceding paragraph.

The hypothesis certainly looks rather startling at first sight, but we can scarcely escape from it, so long as we persist in regarding the ether as immovable. We may, I think, even go so far as to say that, on this assumption, Michelson's experiment *proves* the changes of dimensions in question, and that the conclusion is no less legitimate than the inferences concerning the dilatation by heat or the changes of the refractive index that have been drawn in many other cases from the observed positions of interference bands.

169. The idea has occurred to some physicists that, like an ordinary mechanical strain, the contractions or dilatations of which we are now speaking, might make a body doubly refracting, and Rayleigh and Brace have therefore attempted to detect a double refraction produced by the motion of the earth. Here again the search has been in vain; no trace of an effect of the kind has been found.

With a view to this question of a double refraction, and for other reasons, it seems proper to enter upon a discussion of the electromagnetic phenomena in a moving system, not only, as we did at first, for velocities very small in comparison with the speed of light c, but for any velocity of translation smaller than c. Though the formulae become somewhat more complicated, we can treat this problem by much the same methods which we used before.

Our aim must again be to reduce, at least as far as possible, the equations for a moving system to the form of the ordinary formulae that hold for a system at rest. It is found that the transformations needed for this purpose may be left indeterminate to a certain extent; our formulae will contain a numerical coefficient l, of which we shall provisionally assume only that it is a function of the velocity of translation w, whose value is equal to unity for $w = 0$, and differs from 1 by an amount of the order of magnitude $\frac{w^2}{c^2}$ for small values of the ratio $\frac{w}{c}$.

If x, y, z are the coordinates of a point with respect to axes fixed in the ether, or, as we shall say, the „absolute" coordinates, and if the translation takes place in the direction of OX, the coordinates with respect to axes moving with the system, and coinciding with the fixed axes at the instant $t = 0$, will be

$$x_r = x - wt, \quad y_r = y, \quad z_r = z. \tag{284}$$

Now, instead of x, y, z, we shall introduce new independent variables differing from these „relative" coordinates by certain factors that are constant throughout the system. Putting

$$\frac{c^2}{c^2 - w^2} = k^2, \tag{285}$$

I define the new variables by the equations[1])

$$x' = klx_r, \quad y' = ly_r, \quad z' = lz_r \tag{286}$$

or

$$x' = kl(x - wt), \quad y' = ly, \quad z' = lz, \tag{287}$$

and to these I add as our fourth independent variable

$$t' = \frac{l}{k} t - kl \frac{w}{c^2}(x - wt) = kl\left(t - \frac{w}{c^2} x\right). \tag{288}$$

We shall again understand by $\mathbf{u}$ the velocity relative to the moving axes, so that the components of the absolute velocity are

$$\mathbf{u}_x + w, \quad \mathbf{u}_y, \quad \mathbf{u}_z,$$

and we shall introduce a new vector $\mathbf{u}'$ whose components are

$$\mathbf{u}_x' = k^2 \mathbf{u}_x, \quad \mathbf{u}_y' = k\mathbf{u}_y, \quad \mathbf{u}_z' = k\mathbf{u}_z. \tag{289}$$

Let us put, similarly,

$$\varrho' = \frac{1}{kl^3} \varrho, \tag{290}$$

and let us define two new vectors $\mathbf{d}'$ and $\mathbf{h}'$ by the equations

$$\left.\begin{aligned} \mathbf{d}_x' &= \frac{1}{l^2} \mathbf{d}_x, \quad \mathbf{d}_y' = \frac{k}{l^2}\left(\mathbf{d}_y - \frac{w}{c} \mathbf{h}_z\right), \quad \mathbf{d}_z' = \frac{k}{l^2}\left(\mathbf{d}_z + \frac{w}{c} \mathbf{h}_y\right), \\ \mathbf{h}_x' &= \frac{1}{l^2} \mathbf{h}_x, \quad \mathbf{h}_y' = \frac{k}{l^2}\left(\mathbf{h}_y + \frac{w}{c} \mathbf{d}_z\right), \quad \mathbf{h}_z' = \frac{k}{l^2}\left(\mathbf{h}_z - \frac{w}{c} \mathbf{d}_y\right) \end{aligned}\right\} \tag{291}$$

Then the fundamental equations take the form[2])

$$\left.\begin{aligned} \operatorname{div}' \mathbf{d}' &= \left(1 - \frac{w \mathbf{u}_x'}{c^2}\right) \varrho', \\ \operatorname{div}' \mathbf{h}' &= 0, \\ \operatorname{rot}' \mathbf{h}' &= \frac{1}{c}\left(\frac{\partial \mathbf{d}'}{\partial t'} + \varrho' \mathbf{u}'\right), \\ \operatorname{rot}' \mathbf{d}' &= -\frac{1}{c} \frac{\partial \mathbf{h}'}{\partial t'}. \end{aligned}\right\} \tag{292}$$

The meaning of the symbols div′, rot′ and grad′, the last of which we shall have to use further on, is similar to that which we formerly gave to div, rot and grad, the only difference being that

1) Note **72***. 2) Note **73**.

the differential coefficients with respect to x, y, z (taken for a constant t) are replaced by those with respect to x', y', z' (taken for a constant value of t').[1])

As to the force $\mathbf{f}$ with which the ether acts on unit of electric charge, its components are found to be

$$\left.\begin{aligned}
\mathbf{f}_x &= l^2 \mathbf{d}_x' + l^2 \cdot \frac{1}{c}(\mathbf{u}_y'\mathbf{h}_z' - \mathbf{u}_z'\mathbf{h}_y') + l^2 \frac{w}{c^2}(\mathbf{u}_y'\mathbf{d}_y' + \mathbf{u}_z'\mathbf{d}_z'),\\
\mathbf{f}_y &= \frac{l^2}{k}\mathbf{d}_y' + \frac{l^2}{k}\cdot\frac{1}{c}(\mathbf{u}_z'\mathbf{h}_x' - \mathbf{u}_x'\mathbf{h}_z') - \frac{l^2}{k}\frac{w}{c^2}\mathbf{u}_x'\mathbf{d}_y',\\
\mathbf{f}_z &= \frac{l^2}{k}\mathbf{d}_z' + \frac{l^2}{k}\cdot\frac{1}{c}(\mathbf{u}_x'\mathbf{h}_y' - \mathbf{u}_y'\mathbf{h}_x') - \frac{l^2}{k}\frac{w}{c^2}\mathbf{u}_x'\mathbf{d}_z'.
\end{aligned}\right\} \quad (293)$$

The determination of the field belonging to a system of electrons may again be made to depend on a scalar potential φ' and a vector potential $\mathbf{a}'$. If these are defined by the equations

$$\left.\begin{aligned}
\Delta'\varphi' - \frac{1}{c^2}\frac{\partial^2\varphi'}{\partial t'^2} &= -\varrho',\\
\Delta'\mathbf{a}' - \frac{1}{c^2}\frac{\partial^2\mathbf{a}'}{\partial t'^2} &= -\frac{1}{c}\varrho'\mathbf{u}',
\end{aligned}\right\} \quad (294)$$

in which the symbol Δ' stands for

$$\frac{\partial^2}{\partial x'^2} + \frac{\partial^2}{\partial y'^2} + \frac{\partial^2}{\partial z'^2},$$

we shall have[2])

$$\mathbf{d}' = -\frac{1}{c}\frac{\partial \mathbf{a}'}{\partial t'} - \operatorname{grad}'\varphi' + \frac{w}{c}\operatorname{grad}'\mathbf{a}_x', \quad (295)$$

$$\mathbf{h}' = \operatorname{rot}'\mathbf{a}'. \quad (296)$$

The analogy between these transformations and those which we formerly used, is seen at a glance. The above formulae are changed into those of §§ 44 and 45 by neglecting all terms which are of an order higher than the first with respect to $\frac{w}{c}$, by which k and l both take the value 1. In the present more general theory, it is the variable t' defined by (288) that may be termed the local time.

It is especially interesting that the final formulae (292) and (294)—(296) have exactly the same form as those which we deduced for small values of w. They differ from the equations for a system without translation in the manner pointed out in §§ 44 and 45, but, as

1) In a paper „Über das Doppler'sche Princip", published in 1887 (Gött. Nachrichten, p. 41) and which to my regret has escaped my notice all these years, Voigt has applied to equations of the form (6) (§ 3 of this book) a transformation equivalent to the formulae (287) and (288). The idea of the transformations used above (and in § 44) might therefore have been borrowed from Voigt and the proof that it does not alter the form of the equations for the *free* ether is contained in his paper.

2) Note **74**.

regards the form of the equations, the consideration of greater velocities of translation has not been attended by any new complications.

170. The problem is greatly simplified when we consider an electrostatic system, i. e. a system of electrons having no other motion than the common translation w. In this case $\mathbf{a}' = 0$, and consequently $\mathbf{h}' = 0$. The scalar potential φ', the vector $\mathbf{d}'$, and the electric force $\mathbf{f}$ are determined by

$$\Delta' \varphi' = -\varrho', \tag{297}$$

$$\mathbf{d}' = -\operatorname{grad}' \varphi', \tag{298}$$

$$\mathbf{f}_x = l^2 \mathbf{d}_x', \quad \mathbf{f}_y = \frac{l^2}{k} \mathbf{d}_y', \quad \mathbf{f}_z = \frac{l^2}{k} \mathbf{d}_z'.$$

These equations admit of a simple interpretation. Let us compare the moving system S, the position of whose points is determined by the relative coordinates x_r, y_r, z_r, with a system S_0 that has no translation, and in which a point with the coordinates x', y', z' corresponds to the point (x_r, y_r, z_r) in S, so that, as is shown by (286), S is changed into S_0 if the dimensions parallel to the axis of x are multiplied by kl, and the dimensions which have the direction of y or that of z, by l. Then, if dS and dS' are corresponding elements of volume, we shall have

$$dS' = kl^3 dS, \tag{299}$$

so that, if we suppose corresponding elements of volume to have equal charges, the density at a point of S_0 will be given by the quantity ϱ' that has been defined by (290).

It follows that the equation which determines the scalar potential in S_0 has the same form as the equation (297) which we have found for φ', and that, therefore, this latter quantity has, at a point P of S, the same value as the ordinary scalar potential at the corresponding point P_0 of S_0. The equation (298) further tells us that the same is true of the vector $\mathbf{d}'$ at the point P and the dielectric displacement at the point P_0. But, in order to find the components of the electric force in S, we must multiply those of $\mathbf{d}'$ by l^2, $\frac{l^2}{k}$, $\frac{l^2}{k}$, whereas, in the system S_0, the components of the electric force are immediately given by those of the dielectric displacement. Hence, there is between these electric forces a relation that is conveniently expressed by the formula

$$\mathbf{F}(S) = \left(l^2, \frac{l^2}{k}, \frac{l^2}{k}\right) \mathbf{F}(S_0), \tag{300}$$

the coefficients between the brackets being those by which we must multiply the components of the force in S_0 in order to get those of the force in S Since corresponding elements have equal charges, the same relation exists between the forces acting on corresponding electrons.

It is to be observed that corresponding electrons in the two systems occupy corresponding parts of space, and that, while their charges are equal, they are geometrically dissimilar; if the electrons in S are spheres, those in S_0 are lengthened ellipsoids.

Let us also remember that the potential at a point P_0 of S_0, and, consequently, the quantity φ' at the corresponding point P of S, can be calculated by means of the formula

$$\varphi' = \frac{1}{4\pi}\int \frac{\varrho' \, dS'}{r'}, \tag{301}$$

where we have denoted by r' the distance between a point Q_0 of the element dS' and the point P_0. The integration is to be extended to all elements in S_0 where there is a charge.

The comparison of a moving system with a stationary one will be found of much use in the remaining part of this chapter, and it is therefore proper to settle once for all that, if we speak of S and S_0, we shall always mean two systems of this kind, and that the index 0 will constantly serve to denote the stationary system.

171. With a view to later developments it will be well to put the foregoing statements in yet another form. Let us, for a while, discard all thoughts of the imaginary system S_0, and confine ourselves to the system S with which we are really concerned. We may introduce for this, as we have already done, the quantities x', y', z', and we may even use them for the determination of the position of a point, because they are related in a definite manner to the values of x_r, y_r, z_r. Let them be called the *effective* coordinates, and let us define the *effective* distance between two points whose effective coordinates are $x_1', y_1', z_1', x_2', y_2', z_2'$ as the quantity

$$r' = \sqrt{(x_1' - x_2')^2 + (y_1' - y_2')^2 + (z_1' - z_2')^2}.$$

If dx_r, dy_r, dz_r are infinitely small increments of the relative coordinates, the corresponding increments of the effective coordinates will be

$$dx' = kl\,dx_r, \quad dy' = l\,dy_r, \quad dz' = l\,dz_r,$$

and, of course, the parallelepiped having dx, dy, dz for its edges may be said to be determined by these increments dx', dy', dz'. If, instead of the ordinary unit of volume, we choose a unit kl^3 times smaller, the volume of the parallelepiped will be expressed by the product $dx'dy'dz'$, and, on the same scale, an element of any form that is given in ordinary measure by dS, will have a volume

$$dS' = kl^3 dS. \tag{302}$$

This is equal to the dS' in the equation (299), but the symbol has got a new meaning. Having already used several times the word „effective“, I shall now — only for the sake of uniformity and without attaching any further meaning to the words — call dS' the effective element of volume. A point within dS will also be said to belong to the effective element dS'.

Finally, if the charge ϱdS of an element dS is divided by the magnitude of the effective element dS', we get the quantity ϱ' that is defined by (290). For this reason it is not inappropriate to call ϱ' the effective density of the charge.

It will now be clear that the operations involved in the symbol on the right-hand side of the equation (301) may be described in terms relating only to the real system, the denominator r' being the effective distance between a point of the effective element dS' and the point P for which we want to calculate φ'. This potential having been determined, its partial differential coefficients with respect to the effective coordinates, taken with the signs reversed, will represent the components of the vector $\mathbf{d}'$.

It is only for moving systems that we have had reason to distinguish between the effective coordinates and the „true“ coordinates, the effective elements of volume and the „true“ ones, etc.; as soon as $w = 0$, we shall have $x' = x_r = x$, $y' = y_r = y$, $z' = z_r = z$, $dS' = dS$, $\varrho' = \varrho$, etc. Yet, for the very reason of these equalities, we are free also to speak of the effective coordinates, the effective density, etc. in the case of a stationary system; only, we must not forget that in this case these quantities are identical with the true coordinates, the true density, etc. Similarly, we may always speak of the vector $\mathbf{d}'$, remembering that it is identical with $\mathbf{d}$ when there is no translation.

I have dwelled at some length on these questions of denomination, because in intricate problems a proper choice of terms is of much value. That which we have now made enables us to condense into few words what was said in the last paragraph about the systems $\mathfrak{S}$ and $\mathfrak{S}_0$, namely: In two electrostatic systems, the one moving and the other not, in which the effective density of the electric charge is the same function of the effective coordinates, the vector $\mathbf{d}'$ will be the same at corresponding points, and the forces will be related to each other in the way expressed by (300).

172. Let us now return from this digression to the hypothesis by which we have tried to account for the result of Michelson's experiment. We can understand the possibility of the assumed change of dimensions, if we keep in mind that the form of a solid body depends on the forces between its molecules, and that, in all probability, these forces are propagated by the intervening ether in a way more or less resembling that in which electromagnetic actions are transmitted through this medium. From this point of view it is natural to suppose that, just like the electromagnetic forces, the molecular attractions and repulsions are somewhat modified by a translation imparted to the body, and this may very well result in a change of its dimensions.

Now, it is very remarkable that we find exactly the amount of change that was postulated in § 168, if we extend to molecular actions the result found for the electric forces, i. e. if, comparing two systems of molecules S and S_0 in which the particles have the same effective coordinates, we admit for the molecular forces the relation expressed by (300).

Indeed, this equation implies that if $\mathbf{F}(S_0) = 0$, $\mathbf{F}(S)$ is so likewise, so that when, in the system S_0, each molecule is in equilibrium under the actions exerted on it by its neighbours, the same will be true for the system S. Hence, taking for granted that there is but one position of equilibrium of the particles, we may assert that, in the moving system S, the molecules will take of themselves the arrangement corresponding, in the manner specified by (286), to the configuration existing in S_0. Since x', y', z' are the true coordinates in this latter system, and x_r, y_r, z_r the relative coordinates in S, the change of dimensions in different directions is given by the coefficients in (286), and the two lines of which we have spoken in § 168 will be to each other in the ratio

$$\frac{L_2}{L_1} = k = \frac{c}{\sqrt{c^2 - w^2}},$$

which agrees with the value (283), if quantities of an order higher than the second are neglected.

173. It is a matter of interest to inquire whether our assumptions demand the same change of dimensions for bodies whose shape and size depend in a smaller or greater measure on their molecular motions. As a preliminary to this question, I shall consider a system of points having, besides a common translation w, certain velocities $\mathbf{u}$. For each of them the coordinates x_r, y_r, z_r are definite functions of the time t, and

$$\frac{dx_r}{dt} = \mathbf{u}_x, \quad \frac{dy_r}{dt} = \mathbf{u}_y, \quad \frac{dz_r}{dt} = \mathbf{u}_z.$$

But we may also say that for each the effective coordinates x', y', z' are functions of the local time t', which I shall henceforth also term the effective time, and we may calculate the differential coefficients of x', y', z' with respect to t' in terms of those of x_r, y_r, z_r with respect to t. In doing so I shall suppose the velocities $\mathbf{u}_x$, $\mathbf{u}_y$, $\mathbf{u}_z$ to be so small that terms that are of the order of magnitude $\frac{|\mathbf{u}|}{c}$ compared with those I am going to write down, may be neglected. Then the result is[1])

$$\frac{dx'}{dt'} = k^2 \frac{dx_r}{dt}, \quad \frac{dy'}{dt'} = k \frac{dy_r}{dt}, \quad \frac{dz'}{dt'} = k \frac{dz_r}{dt},$$

$$\frac{d^2x'}{dt'^2} = \frac{k^3}{l} \frac{d^2x_r}{dt^2}, \quad \frac{d^2y'}{dt'^2} = \frac{k^2}{l} \frac{d^2y_r}{dt^2}, \quad \frac{d^2z'}{dt'^2} = \frac{k^2}{l} \frac{d^2z_r}{dt^2} \tag{303}$$

The first set of equations shows that $\frac{dx'}{dt'}, \frac{dy'}{dt'}, \frac{dz'}{dt'}$ are the components of the vector $\mathbf{u}'$ that has been defined in § 169, and it appears from the second set that, if there are two systems of points S and S_0 moving in such a way that in both the effective coordinates are the same functions of the effective time, we shall have the following relation between the accelerations $\mathbf{j}$

$$\mathbf{j}(S) = \left(\frac{l}{k^3}, \frac{l}{k^2}, \frac{l}{k^2}\right) \mathbf{j}(S_0). \tag{304}$$

This formula, in which the mode of expression is the same as that which we have used in (300), follows immediately from (303), the components of the acceleration in S_0 being $\frac{d^2x'}{dt'^2}, \frac{d^2y'}{dt'^2}, \frac{d^2z'}{dt'^2}$, and those of the acceleration in S $\frac{d^2x_r}{dt^2}, \frac{d^2y_r}{dt^2}, \frac{d^2z_r}{dt^2}$.

174. [2])It remains to apply this to a body in which molecular motions are going on. At ordinary temperatures the velocities of these are so small in comparison with that of light, that the approximations used in the above formulae seem to be allowable. On the same ground we may regard the interactions of the molecules to be independent of the velocities $\mathbf{u}$, and to be determined solely by the relative positions and the velocity of translation w.

Let S and S_0 be two systems of molecules moving in such a manner that in both the effective coordinates are the same functions of the effective time. Let us fix our attention on two corresponding particles P and P_0 in the positions which they occupy for a definite value, say t', of the effective time. If we wish to know the simultaneous positions of the neighbouring particles of S_0, which are sufficiently near P_0 sensibly to act on it, we have only to consider the values of their coordinates x', y', z' for the same value t' of the effective, i. e. in this case, the true time. It is otherwise with the moving system S. Here the instants for which the effective (i. e. now, the local) time, has a definite value t' at different points, are *not* simul-

1) Note 75. 2) See for several questions discussed in this article Note **75***.

taneous, and this would greatly complicate the comparison of S and S_0, were it not for the relative slowness of the molecular motions, to which we have already had recourse a moment ago. As it is, we may, I think, skip over the difficulty. If Δ is the distance between the molecule P and another Q near it, the interval between the moments at which the effective time of P and that of Q have the chosen value t', is of the order of magnitude $\frac{w\Delta}{c^2}$, as appears from (288). The changes which the relative coordinates of Q with respect to P undergo during an interval of this length. are of the order $\frac{w\,|\mathbf{u}|\,\Delta}{c^2}$, or of the order $\frac{w\,|\mathbf{u}|}{c^2}$ compared with Δ. The corresponding changes in the components of the force between P and Q are of the same order in comparison with the force itself, and may therefore be neglected since $\frac{|\mathbf{u}|}{c}$ is very small. In other terms, in order to find the force acting on the molecule P, we may consider as simultaneous the positions which the surrounding particles occupy at the instants at which their local times have the value t'. In virtue of our assumption, the relative coordinates in these positions bear to x', y', z', i. e. to the corresponding coordinates in S_0, the ratios determined by (286), so that, within the small compass containing P and the molecules acting on it, the body may be said to have its dimensions changed in the way that has often been mentioned. We infer from this that the forces acting on corresponding particles, in S and S_0, are subjected to the relation (300).

On the other hand we have the relation (304) between the accelerations. Now, if the ratios occurring in (304) und (300) were the same, we might conclude that, if the state of motion existing in S_0 is a possible one, so that for each particle the force acting on it is equal to the product of its acceleration and its mass, and if the particles have equal masses in S and S_0, the state of motion in the former system which corresponds to that in the latter will also be possible.

As it is, however, the ratios in (300) and (304) are not equal. The above considerations cannot, therefore, lead us to a theorem of corresponding states existing in S and S_0, unless we give up the equality of the masses in these systems. We need not, I think, be afraid to make this step. We have seen that the mass of a free electron is a function of the velocity, so that, if the corpuscle has already the translation w of the body to which it belongs, the force required for a change of the velocity will thereby be altered; we have further been led to distinguish between a longitudinal and a transverse mass. Now that we have already extended to the molecular interactions the rule that had been deduced for the electric forces, it will perhaps not be too rash to imagine an alteration in the masses of the molecules caused by the translation, and even, if it should prove necessary, to conceive two different masses, one m' (the longitudinal mass) with which we must reckon when we consider the accelerations parallel to OX, and another, m'' (the transverse mass) which comes into play when we are concerned with an acceleration, either in the direction of OY or in that of OZ.

Dividing the ratios in (300) by the corresponding ones in (304), we see that, if m_0 is the mass of a molecule in the absence of a translation, the formulae

$$m' = \left(l^2 : \frac{l}{k^3}\right) m_0, \quad m'' = \left(\frac{l^2}{k} : \frac{l}{k^2}\right) m_0,$$

or

$$m' = k^3 l m_0, \quad m'' = k l m_0 \tag{305}$$

contain the assumptions required for the establishment of the theorem, that the systems $\mathfrak{S}$ and $\mathfrak{S}_0$ can be the seat of molecular motions of such a kind that in both the effective coordinates of the molecules are the same functions of the effective time.[1])

Now, if the molecules of $\mathfrak{S}_0$, in their irregular motion, remain confined within a surface having a constant position, those in $\mathfrak{S}$ will be continually enclosed by the corresponding surface, i. e. by the one that is determined by the same equation in x', y', z'. Hence, the translation produces the same changes in the dimensions of the bounding surface as in those of a body without molecular motions.

The result may be extended to bodies whose shape and size are partly determined by external forces, such as a pressure exerted by an adjacent system of molecules, provided only that these forces be altered equally with those between the particles of the body itself.

175. We are now prepared for a theorem concerning corresponding states of electromagnetic vibration, similar to that of § 162, but of a wider scope. To the assumptions already introduced, I shall add two new ones, namely 1. that the elastic forces which govern the vibratory motions of the electrons are subjected to the relation (300), and 2. that the longitudinal and transverse masses m' and m'' of the electrons differ from the mass m_0 which they have when at rest in the way indicated by (305). The theorem amounts to this, that in two systems $\mathfrak{S}$ and $\mathfrak{S}_0$, the one moving and the other stationary, there can be motions of such a kind, that not only the effective coordinates which determine the positions of the molecules are in both the same functions of the effective time (so that the translation is attended with the change of dimensions which we have discussed) but

1) Note **75***.

that the same rule holds for the effective coordinates of the separate electrons. Moreover, the components of the vectors $\mathbf{d}'$ and $\mathbf{h}'$ will be found to be identically determined by x', y', z', t', both in S and in S_0.

In our demonstration we shall regard the displacements of the electrons from their positions of equilibrium, and the velocities of vibration as very small quantities, the squares and products of which may be neglected. We shall also leave aside the resistance that may tend to damp the vibrations.

Let M and M_0 be corresponding particles of S and S_0, and let us calculate for these, and for a definite value of the effective time, say the value $\underline{t}'$, the vector $\mathbf{p}'$ whose components are

$$\mathbf{p}_x' = \Sigma e x', \quad \mathbf{p}_y' = \Sigma e y', \quad \mathbf{p}_z' = \Sigma e z', \tag{306}$$

where the sums are extended to all the electrons of the particle considered. If we suppose the positions and the motions of the electrons to be such as is stated in the theorem, this vector $\mathbf{p}'$ will be found to be the same for M and for M_0. For the latter particle, $\mathbf{p}'$ is obviously the electric moment at the time chosen. As to the particle M, it is to be noticed that if we calculate the sums for the chosen value $\underline{t}'$ of the effective time of each electron, the values of x', y', z' in the sums will not be, strictly speaking, the coordinates which the different electrons have simultaneously. On account of the small values of the vibratory velocities $\mathbf{u}$, we may however simplify the meaning of the sums by considering x', y', z' as the effective coordinates of the several electrons, such as they are at one and the same moment, namely the moment when the effective time, taken for a definite point of the molecule, which may be called its centre, has the special value $\underline{t}'$. Then, since the components of the moment of M at that instant may be represented by

$$\mathbf{p}_x = \Sigma e x_r, \quad \mathbf{p}_y = \Sigma e y_r, \quad \mathbf{p}_z = \Sigma e z_r, \tag{307}$$

we shall have, in virtue of (286),

$$\mathbf{p}_x' = kl\mathbf{p}_x, \quad \mathbf{p}_y' = l\mathbf{p}_y, \quad \mathbf{p}_z' = l\mathbf{p}_z.$$

It may be shown that the values of the potentials φ' and $\mathbf{a}'$ of which we have spoken in § 169, are given by the equations, similar to (35) and (36),

$$\varphi' = \frac{1}{4\pi}\int \frac{1}{r'}[\varrho']dS',$$

$$\mathbf{a}' = \frac{1}{4\pi c}\int \frac{1}{r'}[\varrho'\mathbf{u}']dS',$$

where r' is the effective distance between the point P considered and a point of the effective element dS'. The square brackets mean that, if we wish to determine φ' and $\mathbf{a}'$ for the value t' of the effective time, we must understand by ϱ' and $\mathbf{u}'$ the values existing in dS' at the effective time $t' - \frac{r'}{c}$.

With the aid of these formulae the electromagnetic field produced by a molecule may be shown to be determined in rather a simple manner by the vector $\mathbf{p}'$, which we may call the effective moment. The final formulae, whose form is identical with that of our previous equations (271) and (272), are[1])

$$\left.\begin{aligned} \mathbf{d}' &= -\frac{1}{4\pi c^2}\frac{\partial^2}{\partial t'^2}\frac{[\mathbf{p}']}{r'} + \frac{1}{4\pi}\operatorname{grad}'\left\{\frac{\partial}{\partial x'}\frac{[\mathbf{p}_x']}{r'} + \frac{\partial}{\partial y'}\frac{[\mathbf{p}_y']}{r'} + \frac{\partial}{\partial z'}\frac{[\mathbf{p}_z']}{r'}\right\},\\ \mathbf{h}' &= \frac{1}{4\pi c}\operatorname{rot}'\left\{\frac{1}{r'}[\dot{\mathbf{p}}']\right\}, \end{aligned}\right\} \quad (308)$$

where r' is the effective distance between the centre of the molecule and the point (x', y', z') considered. The square brackets mean that, if we want to know the values of $\mathbf{d}'$ and $\mathbf{h}'$ for the instant at which the local time belonging to this point is t', we must take the values of $\mathbf{p}_x'$, $\mathbf{p}_y'$, $\mathbf{p}_z'$ for the instant at which the local time of the centre of the molecule is $t' - \frac{r'}{c}$. The dot indicates a differentiation with respect to t', and the equations apply as well to the system S_0 as to S.

176. We have next to fix our attention on some molecule M of the body S, and on the one movable electron which we shall suppose it to contain. The field produced in M by all the other molecules of the body may be represented by $\Sigma\mathbf{d}'$ and $\Sigma\mathbf{h}'$ (cf. § 160), but to this we must add the field due to causes outside the body, for which the equations are

$$\left.\begin{aligned} \operatorname{div}'\mathbf{d}_0' &= 0,\\ \operatorname{div}'\mathbf{h}_0' &= 0,\\ \operatorname{rot}'\mathbf{h}_0' &= \frac{1}{c}\dot{\mathbf{d}}_0',\\ \operatorname{rot}'\mathbf{d}_0' &= -\frac{1}{c}\dot{\mathbf{h}}_0', \end{aligned}\right\} \quad (309)$$

as is seen by putting $\varrho' = 0$ in the formulae (292).

After having found the total values of $\mathbf{d}'$ and $\mathbf{h}'$, we can use the equations (293), which, however, may be replaced by

$$\mathbf{f}_x = l^2\mathbf{d}_x', \quad \mathbf{f}_y = \frac{l^2}{k}\mathbf{d}_y', \quad \mathbf{f}_z = \frac{l^2}{k}\mathbf{d}_z'. \quad (310)$$

Indeed, so far as $\mathbf{d}'$ and $\mathbf{h}'$ are due to the vibrations in the other molecules of the body, these vectors are proportional to the ampli-

1) Note **76.**

tudes, so that all the terms in which their components are multiplied by $\mathbf{u}_x'$, $\mathbf{u}_y'$ or $\mathbf{u}_z'$ may be neglected. The corresponding terms with components of $\mathbf{d}_0'$ and $\mathbf{h}_0'$ may likewise be omitted, if the intensity of the external field is sufficiently small, if, for example, this field is produced by vibrations of very small amplitude in a source of light.

Returning to the comparison of our two systems, we can finish it in few words. On account of what we know of the accelerations, and of what has been assumed of the masses, it is clear that the state of things we have imagined can exist both in S and in S_0, if all the forces acting on the electrons satisfy the condition (300). We have assumed this for the elastic forces, and we can deduce it for the electric forces from the equations (310), (308) and (309). The effective moments being the same functions of t' in corresponding particles of S and S_0, the vectors $\Sigma \mathbf{d}'$ will be so likewise at corresponding points, and we may suppose the same to be true of the vector $\mathbf{d}_0'$, since one and the same set of equations, namely (309), determines it (together with $\mathbf{h}_0'$), both for S and for S_0. As the components of the force acting on unit charge are given by $\mathbf{d}_x'$, $\mathbf{d}_y'$, $\mathbf{d}_z'$ for S_0, and by the formulae (310) for S, the condition (300) is really fulfilled.

177. The generalized theorem of corresponding states may now serve for the same conclusions which we have drawn from it in its more restricted form (§ 165). Attention must, however, be called to the difference in frequency between the corresponding vibrations in S and S_0. If, for definite values of the effective coordinates, i. e. at a definite point of the system, a quantity varies as $\cos nt'$, n will be the frequency in the stationary system, because here t' is the true time, but for the moving system we shall have

$$\cos nt' = \cos n\left(\frac{l}{k}t - kl\frac{w}{c^2}x_r\right),$$

so that here the frequency at a definite point of the system is

$$\frac{l}{k}n.$$

It is remarkable that, when the source of light forms part of the system, so that it shares the translation w, this frequency will be produced by the actions going on in the radiating particles, if these actions are such that the frequency would be n if the source did not move. At least, this is true if we make the natural assumption that in the source the masses of the electrons and the elastic forces to which they are subjected, are altered in the same manner as in a body through which the light is propagated. Then we may assert that in the source of light too, the effective coordinates of the electrons can be the same functions of the effective time, whether the source move or not. If the vibrations are represented in both cases by formulae containing the factor nt', the frequency will be n when the source is at rest, and $\frac{l}{k}n$ when it moves. This shows that in all experiments made with a terrestrial source of light, the phenomena will correspond quite accurately to those which one would observe, using the same source on a stationary planet; the course of the relative rays, the position of interference fringes, and, in general, the distribution of light and darkness will be unaltered.

The case of experiments made with a celestial source of light is somewhat different. In these, the relative frequency n at a point of our apparatus is equal to the frequency of the source, modified according to Doppler's principle (a modification that will not exist when we employ sunlight, as our distance from the sun may be considered as constant), and the phenomena will correspond to those taking place with the frequency $\frac{k}{l}n$ in a stationary system. Thus, in a dispersive medium the courses of the relative rays observed with the D-lines in sunlight and with a sodium flame, would not coincide exactly. If, supposing the sun to be at rest relatively to the ether, we call n the relative frequency in the first case, it will be $\frac{l}{k}n$ in the second case. It is scarcely necessary to add that this is of a purely theoretical interest, as no phenomenon that can be accurately observed can be perceptibly altered by this change in the frequency of the order $\frac{w^2}{c^2}$.

It should further be noticed that, in an experiment planned for the detection of an influence of the earth's translation, in which we turn round our apparatus, or repeat our observations after a certain number of hours, during which it has rotated on account of the earth's diurnal motion, we are constantly working with the same relative frequency (whatever be the source of light employed). This constant frequency ν will correspond to a determinate frequency $\frac{k}{l}\nu$ in a system without translation, and the rotation can no more produce an effect than it would do if we rotated our instruments on a body without translation, on which we were working with rays of the frequency $\frac{k}{l}\nu$.

But perhaps I am dwelling for too long a time upon these subtle questions. What must now be pointed out particularly, is, that our theorem explains why Rayleigh and Brace have failed to detect a double refraction. In the experiments of the latter of these physicists the beam of light that was received by the observer's eye consisted of two parts, travelling side by side, and having the same state of polarization and also, though they had been passed through different media, the same intensity. It is clear that, whenever this equality exists for two such beams in a system without translation, it must, by our theorem, also be found in the corresponding state in a moving system.

178. When, in our comparison of two electrostatic systems S and S_0 (§ 171), it was stated that, in both of them, the effective density of the charge had to be the same function of the effective coordinates, this implied that the electrons in the two systems are not of the same shape. In the discussion given in § 175, however, we have not assumed this, confining ourselves to the two assumptions stated in the beginning of that paragraph. Indeed, in dealing with the motion of the electrons we are concerned only with their charges, their masses and the elastic forces acting on them; all other particulars are irrelevant to our final results. Consequently, we may very well conceive the electrons not to change their form and size when a body is put in motion (though the dimensions of the body itself be altered in the above mentioned manner), provided only that the necessary relations between the elastic forces and the masses of the electrons, before and after the translation is imparted to the system, be maintained.

Now, in a theory that attempts to explain phenomena by means of these minute particles, the simplest course is certainly to consider the electrons themselves as wholly immutable, as perfectly rigid spheres, for instance, with a constant uniformly distributed surface-charge. This is the idea that has been worked out by Abraham, and on which many of the formulae I have given in Chap. I are based. But, unfortunately, it is at variance with our theorem of corresponding states. This requires, as is seen from (305), that the longitudinal and the transverse mass of an electron be to each other in the ratio

$$\frac{m'}{m''} = k^2 = \frac{c^2}{c^2 - w^2},$$

or, up to quantities of the second order,

$$\frac{m'}{m''} = 1 + \frac{w^2}{c^2},$$

whereas, according to the formulae (68) and (69), and with the same degree of approximation, it would be

$$\frac{m'}{m''} = 1 + \frac{4}{5}\frac{w^2}{c^2}.$$

179. It is for this reason that I have examined what becomes of the theory, if the electrons themselves are considered as liable to the same changes of dimensions as the bodies in which they are contained. This assumption brings out the proper ratios between the masses m_0, m', m'', provided that we assign the value 1 to the coefficient l, which we have hitherto left undeterminate.

The electromagnetic mass of the deformable electron is easily deduced from the theory of electromagnetic momentum, since we can always apply the general formulae of § 24, whatever be the changes in the form and size of an electron taking place during its motion. By calculating the electromagnetic momentum $\mathbf{G}$ and its rate of change $\dot{\mathbf{G}}$, we shall find the force acting on the electron; next, when we divide by the acceleration, the electromagnetic mass, either the longitudinal or the transverse one, will become known.

In our calculations we shall ascribe to the electromagnetic momentum the value which it would have, if the electron were continually moving with the velocity that exists at the moment considered, a procedure the legitimacy of which will be discussed in a subsequent paragraph.

The determination of the momentum is even more simple than it was in the case of a rigid sphere. We have seen that the field of a moving electrostatic system is known, when the field of another system that is supposed to be at rest, and whose dimensions differ in a definite manner from those of the moving one, is given. Now, if the system consists of a single electron, of spherical shape and with uniformly distributed surface charge, so long as it stands still, but ellipsoidal when in motion, as determined by (286), the stationary system to the consideration of which the problem is reduced, is found to be precisely the original sphere, so that the field is determined very easily.

Calling e the charge, and R the radius of the sphere, I find for the electromagnetic momentum corresponding to the velocity w[1])

$$|\mathbf{G}| = \frac{e^2}{6\pi c^2 R} klw, \tag{311}$$

from which, using the formulae (64) and (65), we deduce

$$m' = \frac{e^2}{6\pi c^2 R} \frac{d(klw)}{dw}, \quad m'' = \frac{e^2}{6\pi c^2 R} kl,$$

or

$$m' = \frac{d(klw)}{dw} m_0, \quad m'' = klm_0. \tag{312}$$

The latter formula agrees with the second of the equations (305), so that the only remaining condition is, that the value of m' shall be equal to that given by the former of those equations. Hence

$$\frac{d(klw)}{dw} = k^3 l,$$

1) Note 77.

from which, on account of

$$\frac{d(kw)}{dw} = k^3,$$

we infer

$$\frac{dl}{dw} = 0, \quad l = \text{const.}$$

The value of this constant must be unity, because, as we know, $l = 1$ for $w = 0$.

We are thus led so far to specialize the hypothesis that was imagined for the explanation of Michelson's experimental result, as to admit, for moving bodies, only a contraction, determined by the coefficient k, in the direction of the line of motion. The electrons themselves become flattened ellipsoids of revolution, their limiting form, which they would reach if the translation had attained the speed of light, being that of a circular disk of radius R, perpendicular to the line of motion.

All this looked very tempting, as it would enable us to predict that no experiment made with a terrestrial source of light will ever show us an influence of the earth's motion, even though it were delicate enough to detect effects, not only of the second, but of any order of magnitude. But, so far as we can judge at present, the facts are against our hypothesis.[1])

According to it, the longitudinal and the transverse mass of an electron would be

$$m' = k^3 m_0, \quad m'' = k m_0,$$

or, if we put $\frac{w}{c} = \beta$,

$$m' = (1 - \beta^2)^{-3/2} m_0, \quad m'' = (1 - \beta^2)^{-1/2} m_0. \qquad (313)$$

When β becomes greater, these values increase more rapidly than those which we have formerly found for the spherical electron. Therefore, the determination of $\frac{e}{m''}$ for the high velocities existing in the β-rays affords the means of deciding between the different theories. Kaufmann, who, as early as 1901[2]), had deduced from his researches on this subject that the value of $\frac{e}{m}$ increases most markedly, so that the mass of an electron may be considered as wholly electromagnetic, has repeated his experiments with the utmost care and for the express purpose of testing my assumption.[3]) His new numbers agree

1) This can no longer be said now. [1915.]

2) W. Kaufmann, Die magnetische und elektrische Ablenkbarkeit der Becquerelstrahlen und die scheinbare Masse der Elektronen, Gött. Nachr., Math.-phys. Kl. 1901, p. 143; Über die elektromagnetische Masse des Elektrons, ibid. 1902, p. 291; 1903, p. 90.

3) Kaufmann, Über die Konstitution des Elektrons, Ann. Phys. 19 (1906), p. 487.

within the limits of experimental errors with the formulae given by Abraham, but not so with the second of the equations (313), so that they are decidedly unfavourable to the idea of a contraction, such as I attempted to work out.[1]) Yet, though it seems very likely that we shall have to relinquish this idea altogether, it is, I think, worth while looking into it somewhat more closely. After that, it will be well also to examine a modification of the hypothesis that has been proposed by Bucherer and Langevin.

180. In the preceding determination of the mass of the deformed electron we have availed ourselves of the electromagnetic momentum, but we have not considered the energy. This was done by Abraham[2]), who found that, besides the ordinary electromagnetic energy, the electron must have an energy of another kind, whose amount is lessened when the particle is made to move. The truth of this becomes apparent when we consider a rectilinear motion of the electron with variable velocity. The mass is given by

$$m' = \frac{e^2}{6\pi c^2 R} k^3 = \frac{e^2}{6\pi c^2 R}\left(1 - \frac{w^2}{c^2}\right)^{-3/2},$$

and the work of the moving force during the element of time dt by

$$\frac{e^2}{6\pi c^2 R}\left(1 - \frac{w^2}{c^2}\right)^{-3/2} \dot{w}\, w\, dt, \tag{314}$$

whereas the electromagnetic energy is found to be[3])

$$\frac{e^2}{6\pi R}\left(1 - \frac{w^2}{c^2}\right)^{-1/2} - \frac{e^2}{24\pi R}\left(1 - \frac{w^2}{c^2}\right)^{1/2}. \tag{315}$$

Now, the increment of the first term during the time dt is exactly equal to the expression (314).

Hence, there must be another energy E of such an amount that, when added to the second term of (315), it gives a constant sum, and which is therefore determined by

$$E = \frac{e^2}{24\pi R}\left(1 - \frac{w^2}{c^2}\right)^{1/2} + C, \tag{316}$$

where C is a constant.

181. The nature of this new energy and the mechanism of the contraction are made much clearer by the remark, first made by Poincaré[4]), that the electron will be in equilibrium, both in its ori-

1) See, however, Note 86.

2) M. Abraham, Die Grundhypothesen der Elektronentheorie, Phys. Zeitschrift 5 (1904), p. 576.

3) Note 78.

4) H. Poincaré, Sur la dynamique de l'électron, Rendiconti del Circolo matematico di Palermo 21 (1906), p. 129.

ginal and in its flattened form, if it has the properties of a very thin, perfectly flexible and extensible shell, whose parts are drawn inwards by a normal stress, having the intensity

$$S = \frac{e^2}{32\pi^2 R^4}$$

per unit of area, and preserving this magnitude however far the contraction may proceed.

The value of S has been so chosen that, so long as the electron is at rest and has therefore the shape of a sphere with radius R, the internal force exactly counterbalances the electromagnetic stress on the outside which is due to the surrounding field.[1]) Now — and herein lies the gist of Poincaré's remark — the electron, when deformed as has been stated, will still be in equilibrium under the joint action of the stress S and the electromagnetic forces.

In order to show this, we shall fix our attention on the components of the internal stress acting on a surface element of the shell; these are found if we multiply S by the projections of the element on the planes of yz, zx, xy. Now, when the deformation takes place, these projections are multiplied by the factors $1, \frac{1}{k}, \frac{1}{k}$, from which it appears that the components of the stress are altered in the same ratios as those of the electromagnetic force (cf. (300)), so that the equilibrium will still persist. When it is stable, the electron will necessarily have the configuration corresponding to it; the electromagnetic forces exerted on its surface by the ether, modified by the translation according to our formulae, conjointly with the invariable internal stress, will make the electron take the flattened ellipsoidal form.

Corresponding to the internal stress S there must be a certain potential energy U, and the above result implies that this energy is equal to the expression (316). Indeed, if v is the volume of the ellipsoid, we obviously may write

$$U = Sv + \text{const} = \frac{e^2}{32\pi^2 R^4} v + \text{const},$$

and we have

$$v = \frac{4}{3}\pi R^3 \left(1 - \frac{w^2}{c^2}\right)^{1/2}.$$

182. Abraham[2]) has raised the objection that I had not shown that the electron, when deformed to an ellipsoid by its translation, would be in stable equilibrium. This is certainly true, but I think the hypothesis need not be discarded for *this* reason. The argument

1) Note **79**.
2) Abraham, l. c., p. 578.

proves only that the electromagnetic actions and the stress of which we have spoken cannot be the only forces which determine the configuration of the electron.

If they were, each problem concerning the relative motion of the parts of the moving ellipsoidal electron would have its counterpart in a problem relating to the spherical electron without translation, because the forces of both kinds would satisfy the relation (300). Now, it is easily seen that, under the joint action of the stresses in the surrounding field and the constant internal stress S, a spherical shell would be in stable equilibrium as regards changes of volume, but that its equilibrium would be unstable with respect to changes of shape.[1]) The same would therefore be true of the moving and flattened shell. In the case of the latter there would even be instability of orientation, because after a small rotation the electron does no longer correspond [after the manner indicated by the formulae (286)] to the original sphere, but to a slightly deformed one.

Notwithstanding all this, it would, in my opinion, be quite legitimate to maintain the hypothesis of the contracting electrons, if by its means we could really make some progress in the understanding of phenomena. In speculating on the structure of these minute particles we must not forget that there may be many possibilities not dreamt of at present; it may very well be that other internal forces serve to ensure the stability of the system, and perhaps, after all, we are wholly on the wrong track when we apply to the parts of an electron our ordinary notion of force.

Leaving aside the special mechanism that has been imagined by Poincaré, we are offered the following alternative. Either a spherical electron must be regarded as a material system between whose parts there are certain forces ensuring the constancy of its size and form, or we must simply assume this constancy as a matter of fact which we have not to analyze any further. In the first case, the form, size and orientation of the moving ellipsoid will also be maintained by the action of the system of forces, provided all of them have the property expressed in our relation (300). In the other case we may rest content with simply admitting for the moving electron, without any further discussion, the ellipsoidal form with the smaller axis in the line of translation.

183. I must also say a few words about another question that is connected with the preceding one. In our calculation of the masses m' and m'' in § 179 we have assumed that at any moment the electromagnetic momentum has the value corresponding, in a

---

1) Note **80**.

stationary state of motion, to the actual velocity. Particularly, in the application of the formula (311), it has been presupposed that in a curvilinear motion the electron constantly has its short axis along the tangent to the path, and that, while the velocity changes, the ratio between the axes of the ellipsoid is changing at the same time.

Strictly speaking, it is not absolutely necessary for our results that the orientation and shape of the electron should follow instantaneously the alterations in direction and velocity of its translation; they may be supposed to lag somewhat behind. But it is clear that, at all events, if we want to apply the values of m' and m'' to optical phenomena, as we have done, the time of lagging must be small in comparison with the period of the vibrations of light.

Now, if we choose the latter of the alternatives that presented themselves in the last paragraph, we may as well simply assert that there is no lagging at all. But we must not proceed in this summary manner if we prefer the first alternative. If the form and the orientation of the electron are determined by forces, we cannot be certain that there exists at every instant a state of equilibrium. Even while the translation is constant, there may be small oscillations of the corpuscle, both in shape and in orientation, and under variable circumstances, i. e. when the velocity of translation is changing either in direction or in magnitude, the lagging behind of which we have just spoken cannot be entirely avoided. The case is similar to that of a pendulum bob acted on by a variable force, whose changes, as is well known, it does not instantaneously follow. The pendulum may, however, approximately be said to do so when the variations of the force are very slow in comparison with its own free vibrations. Similarly, the electron may be regarded as being, at every instant, in the state of equilibrium corresponding to its velocity, provided that the time in which the velocity changes perceptibly be very much longer than the period of the oscillations that can be performed under the influence of the regulating forces. If these vibrations are much more rapid than those of light, the values (313) of the masses m' and m'' may be confidently applied to the electrons in a body traversed by a beam of light, and with even more right to free electrons that are deflected from their line of motion by a magnetic or an electric field.

Of course, since we know next to nothing of the structure of an electron, it is impossible to form an opinion about the period of its free oscillations, but perhaps we shall not be far from the mark if we suppose it to correspond to a wave-length of the same order of magnitude as the diameter.

It appears from these considerations that the idea of a deformability of the electrons would give rise to several new problems. One of these would be that of the rotation of these particles. An electron is set spinning whenever a magnetic force to which it is exposed undergoes a change, and it would be necessary to obtain an insight into the peculiarities of the motion imparted in cases of this kind to our flattened ellipsoids.

184. As has already been observed (§ 178), the often mentioned changes in the internal forces, and consequently in the dimensions of a body can be imagined without extending the assumption to the electrons themselves and the question therefore naturally arises, whether after all we may not get a satisfactory theory by simply adhering to the idea of rigid spherical electrons. This course would be open to us, if the discrepancy between the values of $\frac{m'}{m''}$ given at the end of § 178 could be shown to have no perceptible influence on observed phenomena. In examining this point we are led back to the question of double refraction of which we have already spoken.

A glance at the formulae that have served us in Chap. IV for treating the propagation of light in a system of molecules, shows that the term $m'n^2 = \frac{mn^2}{Ne^2}$ in equation (201) is the only one which contains the mass of an electron. Moreover if, confining ourselves to perfectly transparent bodies (not subjected to an external magnetic force), we leave aside the resistance to the vibrations, that term is also the only one in which there is any question of the frequency. It follows that all depends on the product mn^2, and that a change of m, say in the ratio of 1 to α, will have the same effect as a change of n in the ratio of 1 to $\alpha^{1/2}$.

Let us now suppose for a moment that the values of the two masses of an electron, though not exactly equal to the expressions (313), are at least proportional to these, say

$$m' = \alpha k^3 m_0, \quad m'' = \alpha k m_0, \tag{317}$$

where the coefficient α is a certain function of the velocity of translation w, equal to unity for $w = 0$, and differing from 1 by a quantity of the second order when w is small. Then, the phenomena in a moving system S and those in a stationary one S_0 will correspond to each other as formerly explained, provided that the mass of the electrons in the system S_0 be not m_0 but αm_0. If the body considered were originally isotropic, a change of the mass of its electrons from m_0 to αm_0 certainly would not make it doubly refracting. Hence, the moving body whose electrons have the masses (317), can be so neither. It must be singly refracting, and we may be sure that practically it will present the same phenomena, in experiments, that is, in which the source of light moves with it, as it would do when kept at rest. It is true that there will be a difference equivalent to that which could be caused by a change of the mass of an electron from m_0 to αm_0, or by one of the frequency to a corresponding amount (of the second order), but certainly this can have no perceptible influence.

We shall next consider the case that the longitudinal and the transverse mass of an electron bear to each other a ratio different from k^2. Let us write for their values

$$m' = h' m_0, \quad m'' = h'' m_0,$$

where h' and h'' are factors having similar properties as the above coefficient α. Then the phenomena in the body $\mathfrak{S}$ correspond to those in a body $\mathfrak{S}_0$ in which the electrons would have a mass

$$\frac{h'}{k^3} m_0$$

with respect to accelerations parallel to OX, and a mass

$$\frac{h''}{k} m_0$$

with respect to accelerations at right angles to that line. A body of this kind would undoubtedly show a double refraction, and so would the moving body $\mathfrak{S}$ corresponding to it. If, for example, a ray of light were propagated along a line perpendicular to OX, say in the direction of OY, the velocity of propagation would be different according as the vibrations were parallel to OX or to OZ. The frequency of the light used being denoted by n, the velocity of propagation of one vibration would be (by the theorem with which we have begun this paragraph) as if the frequency were

$$h'^{1/2} k^{-3/2} n,$$

and that of the other as if it were

$$h''^{1/2} k^{-1/2} n,$$

the masses being taken equal to m_0 in both cases.

185. For a spherical electron we have, according to the formulae (70) and (71), if we neglect terms of an order higher than the second,

$$h' = 1 + \frac{6}{5}\beta^2, \quad h'' = 1 + \frac{2}{5}\beta^2$$

and, as we may put

$$k = 1 + \frac{1}{2}\beta^2,$$

the above values become

$$\left(1 - \frac{3}{20}\beta^2\right) n \quad \text{and} \quad \left(1 - \frac{1}{20}\beta^2\right) n,$$

showing a difference of

$$\frac{1}{10}\beta^2 n = 10^{-9} n,$$

since the velocity of the earth is one ten-thousandth part of the speed of light. In the case of water, and for yellow light, this change of frequency would produce a change in the index of refraction of about $2 \cdot 10^{-11}$, and this, therefore, would be the difference between the two principal refractive indices which we might expect in the double refraction experiment.

It is scarcely necessary to say that Rayleigh's[1]) and Brace's[2]) observations were conducted in such a manner that a double refraction in which one of the principal directions of vibration would be parallel to the earth's motion could manifest itself. As I mentioned already, the results were invariably negative, though Brace's means of observation were so sensitive that a difference between the principal refractive indices of 10^{-12} could not have escaped him. This is about the twentieth part of the value which we have just computed.

It is true that we have based our calculations on certain assumptions that could be changed for others, and Brace himself has made the calculation in a different manner. Yet, I think, we may confidently conclude that it will be extremely difficult to reconcile the result of his observations with the idea of rigid spherical electrons.

It must be added that, if we adhered to this idea, our considerations concerning the molecular motions in a moving system would also require some modification.

186. We have seen in § 184 that there would be no contradiction with Brace's results, if the ratio between the longitudinal and the transverse mass had the value k^2. This raises the question as to whether this latter ratio can be obtained without the assumption $l = 1$, which has been the origin of all our difficulties. Unfortunately, this way out is barred to us, the equation

$$\frac{d(klw)}{dw} : kl = k^2$$

being satisfied only by a constant value of l.

For this reason the optical experiments do not allow us to suppose, as has been done by Bucherer[3]) and Langevin[4]), that a

1) Rayleigh, Does motion through the aether cause double refraction? Phil. Mag. (6) **4** (1902), p. 678.

2) D. B. Brace, On double refraction in matter moving through the aether, Phil. Mag. (6) **7** (1904), p. 317.

3) A. H. Bucherer, Mathematische Einführung in die Elektronentheorie, Leipzig, 1904, p. 57 a. 58.

4) P. Langevin, La physique des électrons, Revue générale des sciences pures et appliquées **16** (1905), p. 257.

moving electron is deformed to an ellipsoid of the form and orientation which I have assigned to it, but having the original volume, instead of the original equatorial radius. This assumption obviously amounts to putting $l = k^{-1/3}$, so that the dimensions of the electron would be altered in the ratios $k^{-2/3}$, $k^{1/3}$, $k^{1/3}$. When we use this value of l, the two electromagnetic masses become

$$m' = (1 - \beta^2)^{-4/3} (1 - \tfrac{1}{3}\beta^2) m_0, \qquad (318)$$

$$m'' = (1 - \beta^2)^{-1/3} m_0,$$

giving for the ratio

$$\frac{m'}{m''} = \frac{1 - \frac{1}{3}\beta^2}{1 - \beta^2},$$

instead of

$$k^2 = \frac{1}{1 - \beta^2}.$$

If we apply to this hypothesis the same mode of calculation as to that of rigid spheres, we are led to a double refraction that is even a little stronger, so that the contradiction with Brace's experiments would remain the same.

This is certainly to be regretted as the new assumption has unmistakeable advantages over my original one.[1]) It is in sufficient agreement with Kaufmann's results, and the idea of a constant volume is indeed very simple. Following it we should not be obliged, as we were in § 180, to admit the existence of another energy than the ordinary electromagnetic one. This is confirmed by the magnitude of the electromagnetic energy [2])

$$\frac{e^2}{8\pi R} (1 - \beta^2)^{-1/3} (1 + \tfrac{1}{3}\beta^2)$$

and the expression

$$\frac{e^2}{6\pi R c^2} (1 - \beta^2)^{-4/3} (1 - \tfrac{1}{3}\beta^2) w \dot{w}\, dt,$$

derived from (318), for the work of the force, in case the electron has a rectilinear motion of variable velocity. The latter quantity is equal to the increment of the former in the time dt.

187. It is interesting, now to turn once more to the hypothesis $l = 1$, combined with the formulae (305) for the masses (assuming as a matter of fact the influence of the translation on the masses expressed by these equations), and to consider the equations

1) With a view to the principle of relativity I should no longer say so. [1915.]
2) Note 81.

for the propagation of light in moving transparent bodies to which it leads. We have seen that the vectors $\mathbf{d}'$, $\mathbf{h}'$, $\mathbf{p}'$ can be the same functions of x', y', z', t' both in a moving system S and in a stationary one S_0. The same must be true of some other vectors that can be derived from them, viz. 1. the vector $\mathbf{E}'$ which we define as the mean value $\overline{\mathbf{d}}'$ of $\mathbf{d}'$, taken, in S_0 for a spherical space, infinitely small in a physical sense, with its centre at the point considered, and in S for the space corresponding to that sphere, 2. the mean value $\overline{\mathbf{h}}'$ defined in the same way, and to be denoted by $\mathbf{H}'$, 3. the vector

$$\mathbf{P}' = N\mathbf{p}', \tag{319}$$

where, in the formulae for both systems, we understand by N the number of molecules which S_0 contains per unit of volume, and 4. a vector $\mathbf{D}'$ defined by the equation

$$\mathbf{D}' = \mathbf{E}' + \mathbf{P}'. \tag{320}$$

Since all these vectors can be, in S_0 and in S, the same functions of x', y', z', t', the equations by which they are determined must be such that they can be written in the same form.

Now, for the system S_0, x', y', z', t' are the true coordinates and the true time, whereas the above vectors are what we formerly called $\mathbf{E}$, $\mathbf{H}$, $\mathbf{P}$ and $\mathbf{D}$. As we know that they satisfy the equations

$$\left.\begin{aligned} &\operatorname{div} \mathbf{D} = 0, \\ &\operatorname{div} \mathbf{H} = 0, \\ &\operatorname{rot} \mathbf{H} = \frac{1}{c}\frac{\partial \mathbf{D}}{\partial t}, \\ &\operatorname{rot} \mathbf{E} = -\frac{1}{c}\frac{\partial \mathbf{H}}{\partial t}, \end{aligned}\right\} \tag{321}$$

we may be sure that, for the moving system,

$$\left.\begin{aligned} &\operatorname{div}' \mathbf{D}' = 0, \\ &\operatorname{div}' \mathbf{H}' = 0, \\ &\operatorname{rot}' \mathbf{H}' = \frac{1}{c}\frac{\partial \mathbf{D}'}{\partial t'}, \\ &\operatorname{rot}' \mathbf{E}' = -\frac{1}{c}\frac{\partial \mathbf{H}'}{\partial t'}, \end{aligned}\right\} \tag{322}$$

where the symbols div′ and rot′ have the meaning that has been explained in § 169.

To (321) must be added the relation between $\mathbf{E}$ and $\mathbf{D}$, and to (322) a corresponding relation between $\mathbf{E}'$ and $\mathbf{D}'$, so that, if we write

$$\mathbf{D} = F(\mathbf{E}), \tag{323}$$

we shall also have

$$\mathbf{D}' = F(\mathbf{E}'). \tag{324}$$

Here, the symbol F must be understood in a very general sense; it is meant to include all forms which the equations may take according to the special properties of the body considered. If the first formula contains, as may very well be[1]), differential coefficients with respect to t, we shall find in the second the corresponding differential coefficients with respect to t'.

Putting $\mathbf{D} = \mathbf{E}$, and similarly $\mathbf{D}' = \mathbf{E}'$, we obtain the equations for the free ether. These, however, may be left in the form

$$\left.\begin{aligned} &\operatorname{div} \mathbf{d} = 0, \\ &\operatorname{div} \mathbf{h} = 0, \\ &\operatorname{rot} \mathbf{h} = \frac{1}{c}\frac{\partial \mathbf{d}}{\partial t}, \\ &\operatorname{rot} \mathbf{d} = -\frac{1}{c}\frac{\partial \mathbf{h}}{\partial t} \end{aligned}\right\} \tag{325}$$

for the system S_0, there being no necessity for considering mean values when there are no molecules, and we may write for them

$$\left.\begin{aligned} &\operatorname{div}' \mathbf{d}' = 0, \\ &\operatorname{div}' \mathbf{h}' = 0, \\ &\operatorname{rot}' \mathbf{h}' = \frac{1}{c}\frac{\partial \mathbf{d}'}{\partial t'}, \\ &\operatorname{rot}' \mathbf{d}' = -\frac{1}{c}\frac{\partial \mathbf{h}'}{\partial t'}, \end{aligned}\right\} \tag{326}$$

when we are concerned with S.

As the ether does not share the translation w, the two last sets of equations serve for exactly the same phenomena. The one is derived from the other by purely mathematical transformations, the only difference between the two being, that the electromagnetic field is referred to axes fixed in the ether and to the „true" time in (325), but to moving axes and „local" time in (326), and that it is described in the two cases by means of different vectors. On the contrary, the phenomena to which the equations (321, 323) and (322, 324) apply, though corresponding to each other, cannot be said to be identical.

188. Having got thus far, we may proceed as is often done in theoretical physics. We may remove the scaffolding by means of which the system of equations has been built up, and, without troubling ourselves any more about the theory of electrons and the

1) Note 82.

difficulties amidst which it has landed us, we may postulate the above equations as a concise and, so far as we know, accurate description of the phenomena. From this point of view, **E**, **H**, **D** in one system, and **E**′, **H**′, **D**′ in the other, are simply „certain“ vectors, about whose meaning we say just so much as is necessary for fixing unequivocally for every case their directions and magnitudes.

As to the grounds on which the equations recommend themselves, these are: 1. that the formulae (321), combined with suitable assumptions concerning the relation between **E** and **D**, can serve for the explanation of optical phenomena in transparent bodies, whether singly or doubly refracting, 2. that the identity in form of (321, 323) and (322, 324) accounts for the failure of all attempts to discover an influence of the earth's motion by experiments with terrestrial sources, and 3. that the equations (322, 324) give the right value for Fresnel's coefficient.

189. The denominations „effective coordinates“, „effective time“ etc. of which we have availed ourselves for the sake of facilitating our mode of expression, have prepared us for a very interesting interpretation of the above results, for which we are indebted to Einstein.[1]) Let us imagine an observer, whom we shall call A_0 and to whom we shall assign a fixed position in the ether, to be engaged in the study of the phenomena going on in the stationary system S_0 We shall suppose him to be provided with a measuring rod and a clock, even, for his convenience, let us say, with a certain number of clocks placed at various points of S_0, and adjusted to each other with perfect accuracy. By these means he will be able to determine the coordinates x, y, z for any point, and the time t for any instant, and by studying the electromagnetic field as it manifests itself at different places and times, he will be led to the equations (321, 323).

Let A be a second observer, whose task it is to examine the phenomena in the system S, and who himself also moves through the ether with the velocity w, without being aware either of this motion or of that of the system S.

Let this observer use the same measuring rod (or an exact copy of it) that has served A_0, the rod having acquired in one way or another the velocity w before coming into his hands. Then, by our assumption concerning the dimensions of moving bodies, the divisions of the scale will in general have a length that differs from the ori-

1) See Ann. d. Phys. **17** (1905), p. 891; **18** (1905), p. 639; **20** (1906), p. 627; **21** (1906), p. 583; **23** (1907), p. 197, 371, and the comprehensive exposition of Einstein's theory: Über das Relativitätsprinzip und die aus demselben gezogenen Folgerungen, Jahrb. d. Radioaktivität u. Elektronik **4** (1908), p. 411.

ginal one, and will even change whenever the rod is turned round, the law of these changes being, that, in corresponding positions in S_0 and S, the rod has equal projections on the plane YOZ, but projections on OX whose ratio is as k to 1. It is clear that, since the observer is unconscious of these changes, he will be unable to measure the true relative coordinates x_r of the points of the system. His readings will give him only the values of the effective coordinates x' and, of course, those of y', z' which, for $l = 1$, are equal to y_r, z_r. Hence, relying on his rod, he will not find the true shape of bodies. He will take for a sphere what really is an ellipsoid, and his cubic centimetre will be, not a true cubic centimetre, but a parallelepiped k times smaller. This, however, contains a quantity of matter, which, in the absence of the translation, would occupy a cubic centimetre, so that, if A counts the molecules in *his* cubic centimetre, he will find the same number N as A_0. Moreover, his unit of mass will be the same as that of the stationary observer, if each of them chooses as unit the mass of the water occupying a volume equal to *his* cubic centimetre.

With the clocks of A the case is the same as with his measuring rod. If we suppose the forces in the clock-work to be liable to the changes determined by (300), the motion of two equal clocks, one in S_0 and the other in S, will be such that the effective coordinates of the moving parts are, in both systems, the same functions of the effective time. Consequently, if the hand of the clock in S_0 returns to its initial position after an interval of time Θ, the hand of the clock in S will do so after an increment equal to Θ of the effective time t'. Therefore, a clock in the system S will indicate the progress of the effective time, and without his knowing anything about it, A's clocks will go k times slower than those of A_0.

190. It follows from what has been said that, if the moving observer measures the speed of light, by making a ray of light travel from a point P to a point Q, and then back to P, he will find the value c. This may be shown for every direction of the line PQ[1]), but it will suffice to give the proof for the case that the line is either parallel to OX, or at right angles to it. If L is the distance between P and Q as measured by A, then in the first case the true distance is $\frac{L}{k}$, and, as both points move through the ether with the velocity w, the time required by the ray of light is

$$\frac{L}{k}\left(\frac{1}{c+w} + \frac{1}{c-w}\right) = \frac{2cL}{k(c^2-w^2)} = \frac{2kL}{c}. \tag{327}$$

1) Note 83.

In the second case the light has to travel along two sides of an isoscele triangle (cf. § 167), whose height is L and whose half base is to one of the sides as w to c. The side is therefore

$$\frac{L}{\sqrt{1-\frac{w^2}{c^2}}} = kL,$$

and the time taken by the beam of light to return to its starting point is again given by (327). As A's clock goes k times too slow, it will mark an interval of time $\frac{2L}{c}$, so that the observer will conclude that the velocity of the rays is equal to c.

Let us now suppose him to be provided with a certain number of clocks placed at different points of his system, and to adjust these clocks to each other by the best means at his disposal. In order to do so with two clocks placed at the points P and Q, at a measured distance L from each other, he may start an optical signal from P the moment at which the first clock marks the time $t' = 0$, and so set the second clock that, at the arrival of the signal, it marks the time $\frac{L}{c}$, making allowance in this way for the time of passage of the light which he judges to be $\frac{L}{c}$.

Let us suppose that P lies at the origin of coordinates, and Q on the positive axis of x; further, that a clock without translation and therefore indicating the true time, marks the instant 0 at the moment of signalling. Then, on account of the different rates of a moving and a stationary clock, we shall have continually for the clock at P

$$t' = \frac{1}{k}t.$$

At the moment of arrival of the signal the true time will be

$$\frac{L}{k(c-w)},$$

since this is the interval required for the passage of the light between the points P and Q, which move with the velocity w and whose true distance is $\frac{L}{k}$.

Now, since at this moment the time indicated by the clock at Q is $\frac{L}{c}$, its indication, at any other true time t, will be

$$t' = \frac{L}{c} + \frac{1}{k}\left[t - \frac{L}{k(c-w)}\right],$$

or, since $L = x'$

$$t' = \frac{1}{k}t - \frac{w}{c^2}x'.$$

This agrees exactly with (288), so that we see that when the clocks are adjusted by means of optical signals, each of them will indicate the local time t' corresponding to its position.

The proof may easily be extended to other directions of the line joining the two places.[1]

191. It is of importance not to forget that, in doing all that has been said, the observer would remain entirely unconscious of his system moving (with himself) through the ether, and of the errors of his rod and his clocks.

Continuing his researches he may now undertake a study of the electromagnetic phenomena in his system, in exactly the same manner in which A_0 has done so in his. We can predict what his results will be, because we know the phenomena by our theorem of corresponding states. From this we can infer that, if the moving observer determines velocities and accelerations in terms of his effective coordinates and his effective time, if he deduces the intensity of forces from the acceleration which they give to unit of mass, and if he measures electric charges in the ordinary way by means of the electrostatic actions which they exert on each other, his unit of electricity will be equal to that chosen by A_0. His density of charge, on the contrary, will not be the true density ϱ, but what we have called the effective density ϱ'. Further, if he determines the force acting on unit charge at some point of the electromagnetic field, he will find the vector $\mathbf{d}'$.[2] Similarly he will be led to consider the vector $\mathbf{h}'$, and, pursuing his study, he will sooner or later come to establishing the equations that determine the field, namely the formulae (326) for the free ether and (322, 324) for a ponderable body.

He may attain this latter object by different courses. Perhaps he will be satisfied with the idea that $\mathbf{D}'$ is a certain vector which he has for the first time occasion to introduce when working with a charged condensor. Or, if he develops a theory of electrons, he will get the notion of the electric moment of a particle, whose components he will naturally define by the expressions $\sum ex'$, $\sum ey'$, $\sum ez'$, so that what he calls the moment is in reality the vector $\mathbf{p}'$ of our equations (306). After having introduced it, the moving observer will define $\mathbf{P}'$ and $\mathbf{D}'$ by the formulae (319) and (320).

We may sum up these considerations by saying that, if both A_0 and A were to keep a record of their observations and the conclusions drawn from them, these records would, on comparison, be found to be exactly identical.

192. Attention must now be drawn to a remarkable reciprocity that has been pointed out by Einstein. Thus far it has been the

1) Note 84. 2) Note 85.

task of the observer A_0 to examine the phenomena in the stationary system, whereas A has had to confine himself to the system S. Let us now imagine that each observer is able to see the system to which the other belongs, and to study the phenomena going on in it. Then, A_0 will be in the position in which we have all along imagined ourselves to be (though, strictly speaking, on account of the earth's motion, we are in the position of A); in studying the electromagnetic field in S, he will be led to introduce the new variables x', y', z', $\mathbf{d}'$, $\mathbf{h}'$, etc. and so he will establish the equations (326) and (322, 324). The reciprocity consists in this that, if the observer A describes in exactly the same manner the field in the stationary system, he will describe it accurately.

In order to see this, we shall revert to the equations (287) and (288), which in our present hypothesis $l = 1$ take the form

$$x' = k(x - wt), \quad y' = y, \quad z' = z, \quad t' = k\left(t - \frac{w}{c^2}x\right). \tag{328}$$

Let P be a point belonging to the system S_0 and let us fix our attention on the coordinate x' which it has with respect to the moving axes of S, for two definite values t' and $t' + \Delta t'$ of the local time. Since x is constant for this point P, we have by the last of the above equations

$$\Delta t = \frac{1}{k} \Delta t',$$

and by the first

$$\Delta x' = -kw\Delta t = -w\Delta t'.$$

Judging by his means of observation, the observer A will therefore ascribe to the system S_0 a velocity w in a direction opposite to that of the positive axis of x'.

Just as A_0, in his theory of the electromagnetic field in S, has changed the coordinates x, y, z, the time t and the electromagnetic vectors $\mathbf{d}$, $\mathbf{h}$, $\mathbf{E}$, $\mathbf{H}$, $\mathbf{P}$, $\mathbf{D}$ for the variables (328), the vectors $\mathbf{d}'$, $\mathbf{h}'$, whose components are

$$\left.\begin{aligned} \mathbf{d}_x' = \mathbf{d}_x, \quad \mathbf{d}_y' = k\left(\mathbf{d}_y - \frac{w}{c}\mathbf{h}_z\right), \quad \mathbf{d}_z' = k\left(\mathbf{d}_z + \frac{w}{c}\mathbf{h}_y\right), \\ \mathbf{h}_x' = \mathbf{h}_x, \quad \mathbf{h}_y' = k\left(\mathbf{h}_y + \frac{w}{c}\mathbf{d}_z\right), \quad \mathbf{h}_z' = k\left(\mathbf{h}_z - \frac{w}{c}\mathbf{d}_y\right), \end{aligned}\right\} \tag{329}$$

and the vectors $\mathbf{E}'$, $\mathbf{H}'$, $\mathbf{P}'$, $\mathbf{D}'$, so the observer A will introduce, instead of the quantities x', y', z', t', $\mathbf{d}'$, etc. which belong to his system, certain new quantities which we shall distinguish by double dashes, and which will serve him in his theory of the system S_0.

He will define these new quantities by equations analogous to (328) and (329), replacing w by $-w$, which however does not affect the constant k. His transformation will therefore be as follows

$$x'' = k(x' + wt'), \quad y'' = y', \quad z' = z', \quad t'' = k\left(t' + \frac{w}{c^2} x'\right), \tag{330}$$

$$\left.\begin{aligned} \mathbf{d}_x'' &= \mathbf{d}_x', \quad \mathbf{d}_y'' = k\left(\mathbf{d}_y' + \frac{w}{c}\mathbf{h}_z'\right), \quad \mathbf{d}_z'' = k\left(\mathbf{d}_z' - \frac{w}{c}\mathbf{h}_y'\right), \\ \mathbf{h}_x'' &= \mathbf{h}_x', \quad \mathbf{h}_y'' = k\left(\mathbf{h}_y' - \frac{w}{c}\mathbf{d}_z'\right), \quad \mathbf{h}_z'' = k\left(\mathbf{h}_z' + \frac{w}{c}\mathbf{d}_y'\right). \end{aligned}\right\} \tag{331}$$

If he also defines the vectors $\mathbf{E}''$, $\mathbf{H}''$, $\mathbf{D}''$ similarly to A_0's definition of $\mathbf{E}'$, $\mathbf{H}'$, $\mathbf{D}'$, the observer A will finally find the following equations, to be applied to the system S_0, and corresponding to (326), (322, 324); for the ether

$$\left.\begin{aligned} \operatorname{div}'' \mathbf{d}'' &= 0, \\ \operatorname{div}'' \mathbf{h}'' &= 0, \\ \operatorname{rot}'' \mathbf{h}'' &= \frac{1}{c}\frac{\partial \mathbf{d}''}{\partial t''}, \\ \operatorname{rot}'' \mathbf{d}'' &= -\frac{1}{c}\frac{\partial \mathbf{h}''}{\partial t''}, \end{aligned}\right\} \tag{332}$$

and for a ponderable body

$$\left.\begin{aligned} \operatorname{div} \mathbf{D}'' &= 0, \\ \operatorname{div} \mathbf{H}'' &= 0, \\ \operatorname{rot}'' \mathbf{H}'' &= \frac{1}{c}\frac{\partial \mathbf{D}''}{\partial t''}, \\ \operatorname{rot}'' \mathbf{E}'' &= -\frac{1}{c}\frac{\partial \mathbf{H}''}{\partial t''}, \end{aligned}\right\} \tag{333}$$

$$\mathbf{D}'' = F(\mathbf{E}'') \tag{334}$$

The symbols div″ and rot″ will require no further explanation.

193. It remains to show that these formulae contain an *accurate* description of the phenomena in S_0. The proof of this is very simple, because, if we look at them somewhat more closely, the equations are found to be the same which A_0 has used for the purpose.

Indeed, if we solve x, y, z, t from the equations (328) and $\mathbf{d}_x$, $\mathbf{d}_y$, $\mathbf{d}_z$, $\mathbf{h}_x$, $\mathbf{h}_y$, $\mathbf{h}_z$ from (329), we find values agreeing exactly with (330) and (331), so that

$$x'' = x, \quad y'' = y, \quad z'' = z, \quad t'' = t,$$
$$\mathbf{d}'' = \mathbf{d}, \quad \mathbf{h}'' = \mathbf{h},$$

by which the identity of the sets of equations (332) and (325) is demonstrated. As to the equations (333, 334) and (321, 323), the only difference between the two sets is, that one contains the vectors $\mathbf{E}''$ and $\mathbf{D}''$, and the other the vectors $\mathbf{E}$ and $\mathbf{D}$. If these four quantities are considered simply as „certain“ vectors (represented by symbols the choice of which is immaterial), this similarity in form, together with our knowledge that in free ether $\mathbf{E}'' = \mathbf{E}$, $\mathbf{D}'' = \mathbf{D}$, $\mathbf{H}'' = \mathbf{H}$ (since for this medium $\mathbf{E}'' = \mathbf{D}'' = \mathbf{d}''$, $\mathbf{E} = \mathbf{D} = \mathbf{d}$, $\mathbf{H}'' = \mathbf{h}''$, $\mathbf{H} = \mathbf{h}$) must, and can, suffice for our conclusion that the phenomena in the system S_0 can be described by means of the equations (333, 334) just as well as by (321, 323).

We may go a step farther if we suppose that the moving and the stationary observer, or rather theorist, as they have now become, establish a theory of molecules and of electrons. A_0 has defined $\mathbf{E}'$, $\mathbf{H}'$ as the mean values of $\mathbf{d}'$, $\mathbf{h}'$, and for the other vectors he has used the equations

$$\mathbf{p}_x' = \sum ex', \quad \mathbf{p}_y' = \sum ey', \quad \mathbf{p}_z' = \sum ez',$$
$$\mathbf{P}' = N\mathbf{p}',$$
$$\mathbf{D}' = \mathbf{E}' + \mathbf{P}'.$$

Similarly, A will define $\mathbf{E}''$ and $\mathbf{H}''$ as the mean values of $\mathbf{d}''$ and $\mathbf{h}''$, so that these vectors become equal to the mean values of $\mathbf{d}$ and $\mathbf{h}$, i. e. to $\mathbf{E}$ and $\mathbf{H}$. He will put for each molecule

$$\mathbf{p}_x'' = \sum ex'', \quad \mathbf{p}_y'' = \sum ey'', \quad \mathbf{p}_z'' = \sum ez'',$$

and further

$$\mathbf{P}'' = N\mathbf{p}'',$$
$$\mathbf{D}'' = \mathbf{E}'' + \mathbf{P}''.$$

Comparing these formulae with (307) (for which we may write $\mathbf{p}_x = \sum ex$, etc.) and the equations $\mathbf{P} = N\mathbf{p}$, $\mathbf{D} = \mathbf{E} + \mathbf{P}$, and keeping in mind that $x'' = x$, $y'' = y$, $z'' = z$, we see that really

$$\mathbf{p}'' = \mathbf{p}, \quad \mathbf{P}'' = \mathbf{P}, \quad \mathbf{D}'' = \mathbf{D}.$$

194. It will be clear by what has been said that the impressions received by the two observers A_0 and A would be alike in all respects. It would be impossible to decide which of them moves or stands still with respect to the ether, and there would be no reason for preferring the times and lengths measured by the one to those determined by the other, nor for saying that either of them is in possession of the „true" times or the „true" lengths. This is a point which Einstein has laid particular stress on, in a theory in which he starts from what he calls the principle of relativity, i. e. the principle that the equations by means of which physical phenomena may be described are not altered in form when we change the axes of coordinates for others having a uniform motion of translation relatively to the original system.

I cannot speak here of the many highly interesting applications which Einstein has made of this principle. His results concerning electromagnetic and optical phenomena (leading to the same contradiction with Kaufmann's results that was pointed out in § 179[1]) agree in the main with those which we have obtained in the preceding pages, the chief difference being that Einstein simply postulates what we have deduced, with some difficulty and not altogether satisfactorily, from the fundamental equations of the electromagnetic field. By doing so, he may certainly take credit for making us see in the negative result of experiments like those of Michelson, Rayleigh and Brace, not a fortuitous compensation of opposing effects, but the manifestation of a general and fundamental principle.

Yet, I think, something may also be claimed in favour of the form in which I have presented the theory. I cannot but regard the ether, which can be the seat of an electromagnetic field with its energy and its vibrations, as endowed with a certain degree of substantiality, however different it may be from all ordinary matter. In this line of thought, it seems natural not to assume at starting that it can never make any difference whether a body moves through the ether or not, and to measure distances and lengths of time by means of rods and clocks having a fixed position relatively to the ether.

It would be unjust not to add that, besides the fascinating boldness of its starting point, Einstein's theory has another marked advantage over mine. Whereas I have not been able to obtain for the equations referred to moving axes *exactly* the same form as for those which apply to a stationary system, Einstein has accomplished this by means of a system of new variables slightly different from those which I have introduced. I have not availed myself of his substitutions, only because the formulae are rather complicated and look somewhat artificial, unless one deduces them from the principle of relativity itself.[2])

---

1) Note **86**. 2) See, however, Note **72***.

NOTES.[1])

1 (Page 6). Equation (4) is equivalent to the three formulae

$$\frac{\partial \mathbf{h}_z}{\partial y} - \frac{\partial \mathbf{h}_y}{\partial z} = \frac{1}{c}\frac{\partial \mathbf{d}_x}{\partial t},$$

$$\frac{\partial \mathbf{h}_x}{\partial z} - \frac{\partial \mathbf{h}_z}{\partial x} = \frac{1}{c}\frac{\partial \mathbf{d}_y}{\partial t},$$

$$\frac{\partial \mathbf{h}_y}{\partial x} - \frac{\partial \mathbf{h}_x}{\partial y} = \frac{1}{c}\frac{\partial \mathbf{d}_z}{\partial t}.$$

When the second of these, differentiated with respect to z, is subtracted from the third, differentiated with respect to y, we find

$$\frac{\partial}{\partial x}\left(\frac{\partial \mathbf{h}_x}{\partial x} + \frac{\partial \mathbf{h}_y}{\partial y} + \frac{\partial \mathbf{h}_z}{\partial z}\right) - \Delta \mathbf{h}_x = \frac{1}{c}\frac{\partial}{\partial t}\left(\frac{\partial \mathbf{d}_z}{\partial y} - \frac{\partial \mathbf{d}_y}{\partial z}\right), \qquad (\mathit{1})$$

or, if (3) and (5) are taken into account,

$$\Delta \mathbf{h}_x = \frac{1}{c^2}\frac{\partial^2 \mathbf{h}_x}{\partial t^2}.$$

Corresponding formulae for $\mathbf{h}_y$, $\mathbf{h}_z$ and for the components of $\mathbf{d}$ are obtained in a similar manner.

It may be noticed that the quantity

$$\frac{\partial}{\partial y}\left(\frac{\partial \mathbf{h}_y}{\partial x} - \frac{\partial \mathbf{h}_x}{\partial y}\right) - \frac{\partial}{\partial z}\left(\frac{\partial \mathbf{h}_x}{\partial z} - \frac{\partial \mathbf{h}_z}{\partial x}\right),$$

which we have calculated in the above transformation, is the first component of the rotation of rot $\mathbf{h}$, or, as we may say, of rot rot $\mathbf{h}$, and that the expression on the left-hand side of (*1*) is the first component of the vector

$$\text{grad div } \mathbf{h} - \Delta \mathbf{h}.$$

In general, denoting by $\mathbf{A}$ any vector, we may write

$$\text{rot rot } \mathbf{A} = \text{grad div } \mathbf{A} - \Delta \mathbf{A}, \qquad (\mathit{2})$$

a theorem which enables us to perform in the terms of vector analysis the elimination of $\mathbf{d}$ from the fundamental equations. Indeed, we may deduce from (4)

$$\text{rot rot } \mathbf{h} = \frac{1}{c} \text{ rot } \dot{\mathbf{d}},$$

---

1) The numbers of the formulae in this Appendix will be printed in italics.

or, since

$$\operatorname{rot} \dot{\mathbf{d}} = \frac{\partial}{\partial t} \operatorname{rot} \mathbf{d},$$

$$\operatorname{grad} \operatorname{div} \mathbf{h} - \Delta \mathbf{h} = \frac{1}{c} \frac{\partial}{\partial t} \operatorname{rot} \mathbf{d},$$

i. e., if we use (3) and (5),

$$\Delta \mathbf{h} = \frac{1}{c^2} \frac{\partial^2 \mathbf{h}}{\partial t^2}.$$

Similarly, the equation

$$\Delta \mathbf{d} = \frac{1}{c^2} \frac{\partial^2 \mathbf{d}}{\partial t^2}$$

is obtained if we begin by considering the vector rot rot $\mathbf{d}$.

2 (Page 16). The definitions given in § 2 lead to the general formula

$$\operatorname{div} \operatorname{rot} \mathbf{A} = 0.$$

Hence the equation (19) requires that

$$\operatorname{div} \mathbf{c} = \operatorname{div} (\dot{\mathbf{d}} + \varrho \mathbf{v}) = 0, \tag{3}$$

i. e. that the total current, which is composed of the displacement current $\dot{\mathbf{d}}$ and the convection current $\varrho \mathbf{v}$, be solenoidally distributed. In order to show that it is so whenever the condition mentioned in the text is fulfilled, we shall fix our attention on an element of the charged matter, situated at the time t at the point (x, y, z), and therefore, at the time $t + dt$, at the point $(x + \mathbf{v}_x dt,\ y + \mathbf{v}_y dt,\ z + \mathbf{v}_z dt)$. By a well known theorem of the theory of infinitely small deformations, the volume of the element, if initially equal to dS, will have become

$$\left\{1 + \left(\frac{\partial \mathbf{v}_x}{\partial x} + \frac{\partial \mathbf{v}_y}{\partial y} + \frac{\partial \mathbf{v}_z}{\partial z}\right) dt\right\} dS \tag{4}$$

at the end of the interval dt.

On the other hand, the time having changed by dt and the coordinates by $\mathbf{v}_x dt$, $\mathbf{v}_y dt$, $\mathbf{v}_z dt$, the density of the charge, which at first was ϱ, has become

$$\varrho + \left(\frac{\partial \varrho}{\partial t} + \mathbf{v}_x \frac{\partial \varrho}{\partial x} + \mathbf{v}_y \frac{\partial \varrho}{\partial y} + \mathbf{v}_z \frac{\partial \varrho}{\partial z}\right) dt.$$

The product of this expression by (*4*) must be equal to the original charge $\varrho\, dS$ of the element, so that we have

$$\varrho \left(\frac{\partial \mathbf{v}_x}{\partial x} + \frac{\partial \mathbf{v}_y}{\partial y} + \frac{\partial \mathbf{v}_z}{\partial z}\right) + \frac{\partial \varrho}{\partial t} + \mathbf{v}_x \frac{\partial \varrho}{\partial x} + \mathbf{v}_y \frac{\partial \varrho}{\partial y} + \mathbf{v}_z \frac{\partial \varrho}{\partial z} = 0,$$

or

$$\frac{\partial \varrho}{\partial t} + \operatorname{div} (\varrho \mathbf{v}) = 0, \tag{5}$$

from which, taking into account (17), we are at once led to the equation (*3*).

3 (Page 17). The method of elimination is exactly like that which we used in Note 1. We may infer from (20) and (19)

$$\text{rot rot } \mathbf{d} = -\frac{1}{c} \text{ rot } \dot{\mathbf{h}},$$

$$\text{rot rot } \mathbf{h} = \frac{1}{c} \text{ rot } \dot{\mathbf{d}} + \frac{1}{c} \text{ rot} (\varrho \mathbf{v}),$$

or, using (*2*),

$$\text{grad div } \mathbf{d} - \Delta \mathbf{d} = -\frac{1}{c} \frac{\partial}{\partial t} (\text{rot } \mathbf{h}),$$

$$\text{grad div } \mathbf{h} - \Delta \mathbf{h} = \frac{1}{c} \frac{\partial}{\partial t} (\text{rot } \mathbf{d}) + \frac{1}{c} \text{ rot} (\varrho \mathbf{v}).$$

and we get the formulae (24) and (25), if we substitute the values of div **d**, rot **h**, div **h** and rot **d** taken from (17), (19), (18) and (20).

4 (Page 18) The following considerations, showing, not only that the function (30) satisfies the differential equation (29) (which might be verified by direct differentiation), but also under what conditions it may be said to be the only solution, are taken from a paper by Kirchhoff on the theory of rays of light.[1])

They are based on Green's theorem and on the proposition that, if r is the distance from a fixed point, and F an arbitrary function, the expression

$$\chi = \frac{1}{r} F\left(t \pm \frac{r}{c}\right)$$

has the property expressed by

$$\Delta \chi = \frac{1}{c^2} \frac{\partial^2 \chi}{\partial t^2}. \tag{6}$$

This follows at once from the formula

$$\Delta \chi = \frac{\partial^2 \chi}{\partial r^2} + \frac{2}{r} \frac{\partial \chi}{\partial r} = \frac{1}{r} \frac{\partial^2 (r\chi)}{\partial r^2},$$

which is true for any function of r, not explicitly containing the coordinates, and in virtue of which (*6*) assumes the form

$$\frac{\partial^2 (r\chi)}{\partial r^2} = \frac{1}{c^2} \frac{\partial^2 (r\chi)}{\partial t^2}.$$

It is well known that

$$r\chi = F\left(t + \frac{r}{c}\right) \quad \text{and} \quad r\chi = F\left(t - \frac{r}{c}\right)$$

are solutions of this equation.

1) Ann. d. Phys. u. Chem. **18** (1883), p. 663.

Let σ be the bounding surface of a space S throughout which ψ is subjected to the equation (29), P the point of S for which we want to determine the function, dS an element of volume situated at the distance r from P, Σ a small spherical surface having P as centre, n and N the normals to σ and Σ, both drawn towards the outside.

Introducing the auxiliary expression

$$\chi = \frac{1}{r} F\left(t + \frac{r}{c}\right),$$

where F is a function to be specified further on, we shall consider the integral

$$J = \int (\psi \Delta \chi - \chi \Delta \psi) \, dS$$

extended to the space between σ and Σ.

In the first place we have by Green's theorem

$$J = \int \left(\psi \frac{\partial \chi}{\partial n} - \chi \frac{\partial \psi}{\partial n}\right) d\sigma - \int \left(\psi \frac{\partial \chi}{\partial N} - \chi \frac{\partial \psi}{\partial N}\right) d\Sigma,$$

and in the second place, on account of (29) and (6),

$$J = -\int \chi \omega \, dS + \frac{1}{c^2} \int \left(\psi \frac{\partial^2 \chi}{\partial t^2} - \chi \frac{\partial^2 \psi}{\partial t^2}\right) dS$$

$$= -\int \chi \omega \, dS + \frac{1}{c^2} \frac{d}{dt} \int \left(\psi \frac{\partial \chi}{\partial t} - \chi \frac{\partial \psi}{\partial t}\right) dS.$$

Hence, combining the two results,

$$-\int \left(\psi \frac{\partial \chi}{\partial N} - \chi \frac{\partial \psi}{\partial N}\right) d\Sigma = -\int \chi \omega \, dS - \int \left(\psi \frac{\partial \chi}{\partial n} - \chi \frac{\partial \psi}{\partial n}\right) d\sigma$$
$$+ \frac{1}{c^2} \frac{d}{dt} \int \left(\psi \frac{\partial \chi}{\partial t} - \chi \frac{\partial \psi}{\partial t}\right) dS.$$

This equation must hold for all values of t. After being multiplied by dt, it may therefore be integrated between arbitrary limits t_1 and t_2, giving

$$\left.\begin{aligned} -\int_{t_1}^{t_2} dt \int \left(\psi \frac{\partial \chi}{\partial N} - \chi \frac{\partial \psi}{\partial N}\right) d\Sigma = -\int_{t_1}^{t_2} dt \int \chi \omega \, dS \\ -\int_{t_1}^{t_2} dt \int \left(\psi \frac{\partial \chi}{\partial n} - \chi \frac{\partial \psi}{\partial n}\right) d\sigma + \frac{1}{c^2} \left| \int \left(\psi \frac{\partial \chi}{\partial t} - \chi \frac{\partial \psi}{\partial t}\right) dS \right|_{t_1}^{t_2} \end{aligned}\right\} \quad (7)$$

From this equation we may draw the solution of our problem by means of a proper choice of the function F, which has thus far been left indeterminate.

We shall suppose that $F(\varepsilon)$ differs from zero only for values of ε lying between 0 and a certain positive quantity δ, this latter being so small that we may neglect the change which any of the other quantities occurring in the problem undergoes during an interval of time equal to ε. As to the function F itself, we shall suppose its values between $\varepsilon = 0$ and $\varepsilon = \delta$ to be so great that

$$\int_0^\delta F(\varepsilon)\, d\varepsilon = 1.$$

Since, for a fixed value of r,

$$\int_{t_1}^{t_2} F\left(t + \frac{r}{c}\right) dt = \int_{t_1 + \frac{r}{c}}^{t_2 + \frac{r}{c}} F(\varepsilon)\, d\varepsilon,$$

it is clear that on the above assumptions

$$\int_{t_1}^{t_2} F\left(t + \frac{r}{c}\right) dt = 1,$$

and

$$\int_{t_1}^{t_2} \varkappa F\left(t + \frac{r}{c}\right) dt = \varkappa_{\left(t = -\frac{r}{c}\right)}, \tag{8}$$

if we understand by $\varkappa$ one of the functions of t with which we are concerned, and by t_1 and t_2 values of t, such that

$$t_1 + \frac{r}{c} < 0 \quad \text{and} \quad t_2 + \frac{r}{c} > \delta.$$

It will presently be seen that, in the discussion of the equation (7), the formula (8) enables us to select as it were the values of ψ and ω corresponding to definite moments.

Let t_2 have a fixed positive value and t_1 a negative one, so great that even for the points of σ most distant from P, $t_1 + \frac{r}{c} < 0$. Then all values of χ occurring in the last term of (7) are zero. So are also the values of $\frac{\partial \chi}{\partial t}$ in that term. Indeed,

$$\frac{\partial \chi}{\partial t} = \frac{1}{r} F'\left(t + \frac{r}{c}\right)$$

and this vanishes for $t = t_1$ and $t = t_2$ because $F'(\varepsilon)$, like $F(\varepsilon)$ itself vanishes for all values of ε outside the interval $(0, \delta)$. The last term on the right-hand side of (7) is thus seen to be zero.

The term containing ω may be written

$$-\int \frac{1}{r}\,dS \int_{t_1}^{t_2} \omega F\left(t+\frac{r}{c}\right)dt,$$

where

$$\int_{t_1}^{t_2} \omega F\left(t+\frac{r}{c}\right)dt$$

relates to a particular element of volume dS, at the distance r from P. Hence, on account of (8)

$$-\int_{t_1}^{t_2} dt \int \chi\omega\,dS = -\int \frac{1}{r}\,\omega_{\left(t=-\frac{r}{c}\right)}\,dS.$$

By similar reasoning it is found that

$$\int_{t_1}^{t_2} dt \int \chi \frac{\partial\psi}{\partial n}\,d\sigma = \int \frac{1}{r}\left(\frac{\partial\psi}{\partial n}\right)_{\left(t=-\frac{r}{c}\right)} d\sigma.$$

We have next to consider the integral containing $\frac{\partial\chi}{\partial n}$. This differential coefficient being equal to

$$\frac{\partial}{\partial n}\left(\frac{1}{r}\right)F\left(t+\frac{r}{c}\right)+\frac{1}{rc}\frac{\partial r}{\partial n}F'\left(t+\frac{r}{c}\right),$$

we have

$$\int_{t_1}^{t_2} dt \int \psi \frac{\partial\chi}{\partial n}\,d\sigma = \int_{t_1}^{t_2} dt \int \frac{\partial}{\partial n}\left(\frac{1}{r}\right)\psi F\left(t+\frac{r}{c}\right)d\sigma$$
$$+\frac{1}{c}\int_{t_1}^{t_2} dt \int \frac{1}{r}\frac{\partial r}{\partial n}\psi F'\left(t+\frac{r}{c}\right)d\sigma.$$

The first integral is

$$\int \frac{\partial}{\partial n}\left(\frac{1}{r}\right)d\sigma \int_{t_1}^{t_2} \psi F\left(t+\frac{r}{c}\right)dt = \int \frac{\partial}{\partial n}\left(\frac{1}{r}\right)\psi_{\left(t=-\frac{r}{c}\right)}\,d\sigma,$$

and the second expression may be integrated by parts:

$$\int_{t_1}^{t_2} dt \int \frac{1}{r}\frac{\partial r}{\partial n}\psi F'\left(t+\frac{r}{c}\right)d\sigma = \int \frac{1}{r}\frac{\partial r}{\partial n}\,d\sigma \int_{t_1}^{t_2} \psi F'\left(t+\frac{r}{c}\right)dt$$

$$=\int \frac{1}{r}\frac{\partial r}{\partial n}\,d\sigma \left|\psi F\left(t+\frac{r}{c}\right)\right|_{t_1}^{t_2} - \int \frac{1}{r}\frac{\partial r}{\partial n}\,d\sigma \int_{t_1}^{t_2} \frac{\partial\psi}{\partial t}F\left(t+\frac{r}{c}\right)dt$$

$$=-\int \frac{1}{r}\frac{\partial r}{\partial n}\,\dot{\psi}_{\left(t=-\frac{r}{c}\right)}\,d\sigma,$$

because both $F\left(t_1+\frac{r}{c}\right)$ and $F\left(t_2+\frac{r}{c}\right)$ vanish.

Combining these results we find for the right-hand member of (7)

$$-\int \frac{1}{r}\,\omega_{\left(t=-\frac{r}{c}\right)}\,dS$$

$$+\int\left\{\frac{1}{r}\left(\frac{\partial\psi}{\partial n}\right)_{\left(t=-\frac{r}{c}\right)}-\frac{\partial}{\partial n}\left(\frac{1}{r}\right)\psi_{\left(t=-\frac{r}{c}\right)}+\frac{1}{cr}\frac{\partial r}{\partial n}\dot{\psi}_{\left(t=-\frac{r}{c}\right)}\right\}d\sigma.$$

We shall now suppose the radius R of the sphere Σ to diminish indefinitely. By this the first integral in our last expression is made to extend to within the immediate neighbourhood of the point P. The remaining terms remain unchanged, but for the quantity on the left-hand side of (7) we must take its limiting value for $\lim R = 0$.

As the integral over the sphere has the same form as that over the surface σ which we have just considered, we may write

$$-\int_{t_1}^{t_2} dt\int\left(\psi\frac{\partial\chi}{\partial N}-\chi\frac{\partial\psi}{\partial N}\right)d\Sigma$$

$$=\int\left\{\frac{1}{r}\left(\frac{\partial\psi}{\partial N}\right)_{\left(t=-\frac{r}{c}\right)}-\frac{\partial}{\partial N}\left(\frac{1}{r}\right)\psi_{\left(t=-\frac{r}{c}\right)}+\frac{1}{cr}\frac{\partial r}{\partial N}\dot{\psi}_{\left(t=-\frac{r}{c}\right)}\right\}d\Sigma,$$

or, since the normal N has the direction of r, and since, at the sphere, $r = R$,

$$\int\left\{\frac{1}{R}\left(\frac{\partial\psi}{\partial N}\right)_{\left(t=-\frac{R}{c}\right)}+\frac{1}{R^2}\psi_{\left(t=-\frac{R}{c}\right)}+\frac{1}{cR}\dot{\psi}_{\left(t=-\frac{R}{c}\right)}\right\}d\Sigma.$$

Now, when R tends towards 0, the integrals with $\frac{1}{R}$ vanish, so that the expression reduces to

$$\frac{1}{R^2}\int\psi_{\left(t=-\frac{R}{c}\right)}\,d\Sigma. \qquad (9)$$

Let ψ_1 and ψ_2 be the extreme values of $\psi_{\left(t=-\frac{R}{c}\right)}$ on the surface of the sphere. Then (9) is included between

$$4\pi\psi_1 \quad\text{and}\quad 4\pi\psi_2.$$

But both ψ_1 and ψ_2 have for their limit the value of ψ at the point P for the instant $t = 0$, say $\psi_{P(t=0)}$, so that the limit of (9) is seen to be

$$4\pi\psi_{P(t=0)},$$

and equation (7) ultimately becomes

$$\psi_{P(t=0)} = -\frac{1}{4\pi}\int \frac{1}{r}\,\omega_{\left(t=-\frac{r}{c}\right)} dS$$

$$+\frac{1}{4\pi}\int\left\{\frac{1}{r}\left(\frac{\partial\psi}{\partial n}\right)_{\left(t=-\frac{r}{c}\right)} - \frac{\partial}{\partial n}\left(\frac{1}{r}\right)\psi_{\left(t=-\frac{r}{c}\right)} + \frac{1}{cr}\frac{\partial r}{\partial n}\dot{\psi}_{\left(t=-\frac{r}{c}\right)}\right\} d\sigma.$$

This determines the value of ψ at the chosen point P for the instant $t = 0$. We are, however, free in the choice of this instant, and therefore the formula may serve to calculate the value of ψ_P for any instant t; for this we have only to replace the values of ω, ψ, $\frac{\partial\psi}{\partial n}$ and $\dot{\psi}$ on the right-hand side by those relating to the time $t - \frac{r}{c}$. Distinguishing these by square brackets, and omitting the index P, we find

$$\psi = -\frac{1}{4\pi}\int\frac{[\omega]}{r} dS + \frac{1}{4\pi}\int\left\{\frac{1}{r}\left[\frac{\partial\psi}{\partial n}\right] - \frac{\partial}{\partial n}\left(\frac{1}{r}\right)[\psi] + \frac{1}{cr}\frac{\partial r}{\partial n}[\dot{\psi}]\right\} d\sigma. \quad (10)$$

The formula (30) given in the text is obtained by making the surface σ recede on all sides to infinite distance, by which in many cases the surface integral is made to vanish. We may suppose, for example, that in distant regions of space, the function ψ has been zero until some definite instant t_0. The time $t - \frac{r}{c}$ to which the quantities $[\psi]$, $\left[\frac{\partial\psi}{\partial n}\right]$, $[\dot{\psi}]$ relate, always falls below t_0 when r increases, so that, finally, all the quantities in square brackets become 0.

5 (Page 19). When a vector $\mathbf{A}$, whose components we shall suppose to be continuous functions of the coordinates (cf. § 7) is solenoidally distributed, so that

$$\operatorname{div}\mathbf{A} = 0, \quad (11)$$

we can always find a second vector $\mathbf{B}$ such that

$$\mathbf{A} = \operatorname{rot}\mathbf{B}.$$

It suffices for this purpose to put

$$\mathbf{B} = \frac{1}{4\pi}\int\frac{\operatorname{rot}\mathbf{A}}{r} dS.$$

Indeed, we find from this, if we use equation (*2*) of Note 1 and the above equation (*11*), that

$$\operatorname{rot}\mathbf{B} = \frac{1}{4\pi}\int\frac{\operatorname{rot}\operatorname{rot}\mathbf{A}}{r} dS = -\frac{1}{4\pi}\int\frac{\Delta\mathbf{A}}{r} dS,$$

and this is equal to $\mathbf{A}$ in virtue of Poisson's theorem.

In this demonstration we have used the theorem that, if ω is continuous, a potential function of the form

$$\int \frac{\omega}{r} dS$$

may be differentiated with respect to one of the coordinates by simply differentiating ω under the sign of integration with respect to the corresponding coordinate of the element dS.

Now, equation (18) shows that the magnetic force $\mathbf{h}$ is solenoidally distributed. Therefore we can always find a vector $\mathbf{a}$ such that

$$\mathbf{h} = \text{rot}\, \mathbf{a}. \qquad (12)$$

After having done so, we may write for the equation (20)

$$\text{rot}\left(\mathbf{d} + \frac{1}{c}\dot{\mathbf{a}}\right) = 0,$$

showing that the vector

$$\mathbf{d} + \frac{1}{c}\dot{\mathbf{a}}$$

must be the gradient of some scalar function $-\varphi$, so that

$$\mathbf{d} = -\frac{1}{c}\dot{\mathbf{a}} - \text{grad}\, \varphi. \qquad (13)$$

It must be observed, however, that the vector $\mathbf{a}$ and the scalar function φ are left indeterminate to a certain extent by what precedes (though in each special case $\mathbf{h}$ and $\mathbf{d}$ have determinate values). Understanding by $\mathbf{a}_0$ and φ_0 special values, we may represent other values that may as well be chosen by

$$\mathbf{a} = \mathbf{a}_0 - \text{grad}\, \chi, \quad \varphi = \varphi_0 + \frac{1}{c}\dot{\chi},$$

where χ is some scalar function. We shall determine it by subjecting $\mathbf{a}$ and φ to the condition

$$\text{div}\, \mathbf{a} = -\frac{1}{c}\dot{\varphi}, \qquad (14)$$

which can always be fulfilled because it leads to the equation

$$\Delta\chi - \frac{1}{c^2}\ddot{\chi} = \text{div}\, \mathbf{a}_0 + \frac{1}{c}\dot{\varphi}_0,$$

which can be satisfied by a proper choice of χ.

The differential equations (31) and (32) follow immediately from (17) and (19), if in these one substitutes the values (*13*) and (*12*) Indeed, (17) assumes the form

$$-\frac{1}{c}\text{div}\, \dot{\mathbf{a}} - \Delta\varphi = \varrho,$$

i. e., in virtue of (*14*)

$$\Delta\varphi - \frac{1}{c^2}\ddot{\varphi} = -\varrho,$$

and (19) becomes

$$\text{rot rot}\,\mathbf{a} = -\frac{1}{c^2}\ddot{\mathbf{a}} - \frac{1}{c}\,\text{grad}\,\dot{\varphi} + \frac{1}{c}\varrho\mathbf{v},$$

or (cf. Note 1)

$$\text{grad div}\,\mathbf{a} - \Delta\mathbf{a} = -\frac{1}{c^2}\ddot{\mathbf{a}} - \frac{1}{c}\,\text{grad}\,\dot{\varphi} + \frac{1}{c}\varrho\mathbf{v},$$

for which, on account of (*14*), we may write

$$\Delta\mathbf{a} - \frac{1}{c^2}\ddot{\mathbf{a}} = -\frac{1}{c}\varrho\mathbf{v}.$$

6 (Page 20). Our solution is not a general one because we have made the assumption that the surface integral in (*10*), Note 4 vanishes when the surface σ recedes to infinite distance. It is to be observed, however, that any other solution may be put in the form

$$\psi = -\frac{1}{4\pi}\int\frac{[\omega]}{r}dS + \psi',$$

where ψ' is some function satisfying the equation

$$\Delta\psi' - \frac{1}{c^2}\ddot{\psi}' = 0.$$

In the terms of the physical problem with which we are concerned, we may say that the electromagnetic field determined by (33)—(36), (which may be considered as *produced* by the electrons), is not the only one that can exist; we can always add a field satisfying at all points of space the equations (2)—(5) for the free ether. Additional terms of this kind are excluded by the assumption made in the text.

Of course, a state of things for which the formulae (2)—(5) hold, can exist in a limited part of space; the beam of plane polarized light represented by the equations (7) is a proper example. Such a beam must however be considered as having its origin in the vibrations of distant electrons, and it is clear that, if we wish to include the source of light, we must have recourse to equations similar to (33)–(36).

7 (Page 21). Let the centre of the electron move along the axis of x. Then it is clear that $\mathbf{a}_y = 0$, $\mathbf{a}_z = 0$, and that φ and $\mathbf{a}_x$ may be regarded as functions of t, x and the distance r from the origin of coordinates. Indeed, φ and $\mathbf{a}_x$ must be constant along a circle having OX for its axis.

Putting

$$\varphi = f_1(t, r, x), \quad \mathbf{a}_x = f_2(t, r, x),$$

one finds

$$\mathbf{d}_x = -\frac{1}{c}\dot{\mathbf{a}}_x - \frac{\partial \varphi}{\partial x} = -\frac{1}{c}\frac{\partial f_2}{\partial t} - \frac{\partial f_1}{\partial x} - \frac{x}{r}\frac{\partial f_1}{\partial r},$$

$$\mathbf{d}_y = -\frac{\partial \varphi}{\partial y} = -\frac{y}{r}\frac{\partial f_1}{\partial r}, \quad \mathbf{d}_z = -\frac{\partial \varphi}{\partial z} = -\frac{z}{r}\frac{\partial f_1}{\partial r}.$$

Hence, $\mathbf{d}$ may be considered as the resultant of two vectors, one having the direction of OX and the magnitude $-\frac{1}{c}\frac{\partial f_2}{\partial t} - \frac{\partial f_1}{\partial x}$, and the other the direction of r and the magnitude $-\frac{\partial f_1}{\partial r}$.

The components of the magnetic force are

$$\mathbf{h}_x = \frac{\partial \mathbf{a}_z}{\partial y} - \frac{\partial \mathbf{a}_y}{\partial z} = 0,$$

$$\mathbf{h}_y = \frac{\partial \mathbf{a}_x}{\partial z} - \frac{\partial \mathbf{a}_z}{\partial x} = \frac{z}{r}\frac{\partial f_2}{\partial r},$$

$$\mathbf{h}_z = \frac{\partial \mathbf{a}_y}{\partial x} - \frac{\partial \mathbf{a}_x}{\partial y} = -\frac{y}{r}\frac{\partial f_2}{\partial r},$$

so that $\mathbf{h}$ is at right angles both to OX and to the line r.

What is said in the text about the electric and the magnetic lines of force follows immediately from these results.

8 (Page 22). In establishing the equation of energy we shall start from the formula (23). For an element of time dt the work of the force exerted by the ether on an element dS of the charge is represented by the scalar product of the force $\mathbf{f}\varrho\, dS$ and the path $\mathbf{v}\,dt$. Hence, the integral

$$A = \int \varrho(\mathbf{f}\cdot\mathbf{v})\,dS$$

represents the total work done by the ether per unit of time, but this work depends entirely on the first part of the vector (23), since the second part $\frac{1}{c}[\mathbf{v}\cdot\mathbf{h}]$ is perpendicular to the velocity $\mathbf{v}$. Consequently

$$A = \int \varrho(\mathbf{f}\cdot\mathbf{v})\,dS = \int \varrho(\mathbf{d}\cdot\mathbf{v})\,dS = \int (\mathbf{d}\cdot\varrho\mathbf{v})\,dS,$$

and, if the value of $\varrho\mathbf{v}$ is taken from the equation (19),

$$A = c\int (\mathbf{d}\cdot \operatorname{rot}\mathbf{h})\,dS - \int (\mathbf{d}\cdot\dot{\mathbf{d}})\,dS. \qquad (15)$$

Written in full, and with the terms rearranged, the first integral is

$$\int\left\{\left(\mathbf{d}_z\frac{\partial \mathbf{h}_y}{\partial x} - \mathbf{d}_y\frac{\partial \mathbf{h}_z}{\partial x}\right) + \left(\mathbf{d}_x\frac{\partial \mathbf{h}_z}{\partial y} - \mathbf{d}_z\frac{\partial \mathbf{h}_x}{\partial y}\right) + \left(\mathbf{d}_y\frac{\partial \mathbf{h}_x}{\partial z} - \mathbf{d}_x\frac{\partial \mathbf{h}_y}{\partial z}\right)\right\} dS, \qquad (16)$$

and here each term may be integrated by parts. Thus, denoting by

α, β, γ the angles between the normal n to the surface σ and the positive axes,

$$\int \mathbf{d}_z \frac{\partial \mathbf{h}_y}{\partial x} dS = \int \mathbf{d}_z \mathbf{h}_y \cos\alpha\, d\sigma - \int \mathbf{h}_y \frac{\partial \mathbf{d}_z}{\partial x} dS,$$

$$\int \mathbf{d}_y \frac{\partial \mathbf{h}_z}{\partial x} dS = \int \mathbf{d}_y \mathbf{h}_z \cos\alpha\, d\sigma - \int \mathbf{h}_z \frac{\partial \mathbf{d}_y}{\partial x} dS,$$

$$\int \left(\mathbf{d}_z \frac{\partial \mathbf{h}_y}{\partial x} - \mathbf{d}_y \frac{\partial \mathbf{h}_z}{\partial x}\right) dS = -\int [\mathbf{d}\cdot\mathbf{h}]_x \cos\alpha\, d\sigma + \int \left(\mathbf{h}_z \frac{\partial \mathbf{d}_y}{\partial x} - \mathbf{h}_y \frac{\partial \mathbf{d}_z}{\partial x}\right) dS,$$

where $[\mathbf{d}\cdot\mathbf{h}]_x$ means the first component of the vector product $[\mathbf{d}\cdot\mathbf{h}]$.

If the remaining parts of (*16*) are treated in a similar way, the first integral in (*15*) becomes

$$\left.\begin{aligned} &\int (\mathbf{d}\cdot \operatorname{rot}\mathbf{h})\, dS = \\ &= -\int \{[\mathbf{d}\cdot\mathbf{h}]_x \cos\alpha + [\mathbf{d}\cdot\mathbf{h}]_y \cos\beta + [\mathbf{d}\cdot\mathbf{h}]_z \cos\gamma\}\, d\sigma \\ &+ \int (\mathbf{h}\cdot \operatorname{rot}\mathbf{d})\, dS = -\int [\mathbf{d}\cdot\mathbf{h}]_n\, d\sigma + \int (\mathbf{h}\cdot\operatorname{rot}\mathbf{d})\, dS. \end{aligned}\right\} \quad (17)$$

The formula (37) is now easily obtained if it is taken into account:

1° that, in virtue of (20), the last term of (*17*) may be replaced by

$$-\frac{1}{c}\int (\mathbf{h}\cdot\dot{\mathbf{h}})\, dS;$$

2° that

$$(\mathbf{d}\cdot\dot{\mathbf{d}}) = \frac{1}{2}\frac{\partial(\mathbf{d}^2)}{\partial t}, \quad (\mathbf{h}\cdot\dot{\mathbf{h}}) = \frac{1}{2}\frac{\partial(\mathbf{h}^2)}{\partial t}.$$

We may notice in passing that the equation (*17*) expresses a general theorem. Denoting by $\mathbf{A}$ and $\mathbf{B}$ any two vectors and by σ the bounding surface of a space S, we always have

$$\int (\mathbf{A}\cdot\operatorname{rot}\mathbf{B})\, dS = -\int [\mathbf{A}\cdot\mathbf{B}]_n\, d\sigma + \int (\mathbf{B}\cdot\operatorname{rot}\mathbf{A})\, dS.$$

9 (Page 26). The deduction of the formulae for $\mathbf{F}$ is much like that of the equation of energy. Instead of (43) we may write

$$\mathbf{F} = \int \left\{\varrho\mathbf{d} + \frac{1}{c}[\varrho\mathbf{v}\cdot\mathbf{h}]\right\} dS,$$

and here, in virtue of (17) and (19), we may replace ϱ by div $\mathbf{d}$, and $\varrho\mathbf{v}$ by c rot $\mathbf{h} - \dot{\mathbf{d}}$. Hence

$$\mathbf{F} = \int \left\{\operatorname{div}\mathbf{d}\cdot\mathbf{d} + [\operatorname{rot}\mathbf{h}\cdot\mathbf{h}] - \frac{1}{c}[\dot{\mathbf{d}}\cdot\mathbf{h}]\right\} dS.$$

But

$$[\dot{\mathbf{d}} \cdot \mathbf{h}] = \frac{\partial}{\partial t}[\mathbf{d} \cdot \mathbf{h}] - [\mathbf{d} \cdot \dot{\mathbf{h}}] = \frac{\partial}{\partial t}[\mathbf{d} \cdot \mathbf{h}] - c[\text{rot}\, \mathbf{d} \cdot \mathbf{d}],$$

o that, if we determine the part $\mathbf{F}_2$ of the resultant force by the ormula

$$\mathbf{F}_2 = -\frac{1}{c}\frac{d}{dt}\int [\mathbf{d} \cdot \mathbf{h}]\, dS = -\frac{1}{c^2}\frac{d}{dt}\int \mathbf{s}\, dS = -\frac{1}{c^2}\int \dot{\mathbf{s}}\, dS,$$

the remaining part is given by

$$\mathbf{F}_1 = \int \{\text{div}\, \mathbf{d} \cdot \mathbf{d} + [\text{rot}\, \mathbf{h} \cdot \mathbf{h}] + [\text{rot}\, \mathbf{d} \cdot \mathbf{d}]\}\, dS.$$

Leaving aside for a moment the term depending on the magnetic force, we have for the first component of $\mathbf{F}_1$

$$\int \left\{ \left(\frac{\partial \mathbf{d}_x}{\partial x} + \frac{\partial \mathbf{d}_y}{dy} + \frac{\partial \mathbf{d}_z}{\partial z} \right) \mathbf{d}_x + \left(\frac{\partial \mathbf{d}_x}{\partial z} - \frac{\partial \mathbf{d}_z}{\partial x} \right) \mathbf{d}_z - \left(\frac{\partial \mathbf{d}_y}{\partial x} - \frac{\partial \mathbf{d}_x}{\partial y} \right) \mathbf{d}_y \right\} dS$$

$$= \int \left\{ \frac{1}{2}\frac{\partial}{\partial x}(\mathbf{d}_x^2 - \mathbf{d}_y^2 - \mathbf{d}_z^2) + \frac{\partial}{\partial y}(\mathbf{d}_x \mathbf{d}_y) + \frac{\partial}{\partial z}(\mathbf{d}_x \mathbf{d}_z) \right\} dS$$

$$= \int \left\{ \frac{1}{2}(\mathbf{d}_x^2 - \mathbf{d}_y^2 - \mathbf{d}_z^2) \cos\alpha + \mathbf{d}_x \mathbf{d}_y \cos\beta + \mathbf{d}_x \mathbf{d}_z \cos\gamma \right\} d\sigma$$

$$= \int \frac{1}{2} \{2\mathbf{d}_x \mathbf{d}_n - \mathbf{d}^2 \cos\alpha\}\, d\sigma.$$

The part of $\mathbf{F}_1$ that depends on $\mathbf{h}$ leads to a result of the same form, the reason being that $\mathbf{F}_1$ becomes symmetrical in $\mathbf{d}$ and $\mathbf{h}$ when we add the term div $\mathbf{h} \cdot \mathbf{h}$, which is zero on account of (18).

10 (Page 29). The stress on a surface element of any direction and situated anywhere in the space considered can be calculated by means of the formulae (48); if one takes the mean values for a long lapse of time, it will be found to be at right angles to the element. In other terms, there is a normal pressure whose magnitude is given by

$$p = \tfrac{1}{2}\{(\mathbf{d}_y^2) + (\mathbf{d}_z^2) - (\mathbf{d}_x^2)\} + \tfrac{1}{2}\{(\mathbf{h}_y^2) + (\mathbf{h}_z^2) - (\mathbf{h}_x^2)\}, \quad (18)$$

if we lay the axis of x normally to the element, and denote by $(\mathbf{d}_x^2)$, etc. the mean values in question.

We shall now apply to two particular cases the result found in § 19. In the first place, we may take for σ a closed surface wholly lying within the envelop. Then (cf. § 20, b), since $\mathbf{F} = 0$ and, in the mean, $\mathbf{F}_2 = 0$, the pressures p acting on the surface must destroy each other. This requires that p be constant all trough the ether.

Next, considering a flat cylindrical box that contains an element of the wall (cf. Fig. 1, p. 28), we can show that the pressure p really may be said to be the force exerted on the walls

The pressure p having the same intensity at all points, we may as well replace it by the mean of the values which, for determinate directions of OX, OY, OZ, the expression (*18*) has at different places. Hence, if mean values of this kind are denoted by a horizontal bar

$$p = \tfrac{1}{2}\{(\overline{\mathsf{d}_y^2}) + (\overline{\mathsf{d}_z^2}) - (\overline{\mathsf{d}_x^2})\} + \tfrac{1}{2}\{(\overline{\mathsf{h}_y^2}) + (\overline{\mathsf{h}_z^2}) - (\overline{\mathsf{h}_x^2})\}.$$

But it is easily seen that the order of the two operations of taking the mean — one relating to time and the other to space — may be inverted, and that in the stationary state which we are considering the mean values indicated by $\overline{\mathsf{d}_x^2}$ etc. are independent of the time, so that, after having calculated them, it is no longer necessary to take their time-averages. Our formula therefore takes the form

$$p = \tfrac{1}{2}(\overline{\mathsf{d}_y^2} + \overline{\mathsf{d}_z^2} - \overline{\mathsf{d}_x^2}) + \tfrac{1}{2}(\overline{\mathsf{h}_y^2} + \overline{\mathsf{h}_z^2} - \overline{\mathsf{h}_x^2}).$$

11 (Page 30). The formula (51) is obtained if, in the transformations given in Note 9, we omit all terms containing ϱ. We may, however, also proceed as follows.

The resultant force in the direction of x, so far as it is due to the electric field, is given by the surface integral

$$\frac{1}{2}\int\{2\mathsf{d}_x\mathsf{d}_n - \mathsf{d}^2\cos\alpha\}\,d\sigma,$$

for which we may write (see the end of Note 9) the first component of

$$\int\{\operatorname{div}\mathsf{d}\cdot\mathsf{d} + [\operatorname{rot}\mathsf{d}\cdot\mathsf{d}]\}\,dS,$$

and to which we must add a similar expression depending on the magnetic field. Hence, since $\operatorname{div}\mathsf{h} = 0$, and, on the assumption now made, $\operatorname{div}\mathsf{d} = 0$,

$$\mathsf{F}_1 = \int\{[\operatorname{rot}\mathsf{h}\cdot\mathsf{h}] + [\operatorname{rot}\mathsf{d}\cdot\mathsf{d}]\}\,dS,$$

or, if we use equations (4) and (5),

$$\mathsf{F}_1 = \frac{1}{c}\int\{[\dot{\mathsf{d}}\cdot\mathsf{h}] - [\dot{\mathsf{h}}\cdot\mathsf{d}]\}\,dS = \frac{1}{c}\int\{[\dot{\mathsf{d}}\cdot\mathsf{h}] + [\mathsf{d}\cdot\dot{\mathsf{h}}]\}\,dS$$

$$= \frac{1}{c}\int\frac{\partial}{\partial t}[\mathsf{d}\cdot\mathsf{h}]\,dS = \frac{1}{c^2}\int\dot{\mathsf{s}}\,dS.$$

12 (Page 32). Let u, v, w be the components of the velocity of the ether at the point (x, y, z) and the time t. Then, by a well known theorem, the acceleration in the direction of x is given by

$$\frac{\partial u}{\partial t} + u\frac{\partial u}{\partial x} + v\frac{\partial u}{\partial y} + w\frac{\partial u}{\partial z},$$

so that, if μ is the density, and X the force acting on the element dS in the direction of x, we have

$$X = \mu \left(\frac{\partial u}{\partial t} + u \frac{\partial u}{\partial x} + v \frac{\partial u}{\partial y} + w \frac{\partial u}{\partial z} \right) dS.$$

When u, v, w are very small, we may neglect the terms $u \frac{\partial u}{\partial x}$ etc., and add the term $u \frac{\partial \mu}{\partial t}$, which is likewise of the second order of magnitude, because in the case of slow motions, the change of the density per unit of time is very small. It follows that

$$X = \frac{\partial}{\partial t} (\mu u dS),$$

the mathematical expression for the statement made in the text.

13 (Page 35). The value φ of the scalar potential that exists at the time t at the point (x, y, z) of the ether, will be found at the time $t + dt$ at a point whose coordinates are $x + w dt$, y, z. As the value of the potential for these new values of the independent variables may be represented by

$$\varphi + \frac{\partial \varphi}{\partial t} dt + \frac{\partial \varphi}{\partial x} w dt,$$

we have

$$\frac{\partial \varphi}{\partial t} dt + \frac{\partial \varphi}{\partial x} w dt = 0,$$

$$\frac{\partial \varphi}{\partial t} = - w \frac{\partial \varphi}{\partial x}.$$

Applying the same reasoning to the function $\frac{\partial \varphi}{\partial t}$, one finds

$$\frac{\partial^2 \varphi}{\partial t^2} = - w \frac{\partial}{\partial x} \left(\frac{\partial \varphi}{\partial t} \right) = w^2 \frac{\partial^2 \varphi}{\partial x^2}.$$

14 (Page 36). Let S' be a system without translation, and let two points, the one in the moving system S, with the coordinates x, y, z, and the other in S' with the coordinates x', y, z — the relation between x and x' being as shown in (58) — be said to correspond to each other. Then corresponding elements of volume, dS and dS', are to each other in the same ratio as x and x', so that

$$dS' = (1 - \beta^2)^{-1/2} dS,$$

and if they are to have equal charges, the density ϱ' in dS' must be related to the density ϱ in dS as follows:

$$\varrho' = (1 - \beta^2)^{1/2} \varrho.$$

Poisson's equation, which determines the scalar potential φ' in the stationary system may therefore be written in the form

$$\frac{\partial^2 \varphi'}{\partial x'^2} + \frac{\partial^2 \varphi'}{\partial y^2} + \frac{\partial^2 \varphi'}{\partial z^2} = -\varrho' = -(1-\beta^2)^{1/2}\varrho,$$

showing, on comparison with (59), that at corresponding points

$$\varphi' = (1-\beta^2)^{1/2}\varphi, \quad \varphi = (1-\beta^2)^{-1/2}\varphi'. \tag{19}$$

The quantities relating to the moving system S may now be expressed in terms of those that belong to S'.

In the first place we have, on account of (58) and (*19*),

$$\frac{\partial \varphi}{\partial x} = (1-\beta^2)^{-1}\frac{\partial \varphi'}{\partial x'}, \quad \frac{\partial \varphi}{\partial y} = (1-\beta^2)^{-1/2}\frac{\partial \varphi'}{\partial y}, \quad \frac{\partial \varphi}{\partial z} = (1-\beta^2)^{-1/2}\frac{\partial \varphi'}{\partial z}.$$

Further, by (33) and (34), since

$$\mathbf{a}_x = \beta\varphi, \quad \mathbf{a}_y = 0, \quad \mathbf{a}_z = 0,$$

$$\dot{\mathbf{a}}_x = -w\frac{\partial \mathbf{a}_x}{\partial x} = -\beta^2 c\frac{\partial \varphi}{\partial x},$$

$$\mathbf{d}_x = -\frac{1}{c}\dot{\mathbf{a}}_x - \frac{\partial \varphi}{\partial x} = -(1-\beta^2)\frac{\partial \varphi}{\partial x},$$

$$\mathbf{d}_y = -\frac{\partial \varphi}{\partial y}, \quad \mathbf{d}_z = -\frac{\partial \varphi}{\partial z},$$

$$\mathbf{h}_x = 0, \quad \mathbf{h}_y = \frac{\partial \mathbf{a}_x}{\partial z} = \beta\frac{\partial \varphi}{\partial z}, \quad \mathbf{h}_z = -\frac{\partial \mathbf{a}_x}{\partial y} = -\beta\frac{\partial \varphi}{\partial y}.$$

The electric energy is therefore given by

$$\left.\begin{aligned} U &= \frac{1}{2}\int\left\{(1-\beta^2)^2\left(\frac{\partial \varphi}{\partial x}\right)^2 + \left(\frac{\partial \varphi}{\partial y}\right)^2 + \left(\frac{\partial \varphi}{\partial z}\right)^2\right\}dS \\ &= \frac{1}{2}\int\left\{(1-\beta^2)^{1/2}\left(\frac{\partial \varphi'}{\partial x'}\right)^2 + (1-\beta^2)^{-1/2}\left[\left(\frac{\partial \varphi'}{\partial y}\right)^2 + \left(\frac{\partial \varphi'}{\partial z}\right)^2\right]\right\}dS', \end{aligned}\right\} \tag{20}$$

and the magnetic energy by

$$\left.\begin{aligned} T &= \tfrac{1}{2}\beta^2\int\left\{\left(\frac{\partial \varphi}{\partial y}\right)^2 + \left(\frac{\partial \varphi}{\partial z}\right)^2\right\}dS \\ &= \tfrac{1}{2}\beta^2(1-\beta^2)^{-1/2}\int\left\{\left(\frac{\partial \varphi'}{\partial y}\right)^2 + \left[\left(\frac{\partial \varphi'}{\partial z}\right)^2\right]\right\}dS'. \end{aligned}\right\} \tag{21}$$

Finally, we have for the components of the flow of energy

$$\mathbf{s}_x = c(\mathbf{d}_y\mathbf{h}_z - \mathbf{d}_z\mathbf{h}_y) = c\beta(1-\beta^2)^{-1}\left\{\left(\frac{\partial \varphi'}{\partial y}\right)^2 + \left(\frac{\partial \varphi'}{\partial z}\right)^2\right\},$$

$$\mathbf{s}_y = c(\mathbf{d}_z\mathbf{h}_x - \mathbf{d}_x\mathbf{h}_z) = -c\beta(1-\beta^2)^{-1/2}\frac{\partial \varphi'}{\partial x'}\frac{\partial \varphi'}{\partial y},$$

$$\mathbf{s}_z = c(\mathbf{d}_x\mathbf{h}_y - \mathbf{d}_y\mathbf{h}_x) = -c\beta(1-\beta^2)^{-1/2}\frac{\partial \varphi'}{\partial x'}\frac{\partial \varphi'}{\partial z},$$

and for those of the electromagnetic momentum

$$\mathsf{G}_x = \frac{1}{c}\beta(1-\beta^2)^{-1/2}\int\left\{\left(\frac{\partial\varphi'}{\partial y}\right)^2+\left(\frac{\partial\varphi'}{\partial z}\right)^2\right\}dS', \tag{22}$$

$$\mathsf{G}_y = -\frac{1}{c}\beta\int\frac{\partial\varphi'}{\partial x'}\frac{\partial\varphi'}{\partial y}\,dS',$$

$$\mathsf{G}_z = -\frac{1}{c}\beta\int\frac{\partial\varphi'}{\partial x'}\frac{\partial\varphi'}{\partial z}\,dS'.$$

15 (Page 37). A charge uniformly distributed over the surface of a sphere may be considered as the limiting case of a charge distributed with uniform volume density over an infinitely thin spherical shell having the same thickness at all points. When the moving system S is of this kind, the stationary system S' of which we have spoken in the preceding Note, is an elongated ellipsoid of revolution whose semi-axis a and equatorial radius b are equal to

$$a = (1-\beta^2)^{-1/2}R, \quad b = R, \tag{23}$$

and which carries a charge uniformly distributed through an infinitely thin shell bounded by the ellipsoid itself and another that is similar to it and similarly placed with respect to the centre. The total charge must be taken equal to e, the charge of the sphere, because corresponding elements of volume in S and S' have been supposed to carry equal charges.

Let the centre of the ellipsoid be chosen as origin of coordinates, OX' being placed along the axis of revolution, and let x', y, z be the coordinates of an external point P. If we understand by λ the positive root of the equation

$$\frac{x'^2}{p^2+\lambda}+\frac{y^2+z^2}{\lambda}=1, \tag{24}$$

where

$$p^2 = a^2 - b^2,$$

the potential at P is equal to

$$\varphi' = \frac{e}{8\pi p}\log\frac{\sqrt{p^2+\lambda}+p}{\sqrt{p^2+\lambda}-p}.$$

It is to be noticed that, for a given value of λ, the equation (*24*) represents an ellipsoid of revolution confocal with the given one; therefore, the equipotential surfaces are ellipsoids of this kind. The charged surface itself is characterized by the value $\lambda = b^2$, and λ increases from this value to ∞ as we pass outwards. The potential is equal to

$$\varphi_0' = \frac{e}{8\pi p}\log\frac{a+p}{a-p}$$

at the charged surface, and has the same value at all internal points. The integrals to which we have been led in the preceding Note need therefore only be extended to the outside space.

In effecting the necessary calculations we shall avail ourselves of the theorem that the integral

$$\frac{1}{2}\int\left\{\left(\frac{\partial\varphi'}{\partial x'}\right)^2+\left(\frac{\partial\varphi'}{\partial y}\right)^2+\left(\frac{\partial\varphi'}{\partial z}\right)^2\right\}dS'$$

is equal to the electric energy $\frac{1}{2}e\varphi_0'$ of the charged ellipsoid. Hence, putting

$$J_1=\int\left(\frac{\partial\varphi'}{\partial x'}\right)^2 dS',\quad J_2=\int\left\{\left(\frac{\partial\varphi'}{\partial y}\right)^2+\left(\frac{\partial\varphi'}{\partial z}\right)^2\right\}dS',$$

we have

$$J_1+J_2=\frac{e^2}{8\pi p}\log\frac{a+p}{a-p}. \tag{25}$$

In order to find the integral J_1, we shall divide the plane $X'OY$ into infinitely small parts by the series of ellipses

$$\frac{x'^2}{p^2+\lambda}+\frac{y^2}{\lambda}=1, \tag{26}$$

and the system of hyperbolae

$$\frac{x'^2}{p^2-\mu}-\frac{y^2}{\mu}=1, \tag{27}$$

where μ ranges from 0 to p^2. Confining ourselves to the part of the plane where x' and y are positive, we have for the coordinates of the point of intersection of (26) and (27)

$$x'=\frac{1}{p}\sqrt{(p^2+\lambda)(p^2-\mu)},\quad y=\frac{1}{p}\sqrt{\lambda\mu}, \tag{28}$$

and for the area of the element bounded by the ellipses λ, $\lambda+d\lambda$ and the hyperbolae μ, $\mu+d\mu$

$$d\sigma=\begin{vmatrix}\frac{\partial x'}{\partial\lambda}, & \frac{\partial x'}{\partial\mu}\\ \frac{\partial y}{\partial\lambda}, & \frac{\partial y}{\partial\mu}\end{vmatrix} d\lambda d\mu=\frac{1}{4}\frac{\lambda+\mu}{\sqrt{\lambda\mu(p^2+\lambda)(p^2-\mu)}}d\lambda d\mu.$$

We shall now take for dS' in our integral the annular element that is generated by the revolution of this plane element around OX', so that

$$dS'=2\pi y d\sigma=\frac{\pi(\lambda+\mu)}{2p\sqrt{(p^2+\lambda)(p^2-\mu)}}d\lambda d\mu.$$

Since φ' depends on λ only, we have

$$\frac{\partial\varphi'}{\partial x'}=\frac{d\varphi'}{d\lambda}\frac{\partial\lambda}{\partial x'},$$

and here the last factor has, in all parts of the ring, the value deduced from (*26*) for a constant y,

$$\frac{\partial \lambda}{\partial x'} = \frac{2\lambda^2(p^2+\lambda)x'}{\lambda^2 x'^2 + (p^2+\lambda)^2 y^2},$$

or, in virtue of (*28*),

$$\frac{\partial \lambda}{\partial x'} = \frac{2\lambda}{(\lambda+\mu)p}\sqrt{(p^2+\lambda)(p^2-\mu)}.$$

It follows from these results that, in order to find J_1, we must integrate the expression

$$\frac{2\pi\lambda^2}{p^3(\lambda+\mu)}\sqrt{(p^2+\lambda)(p^2-\mu)}\left(\frac{d\varphi'}{d\lambda}\right)^2 d\lambda\, d\mu.$$

If we take 0 and p^2 as the limits of μ, b^2 and ∞ as those of λ, we shall find the part of J_1 that is due to the field on the positive side of the yz-plane; we must, therefore, multiply the result by 2.

Since

$$\int \frac{\sqrt{p^2-\mu}}{\lambda+\mu}\, d\mu = 2\sqrt{p^2-\mu} - \sqrt{p^2+\lambda}\log\frac{\sqrt{p^2+\lambda}+\sqrt{p^2-\mu}}{\sqrt{p^2+\lambda}-\sqrt{p^2-\mu}},$$

$$\int_0^{p^2} \frac{\sqrt{p^2-\mu}}{\lambda+\mu}\, d\mu = -2p + \sqrt{p^2+\lambda}\log\frac{\sqrt{p^2+\lambda}+p}{\sqrt{p^2+\lambda}-p},$$

and

$$\left(\frac{d\varphi'}{d\lambda}\right)^2 = \frac{e^2}{64\pi^2\lambda^2(p^2+\lambda)},$$

the final result is

$$J_1 = \frac{e^2}{16\pi p^3}\int_{b^2}^{\infty}\left\{\log\frac{\sqrt{p^2+\lambda}+p}{\sqrt{p^2+\lambda}-p} - \frac{2p}{\sqrt{p^2+\lambda}}\right\} d\lambda.$$

The indefinite integral is

$$\lambda\log\frac{\sqrt{p^2+\lambda}+p}{\sqrt{p^2+\lambda}-p} - 2p\sqrt{p^2+\lambda},$$

and since this vanishes for $\lambda = \infty$, and is equal to

$$b^2\log\frac{a+p}{a-p} - 2ap$$

for $\lambda = b^2$, the integral J_1 has the value

$$J_1 = \frac{e^2}{16\pi p^3}\left\{2ap - b^2\log\frac{a+p}{a-p}\right\}.$$

In our present problem the values of a and b are given by (*23*), so that

$$p = R\beta(1-\beta^2)^{-1/2},$$

$$J_1 = \frac{e^2}{16\pi R\beta^3}(1-\beta^2)^{3/2}\left[2\beta(1-\beta^2)^{-1} - \log\frac{1+\beta}{1-\beta}\right],$$

$$J_2 = \frac{e^2}{16\pi R\beta^3}(1-\beta^2)^{1/2}\left[-2\beta + (1+\beta^2)\log\frac{1+\beta}{1-\beta}\right].$$

Substituting these values in the formulae (*20*), (*21*) and (*22*), we get the equations (61), (62) and (63).

16 (Page 38). The electromagnetic momentum $\mathbf{G}$ and the velocity $\mathbf{w}$ having the same direction, we may write

$$\mathbf{G} = \alpha\mathbf{w},$$

where α is the ratio between their magnitudes $|\mathbf{G}|$ and $|\mathbf{w}|$. It is a function of $|\mathbf{w}|$.

Differentiating with respect to t, we find

$$\mathbf{F} = -\frac{d\mathbf{G}}{dt} = -\alpha\frac{d\mathbf{w}}{dt} - \frac{d\alpha}{dt}\mathbf{w} = -\alpha\frac{d\mathbf{w}}{dt} - \frac{d\alpha}{d|\mathbf{w}|}\frac{d|\mathbf{w}|}{dt}\mathbf{w}.$$

But

$$\mathbf{w}\frac{d|\mathbf{w}|}{dt} = |\mathbf{w}|\,\mathbf{j}', \quad \frac{d\mathbf{w}}{dt} = \mathbf{j}' + \mathbf{j}'',$$

so that

$$\mathbf{F} = -\alpha(\mathbf{j}'+\mathbf{j}'') - |\mathbf{w}|\frac{d\alpha}{d|\mathbf{w}|}\mathbf{j}' = -\frac{d}{d|\mathbf{w}|}\{\alpha|\mathbf{w}|\}\mathbf{j}' - \alpha\mathbf{j}''$$

$$= -\frac{d|\mathbf{G}|}{d|\mathbf{w}|}\mathbf{j}' - \frac{|\mathbf{G}|}{|\mathbf{w}|}\mathbf{j}'' = -m'\mathbf{j}' - m''\mathbf{j}''.$$

16* (Page 44) [1915]. In these last years highly interesting experiments have been made, especially by Ehrenhaft[1]) and Millikan[2]), in which small electric charges carried by minute metallic particles or liquid drops could be measured.

It is well known that the velocity v acquired by a small body falling in a gas is determined by the rule that the resistance to the motion ultimately becomes equal to the weight G of the particle. For slow motions the resistance is proportional to the velocity and we may therefore write

$$G = \mu v,$$

where μ is a coefficient which, in the case of a spherical particle, may be deduced from its radius and the coefficient of viscosity of the surrounding gas.

---

1) F. Ehrenhaft, Wiener Sitzungsber. (IIa) **123** (1914), p. 53.
2) R. A. Millikan, Phys. Zeitschr. **11** (1910), p. 1097.

A similar equation holds when the particle is subjected to a vertical electric force E. Let e the charge of the particle, and let E be positive when it is directed downward. Then the velocity of fall will be determined by

$$G + eE = \mu v'.$$

It can be made much smaller than v, if eE is negative.

It is clear that by measuring v and v', we can determine the ratio between eE and G; hence, the value of e becomes known if E and G are measured.

Millikan has found values for e which can be considered as multiples of a definite „elementary“ charge. Ehrenhaft, however, has been led to the conclusion that in some cases the charges are no multiples of the elementary one and may even be smaller than it.

The question cannot be said to be wholly elucidated.

17 (Page 48). Take the simple case of an infinitely long circular metallic cylinder of radius a_1, surrounded by a coaxial tube whose inner radius is a_2. When a current i is passed along the core and returned through the tube, the magnetic energy, so far as it is contained in the space between the two conductors, is equal to

$$\frac{i^2}{4\pi c^2} \log \frac{a_2}{a_1}$$

per unit of length; this expression is of the order of magnitude

$$\frac{i^2}{4\pi c^2} \tag{29}$$

when $\frac{a_2}{a_1}$ is some moderate number.

On the other hand, if, per unit of length, the two conductors contain N_1 and N_2 electrons, moving with the velocities v_1 and v_2, the sum of the amounts of energy that would correspond to the motion of each of them is

$$\frac{1}{2} m (N_1 v_1^2 + N_2 v_2^2) = \frac{e^2}{12\pi R c^2} (N_1 v_1^2 + N_2 v_2^2),$$

if we suppose the mass of the corpuscles to be wholly electromagnetic. The current being

$$i = eN_1 v_1 = eN_2 v_2,$$

we may write for our last expression

$$\frac{i^2}{12\pi R c^2} \left(\frac{1}{N_1} + \frac{1}{N_2}\right). \tag{30}$$

The experiments on self-induction have never shown an effect that may not be accounted for by the ordinary formulae for this phenomenon. Therefore, in ordinary cases, the value of (*30*) must be much smaller than that of (*29*), from which it may be inferred that $N_1 R$ and $N_2 R$ are great numbers.

18 (Page 49). In the following proof of the formula (76) we shall confine ourselves to an electron having a rectilinear translation parallel to OX with variable velocity v. Let Q be a definite point of this electron and P a point of the ether, within the space occupied by the particle at the time t for which we wish to calculate the force. Let x', y', z' be the coordinates of P, and x, y, z those of the point Q at the time t.

Among the successive positions of Q there is one Q_e such that an action proceeding from it the moment it is reached, and travelling onward with the speed of light c, will arrive at the point P at the time t. If we denote by $t-\tau$ the time at which this „effective" position, so we may call it, is reached, we have for the coordinates of Q_e

$$x_e = x - v\tau + \tfrac{1}{2}\dot{v}\tau^2 - \tfrac{1}{6}\ddot{v}\tau^3 + \cdots \qquad (31)$$

$$y_e = y, \quad z_e = z,$$

and, since $Q_e P$ must be equal to $c\tau$,

$$(x_e - x')^2 + (y_e - y')^2 + (z_e - z')^2 = c^2\tau^2. \qquad (32)$$

By means of these relations x_e and τ may be expressed in terms of x, y, z. Putting $QP = r$, so that

$$r^2 = (x-x')^2 + (y-y')^2 + (z-z')^2,$$

and considering $v, \dot{v}, \ddot{v}, \ldots$ as so small that terms of the second order with respect to these quantities may be neglected, we may substitute in (*31*) $\tau = \frac{r}{c}$, by which we find

$$x_e = x - \frac{v}{c}r + \frac{\dot{v}}{2c^2}r^2 - \frac{\ddot{v}}{6c^3}r^3 + \cdots \qquad (33)$$

Substituting this value in (*32*), we get

$$\tau = \frac{r}{c} - \frac{v}{c^2}(x-x') + \frac{\dot{v}}{2c^3}(x-x')r - \frac{\ddot{v}}{6c^4}(x-x')r^2 - \cdots$$

It follows from (*33*) that the points Q which, at the time t, are situated in an element $dx\,dy\,dz$, have their effective positions in an element $dx_e dy\,dz$, where

$$dx_e = \left\{1 - \frac{v}{c}\frac{x-x'}{r} + \frac{\dot{v}}{c^2}(x-x') - \frac{\ddot{v}}{2c^3}(x-x')r + \cdots\right\} dx.$$

Hence, to each element dS of the electron taken in the position which it has at the time t, there corresponds an element of space

$$dS_e = \left\{1 - \frac{v}{c}\frac{x-x'}{r} + \frac{\dot{v}}{c^2}(x-x') - \frac{\ddot{v}}{2c^3}(x-x')r + \cdots\right\} dS,$$

in which, at the time $t-\tau$, there was a density ϱ equal to that existing at the time t in the element dS, this charge having a velocity

$$v - \dot{v}\tau + \tfrac{1}{2}\ddot{v}\tau^2 - \cdots,$$

or, with a sufficient degree of approximation

$$v - \frac{\dot{v}}{c}r + \frac{\ddot{v}}{2c^2}r^2 - \cdots\cdots. \tag{34}$$

The distance of the element dS_e from the point P is given by

$$c\tau = r\left\{1 - \frac{v}{c}\frac{x-x'}{r} + \frac{\dot{v}}{2c^2}(x-x') - \frac{\ddot{v}}{6c^3}(x-x')r + \cdots\right\},$$

so that the quotient $\frac{dS}{r}$ in the equation (35) must be replaced by

$$\frac{dS_e}{c\tau} = \left[1 + \frac{\dot{v}}{2c^2}(x-x') - \frac{\ddot{v}}{3c^3}(x-x')r + \cdots\right]\frac{dS}{r}.$$

The factor here enclosed in square brackets may be omitted in the formula for the first component of the vector potential; here, however, we must replace v by the expression (*34*). In this way we find

$$\varphi = \frac{1}{4\pi}\int \varrho\left[1 + \frac{\dot{v}}{2c^2}(x-x') - \frac{\ddot{v}}{3c^3}(x-x')r + \cdots\right]\frac{dS}{r},$$

$$\mathrm{a}_x = \frac{1}{4\pi c}\int \varrho\left(v - \frac{\dot{v}}{c}r + \frac{\ddot{v}}{2c^2}r^2 - \cdots\right)\frac{dS}{r},$$

the integrations being extended to the space occupied by the electron at the time t.

Whe shall now proceed to calculate the electric force $\mathbf{f}$ at the point P. It may be observed in the first place that we need not consider the term $\frac{1}{c}[\mathbf{v}\cdot\mathbf{h}]$ in (23), because the magnetic force $\mathbf{h}$ itself is proportional to v. Hence, by (33), the first component of $\mathbf{f}$, to which we may limit ourselves, is equal to

$$\mathbf{f}_x = -\frac{\partial\varphi}{\partial x'} - \frac{1}{c}\dot{\mathrm{a}}_x.$$

As the differentiations may be effected under the sign of integration, we have

$$\frac{\partial \varphi}{\partial x'} = \frac{1}{4\pi}\int \varrho \frac{x-x'}{r^3}\, dS + \frac{\dot{v}}{8\pi c^2}\int \varrho \left\{-\frac{1}{r} + \frac{(x-x')^2}{r^3}\right\} dS$$
$$+ \frac{\ddot{v}}{12\pi c^3}\int \varrho\, dS + \cdots,$$

$$\dot{\mathfrak{a}}_x = \frac{\dot{v}}{4\pi c}\int \frac{\varrho}{r}\, dS - \frac{\ddot{v}}{4\pi c^2}\int \varrho\, dS + \cdots,$$

and, since $\int \varrho\, dS = e$,

$$\mathsf{f}_x = \frac{1}{4\pi}\int \varrho \frac{x'-x}{r^3}\, dS - \frac{\dot{v}}{8\pi c^2}\int \varrho \left\{\frac{1}{r} + \frac{(x-x')^2}{r^3}\right\} dS + \frac{\ddot{v}}{6\pi c^3} e. \quad (35)$$

In order to find the resultant force we must multiply this by $\varrho' dS'$, where dS' is an element of volume at the point P, and ϱ' the density at this point; we have next to integrate with respect to dS'. From the first term in (35) we find 0, and from the last term

$$\frac{e^2 \ddot{v}}{6\pi c^3},$$

agreeing with the expression (76); these results are independent of the shape of the electron and the distribution of its charge. As to the middle term in (35), it leads to the force

$$-\frac{\dot{v}}{8\pi c^2}\int \varrho' dS' \int \varrho \left\{\frac{1}{r} + \frac{(x-x')^2}{r^3}\right\} dS.$$

In the case of a spherical electron the charge of which is distributed symmetrically around the centre, we may write $\frac{1}{3}r^2$ instead of $(x-x')^2$, so that we get

$$-\frac{\dot{v}}{6\pi c^2}\int \varrho' dS' \int \frac{\varrho}{r}\, dS. \quad (36)$$

Now, if the charge lies on the surface, the integral $\int \frac{\varrho}{r}\, dS$ has the value $\frac{e}{R}$ at all the points where the density ϱ' is different from zero. Therefore (36) becomes

$$-\frac{e\dot{v}}{6\pi R c^2}\int \varrho' dS' = -\frac{e^2 \dot{v}}{6\pi R c^2},$$

in accordance with the result expressed in (72).

What has been said in § 37 about the representation of the resultant force by a series, each term of which is of the order of magnitude $\frac{R}{c\tau}$ in comparison with the preceding one, is also confirmed by the above calculations.

19 (Page 50). Let us fix our attention on the effective position M (cf. Note 18) of a determinate point of the electron, for instance of its centre. If this position is reached at the time t_0, previous to the time t for which we wish to calculate the potentials at the distant point P, and if the distance MP is denoted by r, we have

$$r = c(t - t_0). \qquad (37)$$

Choosing M as origin of coordinates, we shall understand by x_P, y_P, z_P the coordinates of P.

Let us further seek the effective position (x_e, y_e, z_e) of a point of the electron whose coordinates at the time t_0 are x, y, z. This effective position M' will be reached at a time t_e, a little different from t_0; if we put

$$t_e = t_0 + \tau,$$

the interval τ will be very small. The coordinates x, y, z are so likewise, and a sufficient approximation is obtained if, in our next formulae, we neglect all terms that are of the second order with respect to these four quantities.

The condition that M' be the effective position of the point considered is expressed by

$$M'P = c(t - t_e) = c(t - t_0 - \tau). \qquad (38)$$

But, if $\mathbf{v}$ is the velocity of the electron at the time t_0, we may write for the coordinates of M'

$$x_e = x + \mathbf{v}_x\tau, \quad y_e = y + \mathbf{v}_y\tau, \quad z_e = z + \mathbf{v}_z\tau, \qquad (39)$$

so that (38) becomes

$$(x_P - x - \mathbf{v}_x\tau)^2 + (y_P - y - \mathbf{v}_y\tau)^2 + (z_P - z - \mathbf{v}_z\tau)^2 = c^2(t - t_0 - \tau)^2,$$

or, on account of (37), and because

$$\frac{x_P\mathbf{v}_x + y_P\mathbf{v}_y + z_P\mathbf{v}_z}{r}$$

is the component $\mathbf{v}_r$ of $\mathbf{v}$ along the line MP,

$$2(x_P x + y_P y + z_P z) + 2\mathbf{v}_r r\tau = 2cr\tau,$$

giving

$$\tau = \frac{x_P x + y_P y + z_P z}{(c - \mathbf{v}_r)r}. \qquad (40)$$

The points of the electron which, at the time t_0, lie in an element dS, have their effective positions in an element of space dS_e, whose magnitude is equal to the product of dS by the functional determinant of the quantities (*39*) with respect to x, y, z. The value of this determinant is

$$1 + \mathsf{v}_x \frac{\partial \tau}{\partial x} + \mathsf{v}_y \frac{\partial \tau}{\partial y} + \mathsf{v}_z \frac{\partial \tau}{\partial z},$$

or, in virtue of (*40*),

$$1 + \frac{\mathsf{v}_x x_P + \mathsf{v}_y y_P + \mathsf{v}_z z_P}{(c - \mathsf{v}_r) r} = 1 + \frac{\mathsf{v}_r}{c - \mathsf{v}_r} = \frac{c}{c - \mathsf{v}_r}.$$

As to the distance r in the denominators of (35) and (36), we may take for it the length of MP, and in the latter of the two formulae we may understand by v the velocity of the electron at the instant t_0. In this way the general equations take the form

$$\varphi = \frac{1}{4\pi r} \int \varrho \, dS_e, \quad \mathsf{a} = \frac{\mathsf{v}}{4\pi c r} \int \varrho \, dS_e,$$

which is equivalent to (79) because (ϱ being equal to the density existing at the time t_0 in the element dS)

$$\int \varrho \, dS_e = \frac{c}{c - \mathsf{v}_r} \int \varrho \, dS = \frac{ce}{c - \mathsf{v}_r}.$$

20 (Page 51). As the field depends on the differential coefficients of the potentials, we have first to determine these. In doing so, we shall denote by x, y, z the coordinates of the distant point P for which we want to know $\mathfrak{d}$ and $\mathfrak{h}$.

If we change by dt the time t for which we seek φ and a, keeping x, y, z constant, it will no longer be the same position of the electron which is to be called the effective one. Besides, the new effective position will be reached at a time slightly differing from t_0 and will lie at a distance from P different from r, the changes being connected with each other by the formula

$$dr = -\mathsf{v}_r dt_0,$$

where v_r has the meaning explained in § 38.

Differentiating equation (*37*), we find

$$-\mathsf{v}_r dt_0 = c(dt - dt_0),$$

$$dt_0 = \frac{c}{c - \mathsf{v}_r} dt.$$

It appears from this that, by the change now considered, the value of some quantity ψ corresponding to the time t_0, is altered by

$$\left[\frac{\partial \psi}{\partial t}\right] dt_0 = \frac{c}{c - \mathsf{v}_r} \left[\frac{\partial \psi}{\partial t}\right] dt,$$

so that we may write

$$\frac{d[\psi]}{dt} = \frac{c}{c - \mathbf{v}_r}\left[\frac{\partial \psi}{\partial t}\right],$$

the square brackets always having the meaning formerly assigned to them.

In applying this to the expressions (79), we shall suppose the distance $r = MP$ to be so much greater than the dimensions of the electron that, in the final formulae for $\mathbf{d}$ and $\mathbf{h}$, we may neglect all terms of the order $\frac{1}{r^2}$. Doing so we may treat as constants the three cosines in the equation

$$\mathbf{v}_r = \mathbf{v}_x \cos(r, x) + \mathbf{v}_y \cos(r, y) + \mathbf{v}_z \cos(r, z);$$

indeed, their differential coefficients are of the order $\frac{1}{r}$, and in φ there is already a factor $\frac{1}{r}$. Consequently,

$$\frac{d\mathbf{v}_r}{dt} = \mathbf{j}_x \cos(r, x) + \mathbf{j}_y \cos(r, y) + \mathbf{j}_z \cos(r, z) = \mathbf{j}_r,$$

and since the factor $\frac{1}{r}$ in φ may be considered as constant

$$\frac{\partial \varphi}{\partial t} = \frac{e}{4\pi c\left[r\left(1 - \frac{\mathbf{v}_r}{c}\right)^2\right]}\frac{d[\mathbf{v}_r]}{dt} = \frac{e}{4\pi c\left[r\left(1 - \frac{\mathbf{v}_r}{c}\right)^3\right]}[\mathbf{j}_r].$$

If, finally, we neglect all terms that are of the second order with respect to the velocity and the acceleration of the electron, we have the further simplification

$$\frac{\partial \varphi}{\partial t} = \frac{e}{4\pi c r}[\mathbf{j}_r].$$

Similarly one finds from the second of the formulae (79)

$$\frac{\partial \mathbf{a}}{\partial t} = \frac{e}{4\pi c r}[\mathbf{j}].$$

We have next to calculate the differential coefficients with respect to the coordinates. Consider first an infinitely small displacement of P in a direction h at right angles to MP. The distance MP not being altered by this, and t being kept constant, neither the instant t_0 nor the effective position M are changed. As we may again leave out of account the change in the direction of r, we conclude that

$$\frac{\partial \varphi}{\partial h} = 0, \quad \frac{\partial \mathbf{a}}{\partial h} = 0.$$

The differential coefficients with respect to the direction of r are easily found by the following device. If P is displaced over a distance dr along MP prolonged, t being increased at the same time by $dt = \frac{dr}{c}$, the effective position of the electron and the time t_0 remain unaltered, so that, since the denominator r need not be differentiated,

$$\frac{\partial \varphi}{\partial r} dr + \frac{\partial \varphi}{\partial t} \frac{dr}{c} = 0, \quad \frac{\partial \varphi}{\partial r} = -\frac{1}{c} \frac{\partial \varphi}{\partial t}, \quad \frac{\partial \mathbf{a}}{\partial r} = -\frac{1}{c} \frac{\partial \mathbf{a}}{\partial t}.$$

Combining this with the former result, we find for any direction k, in the case both of the scalar and of the vector potential,

$$\frac{\partial}{\partial k} = \cos(r, k) \frac{\partial}{\partial r},$$

and particularly

$$\frac{\partial}{\partial x} = \cos(r, x) \frac{\partial}{\partial r}, \quad \frac{\partial}{\partial y} = \cos(r, y) \frac{\partial}{\partial r}, \quad \frac{\partial}{\partial z} = \cos(r, z) \frac{\partial}{\partial r}.$$

Using these relations one will find without difficulty the formulae (80) and (81).

21 (Page 51). In the formulae (80) each component of $\mathbf{d}$ is represented as the difference of two terms. The terms with the negative sign may be considered as the components of the vector

$$-\frac{e}{4\pi c^2 r} \mathbf{j}$$

and the terms with the positive sign as those of the vector

$$\frac{e}{4\pi c^2 r} (\mathbf{j}_r),$$

where we have used the parentheses in order to indicate that the component $\mathbf{j}_r$ is here itself regarded as a vector. Understanding $(\mathbf{j}_p)$ in a similar sense, so that

$$\mathbf{j} = (\mathbf{j}_r) + (\mathbf{j}_p),$$

we have

$$\mathbf{d} = \frac{e}{4\pi c^2 r} \{-\mathbf{j} + (\mathbf{j}_r)\} = -\frac{e}{4\pi c^2 r} (\mathbf{j}_p),$$

$$\mathbf{h} = \frac{e}{4\pi c^2 r} [\mathbf{j} \cdot \mathbf{k}] = -[\mathbf{d} \cdot \mathbf{k}].$$

The magnetic force is therefore perpendicular both to $\mathbf{d}$ and to $\mathbf{k}$, and its direction is such that the flow of energy $c[\mathbf{d} \cdot \mathbf{h}]$ has the direction of $\mathbf{k}$, away from the electron. The intensity of the flow is $c|\mathbf{d}|\,|\mathbf{h}| = c\mathbf{d}^2$.

21* (Page 52) [1915]. The experiments on the diffraction of Röntgen rays by crystals first made by v. Laue, Knipping and Friedrich[1]) and afterwards by W. H. and W. L. Bragg[2]) have shown that these rays are much more like light than was formerly thought, the only difference being the wave-length, which is of the order of 10^{-9} cm. Part of the Röntgen radiation consists of homogeneous rays characteristic of the metal of the anti-cathode. Another part is continuously spread over a certain interval of frequencies, so that it may be compared with white light.

22 (Page 53). As an interesting application of the formula found for the resistance, we shall calculate the damping of the vibrations of an electron. Suppose the particle to be subjected to an elastic force $-f\mathfrak{q}$, where $\mathfrak{q}$ is the displacement from the position of equilibrium, and f a positive constant. The motion in the direction of OX ist determined by the equation

$$m\ddot{\mathfrak{q}}_x = -f\mathfrak{q}_x + \frac{e^2}{6\pi c^3}\dddot{\mathfrak{q}}_x,$$

a particular solution of which is found by taking for $\mathfrak{q}_x$ the real part of

$$\varepsilon^{\alpha t},$$

where ε is the basis of natural logarithms, and α a complex constant determined by the condition

$$m\alpha^2 = -f + \frac{e^2}{6\pi c^3}\alpha^3. \qquad (41)$$

If the last term has but a small influence, we may replace in it α by the value given by the equation

$$m\alpha^2 = -f.$$

Hence, putting

$$\frac{f}{m} = n^2,$$

we have

$$\alpha = in - \frac{e^2 n^2}{12\pi m c^3},$$

and introducing two constants a and p,

$$\mathfrak{q}_x = a\varepsilon^{-\frac{e^2 n^2}{12\pi m c^3}t}\cos(nt + p).$$

---

1) Friedrich, Knipping u. Laue, Ann. Phys. **41** (1913), p. 971.
2) W. H. a. W. L. Bragg, X Rays and crystal structure London, 1915.

This formula shows that in a time equal to

$$\tau = \frac{12\pi m c^3}{e^2 n^2}$$

the amplitude falls to $\frac{1}{\varepsilon}$ of its original value.

Taking for m the value (72), and writing T for the time of vibration $\frac{2\pi}{n}$, λ for the wave-length, we find

$$\tau = \frac{\lambda}{2\pi^2 R} T.$$

If we substitute for R the value given in § 35 we have for yellow light ($\lambda = 0{,}00006$ cm)

$$\tau = 2 \cdot 10^7 T,$$

showing that the damping would be very feeble, and that we have been right in supposing the last term in (*41*) to be very small.

This question of the damping of the vibrations is important because, the slower the damping, the more will the radiation present the character of truly homogeneous light. We can form an opinion of the degree of homogeneousness by making experiments on the visibility of interference fringes for various values of the difference of phase; in fact, when this difference is continually increased, the fringes can remain clearly visible for a long time only if the light is fairly homogeneous. A small degree of damping is thus found to be conducive to a good visibility of the fringes, a conclusion that is readily understood if one considers that the interference becomes indistinct when the intensities of the two rays are very different. This must be the case whenever the vibrations in the source have considerably diminished in amplitude between the instants at which the interfering rays have been emitted.

The result of the above calculation is in satisfactory agreement with the experiments of Lummer and Gehrcke in which, under favourable conditions, interferences up to a phase difference of two millions of periods were observed. Similar results have been obtained by Buisson and Fabry who studied the emission of helium, krypton and neon contained in vacuum tubes.

23 (Page 56). In each successive differentiation with respect to one of the coordinates, of the expression found for $\frac{[\mathfrak{p}_x]}{r}$, we have to differentiate both the goniometric function and the factor preceding it. These operations introduce factors of the order of magnitude $\frac{n}{c} = \frac{2\pi}{\lambda}$

(if λ denotes the wave-length) and $\frac{1}{r}$. Consequently, in as much as r is very much greater than λ, we may confine ourselves to the differentiation of the goniometric function.

Thus, for example,

$$\varphi = -\frac{1}{4\pi}\frac{\partial}{\partial x}\frac{[\mathbf{p}_x]}{r} = -\frac{nb}{4\pi c r}\cdot\frac{x}{r}\sin\left\{n\left(t-\frac{r}{c}\right)+p\right\},$$

$$\mathbf{a}_x = \frac{1}{4\pi c}\frac{\partial}{\partial t}\frac{[\mathbf{p}_x]}{r} = -\frac{nb}{4\pi c r}\sin\left\{n\left(t-\frac{r}{c}\right)+p\right\},$$

$$\mathbf{d}_x = -\frac{\partial\varphi}{\partial x} - \frac{1}{c}\frac{\partial \mathbf{a}_x}{\partial t} = \frac{n^2 b}{4\pi c^2 r}\left(-\frac{x^2}{r^2}+1\right)\cos\left\{n\left(t-\frac{r}{c}\right)+p\right\}.$$

It is easily verified by means of the expressions (95) that $\mathbf{d}$ and $\mathbf{h}$ are at right angles both to each other and to the line r, and that they have equal amplitudes. The formulae represent a system of plane polarized waves, whose amplitude changes in the inverse ratio of the distance r as we pass along a straight line drawn from the radiating particle. The flow of energy changes as $\frac{1}{r^2}$.

24 (Page 58). Considering any one of the dependent variables, say ψ, first as a function of x, y, z, t, and then as a function of x', y', z', t', we have the following relations, arising from (96) combined with

$$t' = t - \frac{1}{c^2}(\mathbf{w}_x x + \mathbf{w}_y y + \mathbf{w}_z z),$$

as we may write instead of (97) if the square of $\frac{\mathbf{w}}{c}$ is neglected,

$$\frac{\partial\psi}{\partial x} = \frac{\partial\psi}{\partial x'}\frac{\partial x'}{\partial x} + \frac{\partial\psi}{\partial y'}\frac{\partial y'}{\partial x} + \frac{\partial\psi}{\partial z'}\frac{\partial z'}{\partial x} + \frac{\partial\psi}{\partial t'}\frac{\partial t'}{\partial x} = \frac{\partial\psi}{\partial x'} - \frac{\mathbf{w}_x}{c^2}\frac{\partial\psi}{\partial t'},$$

$$\frac{\partial\psi}{\partial y} = \frac{\partial\psi}{\partial y'} - \frac{\mathbf{w}_y}{c^2}\frac{\partial\psi}{\partial t'}, \quad \frac{\partial\psi}{\partial z} = \frac{\partial\psi}{\partial z'} - \frac{\mathbf{w}_z}{c^2}\frac{\partial\psi}{\partial t'},$$

$$\frac{\partial\psi}{\partial t} = \frac{\partial\psi}{\partial t'} - \mathbf{w}_x\frac{\partial\psi}{\partial x'} - \mathbf{w}_y\frac{\partial\psi}{\partial y'} - \mathbf{w}_z\frac{\partial\psi}{\partial z'}.$$

By this the equation (17) becomes

$$\frac{\partial \mathbf{d}_x}{\partial x'} + \frac{\partial \mathbf{d}_y}{\partial y'} + \frac{\partial \mathbf{d}_z}{\partial z'} - \frac{1}{c^2}\left[\mathbf{w}_x\frac{\partial \mathbf{d}_x}{\partial t'} + \mathbf{w}_y\frac{\partial \mathbf{d}_y}{\partial t'} + \mathbf{w}_z\frac{\partial \mathbf{d}_z}{\partial t'}\right] = \varrho.$$

In the terms multiplied by $\mathbf{w}_x$, $\mathbf{w}_y$, $\mathbf{w}_z$ we need not distinguish between the differential coefficients with respect to t', x', y', z', and those with respect to t, x, y, z. Hence, in virtue of (19), we write for the terms enclosed in square brackets

$$c\mathbf{w}_x\left(\frac{\partial \mathbf{h}_z}{\partial y'} - \frac{\partial \mathbf{h}_y}{\partial z'}\right) + c\mathbf{w}_y\left(\frac{\partial \mathbf{h}_x}{\partial z'} - \frac{\partial \mathbf{h}_z}{\partial x'}\right) + c\mathbf{w}_z\left(\frac{\partial \mathbf{h}_y}{\partial x'} - \frac{\partial \mathbf{h}_x}{\partial y'}\right) - (\mathbf{w}\cdot\mathbf{v})\varrho.$$

In the last term $\mathbf{v}$ may be replaced by $\mathbf{u}$, because we are constantly neglecting the square of $\mathbf{w}$, and we are led at once to equation (100) if we keep in mind that

$$\mathbf{d}_x + \frac{1}{c}(\mathbf{w}_y \mathbf{h}_z - \mathbf{w}_z \mathbf{h}_y) = \mathbf{d}_x', \text{ etc.}$$

Let us next transform the first of the three equations taken together in (19), namely

$$\frac{\partial \mathbf{h}_z}{\partial y} - \frac{\partial \mathbf{h}_y}{\partial z} = \frac{1}{c}\left(\varrho \mathbf{v}_x + \frac{\partial \mathbf{d}_x}{\partial t}\right).$$

It assumes the form

$$\frac{\partial \mathbf{h}_z}{\partial y'} - \frac{\mathbf{w}_y}{c^2}\frac{\partial \mathbf{h}_z}{\partial t'} - \frac{\partial \mathbf{h}_y}{\partial z'} + \frac{\mathbf{w}_z}{c^2}\frac{\partial \mathbf{h}_y}{\partial t'}$$

$$= \frac{1}{c}\left(\varrho \mathbf{w}_x + \varrho \mathbf{u}_x + \frac{\partial \mathbf{d}_x}{\partial t'} - \mathbf{w}_x \frac{\partial \mathbf{d}_x}{\partial x'} - \mathbf{w}_y \frac{\partial \mathbf{d}_x}{\partial y'} - \mathbf{w}_z \frac{\partial \mathbf{d}_x}{\partial z'}\right),$$

or, if $\varrho \mathbf{w}_x$ is replaced by

$$\mathbf{w}_x\left(\frac{\partial \mathbf{d}_x}{\partial x'} + \frac{\partial \mathbf{d}_y}{\partial y'} + \frac{\partial \mathbf{d}_z}{\partial z'}\right),$$

and if the terms are arranged in a different order,

$$\frac{\partial}{\partial y'}\left\{\mathbf{h}_z - \frac{1}{c}(\mathbf{w}_x \mathbf{d}_y - \mathbf{w}_y \mathbf{d}_x)\right\} - \frac{\partial}{\partial z'}\left\{\mathbf{h}_y - \frac{1}{c}(\mathbf{w}_z \mathbf{d}_x - \mathbf{w}_x \mathbf{d}_z)\right\}$$

$$= \frac{1}{c}\varrho \mathbf{u}_x + \frac{1}{c}\frac{\partial}{\partial t'}\left\{\mathbf{d}_x + \frac{1}{c}(\mathbf{w}_y \mathbf{h}_z - \mathbf{w}_z \mathbf{h}_y)\right\}.$$

This is the first of the equations contained in (102).

25 (Page 59). We shall begin by observing that the potentials φ' and $\mathbf{a}'$ satisfy the differential equations

$$\Delta \varphi' - \frac{1}{c^2}\frac{\partial^2 \varphi'}{\partial t'^2} = -\varrho, \tag{42}$$

$$\Delta \mathbf{a}' - \frac{1}{c^2}\frac{\partial^2 \mathbf{a}'}{\partial t'^2} = -\frac{1}{c}\varrho \mathbf{u} \tag{43}$$

(ct. Note 4), where Δ is now an abbreviation for $\frac{\partial^2}{\partial x'^2} + \frac{\partial^2}{\partial y'^2} + \frac{\partial^2}{\partial z'^2}$, and that they are mutually connected in the following manner:

$$\operatorname{div} \mathbf{a}' = -\frac{1}{c}\frac{\partial \varphi'}{\partial t'} + \frac{1}{c^2}(\mathbf{w} \cdot \dot{\mathbf{a}}'). \tag{44}$$

In order to prove this latter formula we shall start from equation (5) of Note 2, which, in terms of the new variables, may be written

$$\frac{\partial \varrho}{\partial t'} - \mathbf{w}_x \frac{\partial \varrho}{\partial x'} - \mathbf{w}_y \frac{\partial \varrho}{\partial y'} - \mathbf{w}_z \frac{\partial \varrho}{\partial z'} + \operatorname{div}(\varrho \mathbf{v}) - \frac{1}{c^2}\left(\mathbf{w} \cdot \frac{\partial(\varrho \mathbf{v})}{\partial t'}\right) = 0,$$

or, if the square of $\mathbf{w}$ is again neglected,

$$\frac{\partial \varrho}{\partial t'} + \operatorname{div}(\varrho \mathbf{u}) - \frac{1}{c^2}\left(\mathbf{w} \cdot \frac{\partial(\varrho \mathbf{u})}{\partial t'}\right) = 0. \qquad (45)$$

If, in an integral of the form (104) or (105), the factor by which $\frac{1}{r}$ is multiplied is a continuous function of the local time t' and the coordinates x', y', z' of the element dS, the partial derivatives of the integral with respect to t' or to the coordinates of the point for which it is calculated, are found by simply differentiating the said factor with respect to t', or x', y', z', the differential coefficient being again taken for the value $t' - \frac{r}{c}$ of the local time.

According to this rule

$$\frac{\partial \varphi'}{\partial t'} = \frac{1}{4\pi}\int \frac{1}{r}\left[\frac{\partial \varrho}{\partial t'}\right] dS,$$

$$\operatorname{div} \mathbf{a}' = \frac{1}{4\pi c}\int \frac{1}{r}[\operatorname{div}(\varrho \mathbf{u})]\, dS,$$

$$\dot{\mathbf{a}}' = \frac{1}{4\pi c}\int \frac{1}{r}\left[\frac{\partial(\varrho \mathbf{u})}{\partial t'}\right] dS,$$

from which we infer that

$$(\mathbf{w} \cdot \dot{\mathbf{a}}') = \frac{1}{4\pi c}\int \frac{1}{r}\left[\left(\mathbf{w} \cdot \frac{\partial(\varrho \mathbf{u})}{\partial t'}\right)\right] dS.$$

In virtue of (*45*) these values verify the equation (*44*) and it is further found by direct substitution that the fundamental equations (100)—(103) are satisfied by (106) and (107) (see, however, Note 6). We have, for example,

$$\operatorname{div} \mathbf{d}' = -\frac{1}{c}\operatorname{div} \dot{\mathbf{a}}' - \Delta\varphi' + \frac{1}{c}\Delta(\mathbf{w} \cdot \mathbf{a}').$$

But by (*44*)

$$\operatorname{div} \dot{\mathbf{a}}' = -\frac{1}{c}\frac{\partial^2 \varphi'}{\partial t'^2} + \frac{1}{c^2}(\mathbf{w} \cdot \ddot{\mathbf{a}}'),$$

so that the foregoing equation assumes the form

$$\operatorname{div} \mathbf{d}' = \frac{1}{c^2}\frac{\partial^2 \varphi'}{\partial t'^2} - \Delta\varphi' - \frac{1}{c^3}(\mathbf{w} \cdot \ddot{\mathbf{a}}') + \frac{1}{c}\Delta(\mathbf{w} \cdot \mathbf{a}').$$

The two terms containing $\mathbf{a}'$ are equal to

$$\frac{1}{c}\left(\mathbf{w} \cdot \left\{\Delta \mathbf{a}' - \frac{1}{c^2}\ddot{\mathbf{a}}'\right\}\right),$$

and in virtue of (*42*) and (*43*), the right-hand side of the equation becomes identical with that of (100).

No difficulty will be found in the verification of (101) and (103). As to equation (102), we find from (107) (cf. Note 1)

$$\text{rot}\,\mathfrak{h}' = \text{rot rot}\,\mathfrak{a}' = \text{grad div}\,\mathfrak{a}' - \Delta\mathfrak{a}',$$

and, if we use (*44*), (*43*) and (106),

$$\text{rot}\,\mathfrak{h}' = -\frac{1}{c}\,\text{grad}\,\dot{\varphi}' + \frac{1}{c^2}\,\text{grad}\,(\mathfrak{w}\cdot\dot{\mathfrak{a}}') + \frac{1}{c}\,\varrho\,\mathfrak{u} - \frac{1}{c^2}\,\ddot{\mathfrak{a}}' = \frac{1}{c}\,(\dot{\mathfrak{d}}' + \varrho\,\mathfrak{u}).$$

26 (Page 59). The problem may be reduced to that of determining the field due to a single moving electron (cf. §§ 38, 41, 42 and Note 19). Let P be the distant point for which we want to calculate the potentials φ' and $\mathfrak{a}'$ at the local time t', and M a definite point of the electron, say its centre, in its effective position, so that, if t_0' is the time (local time of M) at which it is reached, and r the length of MP,

$$r = c(t' - t_0'). \tag{46}$$

Choosing M as origin we shall call x'_P, y'_P, z'_P the coordinates of P, x', y', z' those of some point Q of the electron at the time t_0' (local time of M), x_e', y_e', z_e' the coordinates of the effective position Q_e of this point, and $t_0' + \tau$ (local time of M) the time at which it is reached, so that, according to (97), the local time of Q_e itself is then represented by

$$t_e' = t_0' + \tau - \frac{1}{c^2}(\mathfrak{w}_x x_e' + \mathfrak{w}_y y_e' + \mathfrak{w}_z z_e').$$

The condition that Q_e be the effective position of the point considered is expressed by an equation similar to (*46*), namely

$$Q_e P = c(t' - t_e'),$$

or, taking the square on both sides,

$$(x'_P - x_e')^2 + (y'_P - y_e')^2 + (z'_P - z_e')^2$$
$$= c^2(t' - t_0' - \tau)^2 + 2(t' - t_0' - \tau)(\mathfrak{w}_x x_e' + \mathfrak{w}_y y_e' + \mathfrak{w}_z z_e').$$

The interval τ being very short, we may write

$$x_e' = x' + \mathfrak{u}_x\tau, \quad y_e' = y' + \mathfrak{u}_y\tau, \quad z_e' = z' + \mathfrak{u}_z\tau,$$

by which, if terms of the second order with respect to x', y', z', τ are neglected, and if (*46*) is used, our condition becomes

$$-(x'_P x' + y'_P y' + z'_P z') - r\mathfrak{u}_r\tau$$
$$= -rc\tau + \frac{r}{c}(\mathfrak{w}_x x' + \mathfrak{w}_y y' + \mathfrak{w}_z z') + \frac{r}{c}(\mathfrak{w}\cdot\mathfrak{u})\tau,$$

$$\tau = \frac{(x'_P x' + y'_P y' + z'_P z') + \frac{r}{c}(\mathfrak{w}_x x' + \mathfrak{w}_y y' + \mathfrak{w}_z z')}{r(c - \mathfrak{u}_r) - \frac{r}{c}(\mathfrak{w}\cdot\mathfrak{u})}. \tag{47}$$

Here $\mathbf{u}_r$ means the component of $\mathbf{u}$ in the direction of MP, the product $r\mathbf{u}_r$ having replaced the expression $x'_P \mathbf{u}_x + y'_P \mathbf{u}_y + z'_P \mathbf{u}_z$.

Having got thus far we can again distinguish between an element dS of the electron in its position at the instant t_0' (local time of M) and the element dS_e which contains the effective positions of the different points of dS, the ratio between the magnitudes of these elements being given by the functional determinant of x_e', y_e', z_e' with respect to x', y', z', i. e. by

$$1 + \mathbf{u}_x \frac{\partial \tau}{\partial x'} + \mathbf{u}_y \frac{\partial \tau}{\partial y'} + \mathbf{u}_z \frac{\partial \tau}{\partial z'}.$$

We shall retain only the terms of the first order with respect to $\mathbf{u}_x, \mathbf{u}_y, \mathbf{u}_z$. Doing so, we may neglect in $\frac{\partial \tau}{\partial x'}, \frac{\partial \tau}{\partial y'}, \frac{\partial \tau}{\partial z'}$ the terms containing these velocities, so that (*47*) gives for the determinant

$$1 + \frac{1}{cr}\left\{ \mathbf{u}_x\left(x'_P + \frac{r\mathbf{w}_x}{c}\right) + \mathbf{u}_y\left(y'_P + \frac{r\mathbf{w}_y}{c}\right) + \mathbf{u}_z\left(z'_P + \frac{r\mathbf{w}_z}{c}\right)\right\}$$

$$= 1 + \frac{\mathbf{u}_r}{c} + \frac{1}{c^2}(\mathbf{u}\cdot\mathbf{w}).$$

Finally we have the following equations, similar to those which we found in Note 19,

$$\varphi' = \frac{e}{4\pi r}\left\{1 + \frac{[\mathbf{u}_r]}{c} + \frac{1}{c^2}[(\mathbf{u}\cdot\mathbf{w})]\right\},$$

$$\mathfrak{a}' = \frac{e[\mathbf{u}]}{4\pi c r}. \qquad (48)$$

Now, if we put

$$\varphi' - \frac{1}{c}(\mathbf{w}\cdot\mathfrak{a}') = (\varphi'),$$

we find

$$(\varphi') = \frac{e}{4\pi r}\left\{1 + \frac{[\mathbf{u}_r]}{c}\right\}, \qquad (49)$$

and, in virtue of (106),

$$\mathbf{d}' = -\frac{1}{c}\dot{\mathfrak{a}}' - \text{grad}\,(\varphi'). \qquad (50)$$

Comparing the formulae (*49*), (*48*), (*50*) and (107) with (79), (33) and (34), keeping in mind that, when $\mathbf{v}$ is very small, the factor $1 - \frac{\mathbf{v}_r}{c}$ may be omitted in the second of the equations (79), and replaced by $1 + \frac{\mathbf{v}_r}{c}$ in the numerator of the first, we see that there is perfect equality of form. Hence, if we speak of corresponding states when the dependency of $\mathbf{d}', \mathbf{h}'$ on x', y', z', t' in a moving system is the same as that of $\mathbf{d}, \mathbf{h}$ on x, y, z, t in a stationary one, we may draw the following conclusion. The field produced at distant points of a moving system by an electron whose coordinates x', y', z' are certain functions of t' (the local time belonging to the instantaneous position of the electron) corresponds to the field produced in a system without translation by an equal electron whose coordinates x, y, z are the same functions of t.

Of course, this theorem may be extended to any number of electrons, so that we may also apply it to a polarized particle. We shall suppose this latter to be so small that the differences between the local times of its various parts may be neglected. Then it makes no difference, whether we say that the coordinates x', y', z' of an electron moving in the particle are certain functions of the local time t' belonging to the instantaneous position of the electron itself, or that they are the same functions of the local time belonging to some fixed point, say the centre, of the particle, and we have the proposition: The field produced in a moving system by an electric moment whose components are certain functions of t' (the local time of the centre of the particle) corresponds to the field existing in a system without translation in which there is an electric moment whose components are the same functions of t. But, in the latter case, the field is determined by (88) und (89). Therefore, we shall have for the moving system

$$(\varphi') = -\frac{1}{4\pi}\left\{\frac{\partial}{\partial x'}\frac{[\mathbf{p}_x]}{r} + \frac{\partial}{\partial y'}\frac{[\mathbf{p}_y]}{r} + \frac{\partial}{\partial z'}\frac{[\mathbf{p}_z]}{r}\right\},$$

$$\mathbf{a}' = \frac{[\dot{\mathbf{p}}]}{4\pi c r},$$

and we shall find $\mathbf{d}'$ and $\mathbf{h}'$ by using the formulae (*50*) and (107).

It follows from this that the expressions for the field belonging to the electric moment represented by (108) may be found as stated in the text.

27 (Page 60). In a stationary system the condition at the surface of a perfectly conducting body is, that the electric force be at right angles to it. This follows from the continuity of the tangential components of the force, combined with the rule that in a perfect conductor the electric force must be zero, because otherwise there would be a current of infinite strength.

Now, in a moving system, an electron that is at rest relatively to it is acted on by a force which, according to (23), is given by

$$\mathbf{d} + \frac{1}{c}[\mathbf{w}\cdot\mathbf{h}].$$

As this is equal to the vector $\mathbf{d}'$ defined by (98), $\mathbf{d}'$ plays exactly the same part as $\mathbf{d}$ in a system without translation, and by going somewhat further into the phenomena in ponderable bodies, one can show that, in a moving system, $\mathbf{d}'$ must be normal to the surface of a perfect conductor. Moreover, for the free ether, the equations which determine $\mathbf{d}'$ and $\mathbf{h}'$, when referred to moving axes and local time, are identical in form with those which we have for $\mathbf{d}$ and $\mathbf{h}$, when we use axes having a fixed position in the ether. This appears at once from the equations (100)—(103).

28 (Page 62). Since $\mathbf{h}_z = \mathbf{d}_y$ and $\mathbf{h}_{z(r)} = - \mathbf{d}_{y(r)}$, we have

$$\mathbf{d}_y \mathbf{d}_{y(r)} = - \mathbf{h}_z \mathbf{h}_{z(r)},$$

and for the energy per unit of volume

$$w_e + w_m = \tfrac{1}{2}\{(\mathbf{d}_y + \mathbf{d}_{y(r)})^2 + (\mathbf{h}_z + \mathbf{h}_{z(r)})^2\}$$
$$= \tfrac{1}{2}(\mathbf{d}_y^2 + \mathbf{h}_z^2) + \tfrac{1}{2}(\mathbf{d}^2_{y(r)} + \mathbf{h}^2_{z(r)}).$$

29 (Page 67). Problems relating to the motion of the innumerable electrons in a piece of metal are best treated by the statistical method which Maxwell introduced into the kinetic theory of gases, and which may be presented in a simple geometrical form so long as we are concerned only with the motion of translation of the particles. Indeed, it is clear that, if we construct a diagram in which the velocity of each electron is represented in direction and magnitude by a vector OP drawn from a fixed point O, the distribution of the ends P of these vectors, the velocity points as we shall say, will give us an image of the state of motion of the electrons.

If the positions of the velocity points are referred to axes of coordinates parallel to those that have been chosen in the metal itself, the coordinates of a velocity point are equal to the components ξ, η, ζ of the velocity of the corresponding electron.

Let $d\lambda$ be an element of volume in the diagram, situated at the point (ξ, η, ζ), so small that we may neglect the changes of ξ, η, ζ from one of its points to another, and yet so large that it contains a great number of velocity points. Then, this number may be reckoned to be proportional to $d\lambda$. Representing it by

$$f(\xi, \eta, \zeta)\, d\lambda \tag{51}$$

per unit volume of the metal, we may say that, from a statistical point of view, the function f determines the motion of the swarm of electrons.

It is clear that the integral

$$\int f(\xi, \eta, \zeta)\, d\lambda,$$

extended over the whole space of the diagram, gives the total number of electrons per unit of volume. In like manner the integral

$$\int \xi f(\xi, \eta, \zeta)\, d\lambda \qquad (52)$$

represents the stream of electrons through a plane perpendicular to OX, i. e. the excess of the number passing through the plane towards the positive side over the number of those which go in the opposite direction, both numbers being referred to unit of area and unit of time. This is seen by first considering a group of electrons having their velocity points in an element $d\lambda$; these may be regarded as moving with equal velocities, and those of them which pass through an element $d\sigma$ of the said direction between the moments t and $t + dt$, have been situated at the beginning of this interval in a certain cylinder having $d\sigma$ for its base, and the height $|\xi|dt$. The number of these particles is found if one multiplies the volume of the cylinder by the number (51).

Hence, if $\int_1$ means an integration over the part of the diagram on the positive side of the $\eta\zeta$-plane, and $\int_2$ an integration over the part on the opposite side, the number of the electrons which go to one side is

$$d\sigma dt \int_1 \xi f(\xi, \eta, \zeta)\, d\lambda,$$

and that of the particles going the other way

$$d\sigma dt \int_2 -\xi f(\xi, \eta, \zeta)\, d\lambda.$$

The expression (52) is the difference between these values divided by $d\sigma dt$.

If all the electrons have equal charges e, the excess of the charge that is carried towards the positive side over that which is transported in the opposite direction is given by

$$J = e \int \xi f\, d\lambda, \qquad (53)$$

and it is easily seen that, denoting by m the mass of an electron and by $r^2 = \xi^2 + \eta^2 + \zeta^2$ the square of its velocity, we shall have

$$W = \tfrac{1}{2} m \int \xi r^2 f\, d\lambda \qquad (54)$$

for the difference between the amounts of energy that are carried through the plane in the two directions. The quantities (53) and (54) are therefore the expressions for the flow of electricity and for that of heat, both in the direction of OX.

The function f is determined by an equation that is to be regarded as the fundamental formula of the theory, and which we now proceed to establish, on the assumption that the electrons are subjected to a force in the direction of OX, giving them an acceleration X equal for all the corpuscles in one of the groups considered.

Let us fix our attention on the electrons lying, at the time t, in an element of volume dS of the metal, and having their velocity points in the element $d\lambda$ of the diagram. If there were no encounters, neither with other electrons nor with metallic atoms, these electrons would be found, at the time $t + dt$, in an element dS' equal to dS and lying at the point $(x + \xi dt,\ y + \eta dt,\ z + \zeta dt)$. At the same time their velocity points would have been displaced to an element $d\lambda'$ equal to $d\lambda$ and situated at the point $(\xi + X dt,\ \eta,\ \zeta)$ of the diagram, so that we should have

$$f(\xi + X dt,\ \eta,\ \zeta,\ x + \xi dt,\ y + \eta dt,\ z + \zeta dt,\ t + dt)\, dS'\, d\lambda'$$
$$= f(\xi,\ \eta,\ \zeta,\ x,\ y,\ z,\ t)\, dS\, d\lambda.$$

The impacts which take place during the interval of time considered require us to modify this equation. The number of electrons constituting, at the time $t + dt$, the group specified by dS' and $d\lambda'$, is no longer equal to the number of those which, at the time t, belonged to the group $(dS,\ d\lambda)$, the latter number having to be diminished by the number of impacts which the group of electrons under consideration undergoes during the time dt, and increased by the number of the impacts by which an electron, originally not belonging to the group, is made to enter it. Writing $a\, dS\, d\lambda\, dt$ and $b\, dS\, d\lambda\, dt$ for these two numbers, we have, after division by $dS\, d\lambda = dS'\, d\lambda'$,

$$f(\xi + X dt,\ \eta,\ \zeta,\ x + \xi dt,\ y + \eta dt,\ z + \zeta dt,\ t + dt)$$
$$= f(\xi,\ \eta,\ \zeta,\ x,\ y,\ z,\ t) + (b - a)\, dt,$$

or, since the function on the left-hand side may be replaced by

$$f(\xi,\ \eta,\ \zeta,\ x,\ y,\ z,\ t) + \left(\frac{\partial f}{\partial \xi} X + \frac{\partial f}{\partial x} \xi + \frac{\partial f}{\partial y} \eta + \frac{\partial f}{\partial z} \zeta + \frac{\partial f}{\partial t}\right) dt,$$

$$X \frac{\partial f}{\partial \xi} + \xi \frac{\partial f}{\partial x} + \eta \frac{\partial f}{\partial y} + \zeta \frac{\partial f}{\partial z} + \frac{\partial f}{\partial t} = b - a. \tag{55}$$

This is the general equation of which we have spoken.

We have now to calculate the values of a and b. We shall simplify this problem by neglecting the mutual encounters of the electrons, considering only their impacts against the metallic atoms. We shall further treat both the atoms and the electrons as perfectly elastic rigid spheres, and we shall ascribe to the atoms masses so great that they may be regarded as unmovable.

Among all the encounters we shall provisionally consider only those in which the line joining the centra of the atom and the electron has, at the instant of impact, a direction lying within a definite cone of infinitely small solid angle $d\omega$. If R is the sum of the radii of an atom and an electron, and n the number of atoms per unit of volume, the number of electrons of the group (*51*) which undergo an impact of the kind just specified during the time dt, is equal to

$$nR^2 f(\xi, \eta, \zeta) r \cos \vartheta \, d\lambda \, d\omega \, dt. \tag{56}$$

Here ϑ is the sharp angle between the line of centra and the direction of the velocity r.

The velocity of the electron at the end of a collision is found by a simple rule. After having decomposed the original velocity into a component along the line of centra and another at right angles to it, we have only to reverse the direction of the first component. Hence, the new velocity point P', whose coordinates I shall call ξ', η', ζ', and the original one (ξ, η, ζ) lie symmetrically on both sides of the plane W passing through O at right angles to the axis of the cone $d\omega$, and when the point P takes different positions in the element $d\lambda$, the new point P' will continually lie in an element $d\lambda'$ that is the image of $d\lambda$ with respect to the plane W, and is therefore equal to $d\lambda$.

This last remark enables us to calculate the number b, so far as it is due to collisions taking place under the specified conditions. By these, a velocity point is made to jump from $d\lambda'$ to $d\lambda$, and the number of these „inverse" encounters is found by a proper change of the expression (*56*). · While we replace ξ, η, ζ by ξ', η', ζ', we must leave the factor $r \cos \vartheta \, d\lambda$ unaltered, for we have $d\lambda' = d\lambda$ $r' = r$ (if r' is the velocity whose components are ξ', η', ζ'), and the line joining the centra makes equal angles with r and r'.

We get therefore

$$nR^2 f(\xi', \eta', \zeta') r \cos \vartheta \, d\lambda \, d\omega \, dt.$$

Subtracting (*56*) from this and integrating the result over all directions of the axis of the cone $d\omega$ which are inclined at sharp angles to the direction of r, we shall obtain the value of $(b - a) \, d\lambda \, dt$.

When the force which produces the acceleration X has a constant intensity, depending only on the coordinate x, there can exist a stationary state, in which the function f contains neither y nor z. For cases of this kind, which occur for instance when the ends of a cylindrical bar are kept at different temperatures, or when it is subjected to a longitudinal electric force, the fundamental equation (*55*) becomes

$$nR^2 r \int \{ f(\xi', \eta', \zeta') - f(\xi, \eta, \zeta) \} \cos \vartheta \, d\omega = X \frac{\partial f}{\partial \xi} + \xi \frac{\partial f}{\partial x} \cdot \tag{57}$$

In performing the integration we must leave ξ, η, ζ unchanged, so that r is a constant, but we must not forget that the values of ξ', η', ζ' depend on the direction of the line joining the centra. Denoting by f, g, h the angles between this line (taken in such a direction that the angle with r is sharp) and the axes, we have

$$\xi' = \xi - 2r\cos\vartheta\cos f,\ \eta' = \eta - 2r\cos\vartheta\cos g,\ \zeta' = \zeta - 2r\cos\vartheta\cos h.$$

So long as the state of things is the same at all points of the metal, the electrons will move equally in all directions. It is natural to assume for this case Maxwell's well known law expressed by

$$f(\xi, \eta, \zeta) = A\varepsilon^{-hr^2}, \tag{58}$$

where A and h are constants.

Using the formulae

$$J_1 = \int_{-\infty}^{+\infty} \varepsilon^{-h\xi^2} d\xi = \sqrt{\frac{\pi}{h}},$$

$$J_2 = \int_{-\infty}^{+\infty} \varepsilon^{-h\xi^2} \xi^2 d\xi = \frac{1}{2}\sqrt{\frac{\pi}{h^3}},$$

we find from (58) for the number of electrons per unit of volume

$$N = A\int_{-\infty}^{+\infty}\int_{-\infty}^{+\infty}\int_{-\infty}^{+\infty} \varepsilon^{-h(\xi^2+\eta^2+\zeta^2)} d\xi\, d\eta\, d\zeta = AJ_1^3 = A\sqrt{\frac{\pi^3}{h^3}}, \tag{59}$$

and for the sum of the values of ξ^2, for which we may write $N\overline{\xi^2}$ if we use a horizontal bar to denote mean values

$$N\overline{\xi^2} = A\int_{-\infty}^{+\infty}\int_{-\infty}^{+\infty}\int_{-\infty}^{+\infty} \varepsilon^{-h(\xi^2+\eta^2+\zeta^2)} \xi^2 d\xi\, d\eta\, d\zeta = AJ_2J_1^2 = \frac{1}{2}A\sqrt{\frac{\pi^3}{h^5}}.$$

It follows from these results that

$$\overline{\xi^2} = \overline{\eta^2} = \overline{\zeta^2} = \frac{1}{2h},$$

and that the mean value of the kinetic energy of an electron is equal to

$$\frac{3m}{4h}.$$

But we have already made the assumption that the mean kinetic energy is equal to αT. Therefore

$$h = \frac{3m}{4\alpha T}, \tag{60}$$

an equation which, conjointly with (59), tells us in what manner the constants h and A are determined by the temperature and the number N of corpuscles per unit of volume.

It is clear that the formula (*58*) can no longer hold when there is an external force or when the ends of a metallic bar are unequally heated. Yet, whatever be the new state of motion, we shall always have a definite number N of electrons per unit of volume, and a definite value of the mean square of their velocities, and, after having assigned to h and A such values that $\frac{3}{2h}$ is equal to this mean square and $A\sqrt{\frac{\pi^3}{h^3}}$ to the number N, we may always write

$$f(\xi, \eta, \zeta) = A\varepsilon^{-hr^2} + \varphi(\xi, \eta, \zeta), \tag{61}$$

where φ is a function that remains to be determined. For this we have the fundamental equation (*57*) and in addition to it the conditions

$$\int \varphi \, d\lambda = 0, \quad \int \varphi r^2 d\lambda = 0, \tag{62}$$

which must be fulfilled because the term $A\varepsilon^{-hr^2}$ has been so chosen that it leads to the values of N and $\overline{r^2}$ really existing.

The function φ is the mathematical expression for the change which an external force or a difference of temperature produces in the state of motion of the system of electrons. Now, this change may be shown to be extremely small in all real cases, so that the value of φ is always small in comparison with that of $A\varepsilon^{-hr^2}$. Hence, on the right-hand side of equation (*57*) we may replace f by $A\varepsilon^{-hr^2}$. On the left-hand side, on the contrary, we must use the complete function (*61*), because here we should find zero, if we omitted the part $\varphi(\xi, \eta, \zeta)$.

The equation therefore becomes

$$nR^2 r \int \{\varphi(\xi', \eta', \zeta') - \varphi(\xi, \eta, \zeta)\} \cos\vartheta \, d\omega$$
$$= \left(-2hAX + \frac{dA}{dx} - r^2 A \frac{dh}{dx}\right) \xi \varepsilon^{-hr^2}. \tag{63}$$

Let us try the solution

$$\varphi(\xi, \eta, \zeta) = \xi \chi(r), \tag{64}$$

where χ is a function of r alone. This assumption is in accordance with the conditions (*62*), so that we have only to consider the principal equation (*63*). Substituting in it the value (*64*) we first find

$$\int \{\varphi(\xi', \eta', \zeta') - \varphi(\xi, \eta, \zeta)\} \cos\vartheta \, d\omega = \chi(r) \int (\xi' - \xi) \cos\vartheta \, d\omega$$
$$= -2r\chi(r) \int \cos^2\vartheta \cos f \, d\omega.$$

Let us imagine two lines OP and OQ, drawn from the origin of coordinates, the first in the direction of the velocity (ξ, η, ζ), and the second in that of the line of centra at the moment of impact, the angle $POQ = \vartheta$ being sharp. Denoting by μ the angle POX and by ψ that between the planes POX and POQ, we have

$$\cos f = \cos\mu \cos\vartheta + \sin\mu \sin\vartheta \cos\psi,$$

$$\int \cos^2\vartheta \cos f\, d\omega = \int_0^{\frac{1}{2}\pi}\int_0^{2\pi} \cos^2\vartheta\,(\cos\mu\cos\vartheta + \sin\mu\sin\vartheta\cos\psi)\sin\vartheta\, d\vartheta\, d\psi$$

$$= 2\pi\cos\mu \int_0^{\frac{1}{2}\pi} \cos^3\vartheta \sin\vartheta\, d\vartheta = \frac{1}{2}\pi\cos\mu = \frac{1}{2}\pi\frac{\xi}{r},$$

by which (*63*) assumes the form

$$-\pi n R^2 \xi r \chi(r) = \left(-2hAX + \frac{dA}{dx} - r^2 A \frac{dh}{dx}\right)\xi\varepsilon^{-hr^2},$$

showing (because ξ disappears on division) that our assumption really leads to a solution of the problem.

If we put

$$\frac{1}{\pi n R^2} = l,$$

the result is

$$\chi(r) = l\left(2hAX - \frac{dA}{dx} + r^2 A \frac{dh}{dx}\right)\frac{1}{r}\varepsilon^{-hr^2}. \qquad (65)$$

Finally we find from (*53*) and (*54*) for the currents of electricity and of heat

$$J = e\int \xi^2 \chi(r)\, d\lambda,$$

$$W = \tfrac{1}{2}m\int \xi^2 r^2 \chi(r)\, d\lambda.$$

In these formulae ξ^2 may be replaced by $\frac{1}{3}r^2$ and $d\lambda$ by $4\pi r^2 dr$; the integration is thereby reduced to one with respect to r from 0 to ∞. Next substituting the value (*65*), and choosing $s = r^2$ as a new variable, we are led to the integrals

$$\int_0^\infty s\varepsilon^{-hs}ds, \quad \int_0^\infty s^2\varepsilon^{-hs}ds \quad \text{and} \quad \int_0^\infty s^3\varepsilon^{-hs}ds.$$

The values of these are

$$\frac{1}{h^2}, \quad \frac{2}{h^3} \quad \text{and} \quad \frac{6}{h^4},$$

so that the two currents are given by

$$J = \frac{2}{3}\pi e l\left\{\frac{1}{h^2}\left(2hAX - \frac{dA}{dx}\right) + 2\frac{A}{h^3}\frac{dh}{dx}\right\},$$

$$W = \frac{2}{3}\pi m l\left\{\frac{1}{h^3}\left(2hAX - \frac{dA}{dx}\right) + 3\frac{A}{h^4}\frac{dh}{dx}\right\}.$$

The coefficient of electric conductivity σ is easily found from the first of these equations. Let the cylindrical bar be kept at uniform temperature throughout its length. Then $\frac{dh}{dx}=0$, $\frac{dA}{dx}=0$, and when there is an electric force E producing an acceleration

$$X=\frac{eE}{m},$$

the electric current will be

$$J=\frac{4\pi l A e^2}{3hm}E.$$

We conclude from this that

$$\sigma=\frac{4\pi l A e^2}{3hm},$$

or, if we use the relations (*59*) and (*60*), introducing at the same time a velocity u whose square is equal to the mean square $\overline{r^2}$, so that $m=\frac{2\alpha T}{u^2}$,

$$\sigma=\sqrt{\frac{2}{3\pi}}\cdot\frac{e^2 l N u}{\alpha T}.$$

In order to find the conductivity for heat we shall consider a bar between whose ends a difference of temperature is maintained, these ends being electrically insulated, so that no electricity can enter or leave the metal. Under these circumstances the unequal heating will produce a difference of potential which increases until the electric force called forth by it makes J vanish. The final state will be characterized by

$$2hAX-\frac{dA}{dx}=-2\frac{A}{h}\frac{dh}{dx},$$

giving

$$W=\frac{2}{3}\pi m l\cdot\frac{A}{h^4}\frac{dh}{dx}=-\frac{8\pi l A\alpha}{9h^2}\frac{dT}{dx},$$

where we have also used the relation (*60*). From this we infer the coefficient of thermal conductivity

$$k=\frac{8\pi l A\alpha}{9h^2}=\frac{8}{9}\sqrt{\frac{2}{3\pi}}\,\alpha l N u.$$

It remains to add that the quantity l may be considered as a certain mean length of free path.

30 (Page 77). As a preliminary to the deduction of Wien's law, we shall extend to the case of an oblique incidence the reasoning given in § 46. A beam of light propagated in a direction lying in the plane XOZ and making an angle ϑ with OX may be represented by expressions of the form

$$a\cos n\left(t-\frac{x\cos\vartheta+z\sin\vartheta}{c}+p\right),$$

and when it falls upon a fixed mirror whose surface coincides with the plane YOZ, we shall have functions containing the factor

$$\cos n\left(t + \frac{x \cos \vartheta - z \sin \vartheta}{c} + p\right)$$

for the quantities relating to the reflected light.

Now, the theorem of corresponding states (§ 45, Note 26) tells us that when the mirror has a translation with velocity w in the direction of OX, there can be a state of things represented by equations in which the above goniometric functions are replaced by

$$\cos n\left(t' - \frac{x' \cos \vartheta + z \sin \vartheta}{c} + p\right) \tag{66}$$

and

$$\cos n\left(t' + \frac{x' \cos \vartheta - z \sin \vartheta}{c} + p\right), \tag{67}$$

where

$$x' = x - wt \quad \text{and} \quad t' = t - \frac{w}{c^2}\, x'.$$

The frequencies of the beams are given by the coefficients of t in these expressions (66) and (67)

$$n\left(1 + \frac{w}{c} \cos \vartheta\right) \quad \text{and} \quad n\left(1 - \frac{w}{c} \cos \vartheta\right),$$

so that, if the frequency of the incident rays is

$$n\left(1 + \frac{w}{c} \cos \vartheta\right) = \mathbf{n},$$

that of the rays reflected by the moving mirror is given by

$$\mathbf{n}\left(1 - \frac{2w}{c} \cos \vartheta\right).$$

It follows from this that a wave-length λ is changed to

$$\lambda\left(1 + \frac{2w}{c} \cos \vartheta\right).$$

We shall also have to speak of the pressure acting on a perfectly reflecting mirror receiving under the angle ϑ a bundle of parallel rays. As it will suffice to know the pressure exerted on the mirror when at rest, we may apply the formula found in § 25. Since all the light is reflected, we have $\bar{\mathbf{s}}'' = 0$, and $|\bar{\mathbf{s}}'| = |\bar{\mathbf{s}}|$, the magnitude of these last vectors being equal to the product by c of the energy i existing in the incident beam per unit of volume. Moreover, if A is the area of the mirror, we have $\Sigma = \Sigma' = A \cos \vartheta$. As the vectors $\bar{\mathbf{s}}$ and $\bar{\mathbf{s}}'$ are in the direction of the rays, it is easily seen that the vector $\bar{\mathbf{s}} - \bar{\mathbf{s}}'$ is directed towards the mirror along the normal. The resultant force is therefore a normal pressure whose magnitude is $2Ai \cos^2 \vartheta$, or $2i \cos^2 \vartheta$ per unit of area.

Turning now to the proof of Wien's law, we shall consider a cylindrical vessel closed by a movable piston and void of ponderable matter. We shall conceive the internal space to be traversed in all directions by rays of light or heat, it being our object to examine the changes in intensity and wave-length that are brought about by the motion of the piston. We suppose the latter to be perfectly reflecting on the inside, whereas the walls and the bottom of the cylinder are „perfectly white", by which we mean that they reflect the rays equally in all directions and without any change in wave-length or any loss of intensity. By making these assumptions, and by supposing the motion of the piston to be extremely slow, we secure for all instants the isotropy of the state of radiation.

Let us fix our attention on the rays existing at a certain time t with wave-lengths between the limits λ and $\lambda + d\lambda$, and let us denote by $\psi(\lambda)d\lambda$ the energy per unit of volume belonging to these rays, or, as we shall say, to the group $(\lambda, \lambda + d\lambda)$. If A is the surface of the piston and h its height above the bottom of the cylinder, the total energy belonging to the group in question is

$$J = Ah\psi(\lambda)\,d\lambda, \tag{68}$$

and we may find a differential equation proper for the determination of ψ as a function of λ and t, by examining the quantities of energy that are lost and gained by the group $(\lambda, \lambda + d\lambda)$.

In the first place a loss is caused by the reflexion of part of the rays against the moving piston, for every ray which falls upon it, has its wave-length changed, so that, after the reflexion, it no longer belongs to the group $(\lambda, \lambda + d\lambda)$. In order to calculate the loss we may observe that the rays of which we are speaking are travelling equally in all directions; hence, if we confine ourselves to those whose direction lies within an infinitely narrow cone of solid angle $d\omega$, we have for the energy per unit of volume

$$\frac{1}{4\pi}\psi(\lambda)\,d\omega\,d\lambda,$$

and for those rays whose direction makes an angle between ϑ and $\vartheta + d\vartheta$ with the normal to the piston (drawn towards the outside) the corresponding value is

$$\tfrac{1}{2}\psi(\lambda)\sin\vartheta\,d\vartheta\,d\lambda.$$

During the interval dt the piston is struck by these rays in so far as, at the time t, they were within a distance $c\cos\vartheta\,dt$ from the piston, i. e. in a part of the cylinder whose volume is $cA\cos\vartheta\,dt$, so that the energy falling upon the piston is

$$\tfrac{1}{2}cA\psi(\lambda)\sin\vartheta\cos\vartheta\,d\vartheta\,d\lambda\,dt.$$

Integrating from $\vartheta = 0$ to $\vartheta = \frac{1}{2}\pi$, one finds for the energy that is lost by the group $(\lambda, \lambda + d\lambda)$

$$\tfrac{1}{4} c A \psi(\lambda)\, d\lambda\, dt. \tag{69}$$

On the other hand a certain amount of energy is restored to the group because rays originally having another wave-length, get one between λ and $\lambda + d\lambda$ by their reflexion against the moving piston.

Let us begin by especially considering the rays whose direction before reflexion is comprised within a cone $d\omega$ whose axis makes an angle $\vartheta (< \frac{1}{2}\pi)$ with the normal to the piston. If λ' is their wave-length before reflexion, it will be changed to

$$\lambda = \left(1 + \frac{2w}{c} \cos \vartheta\right) \lambda',$$

where w is to be reckoned positive when the motion of the piston is outward. Hence, if the new wave-length is to lie between λ and $\lambda + d\lambda$, the original one must be between λ' and $\lambda' + d\lambda'$, where

$$\lambda' = \left(1 - \frac{2w}{c} \cos \vartheta\right) \lambda,$$

$$d\lambda' = \left(1 - \frac{2w}{c} \cos \vartheta\right) d\lambda.$$

The energy of these rays per unit of volume is

$$i = \frac{1}{4\pi} \psi(\lambda')\, d\omega\, d\lambda'$$

and one sees by a reasoning similar to that used above that the amount of energy belonging to the group of rays defined by $d\omega$, λ', $d\lambda'$, which falls upon the piston during the time dt, is equal to

$$c A i \cos \vartheta\, dt.$$

Part of this energy is spent in doing work on the piston, and it is only the remaining part that is gained by the group $(\lambda, \lambda + d\lambda)$.

The pressure exerted on the piston by the rays of which we are now speaking being

$$2 A i \cos^2 \vartheta,$$

and its work during the time dt

$$2 w A i \cos^2 \vartheta\, dt,$$

the amount of energy restored to the group $(\lambda, \lambda + d\lambda)$ is given by

$$c A i \cos \vartheta\, dt - 2 w A i \cos^2 \vartheta\, dt. \tag{70}$$

As we constantly neglect the square of w, we shall replace i in the second term by

$$\frac{1}{4\pi} \psi(\lambda)\, d\omega\, d\lambda$$

and in the first term by

$$\frac{1}{4\pi}\left(1-\frac{2w}{c}\cos\vartheta\right)\psi(\lambda')\,d\omega\,d\lambda$$

$$=\frac{1}{4\pi}\left\{\left(1-\frac{2w}{c}\cos\vartheta\right)\psi(\lambda)-\frac{2w}{c}\cos\vartheta\cdot\lambda\frac{\partial\psi}{\partial\lambda}\right\}d\omega\,d\lambda,$$

since

$$\psi(\lambda')=\psi(\lambda)-\frac{2w}{c}\cos\vartheta\cdot\lambda\frac{\partial\psi}{\partial\lambda}.$$

By this we get for the expression *(70)*

$$\frac{cA}{4\pi}\left[\cos\vartheta\cdot\psi(\lambda)-\frac{2w}{c}\cos^2\vartheta\left\{2\psi(\lambda)+\lambda\frac{\partial\psi}{\partial\lambda}\right\}\right]d\omega\,d\lambda\,dt.$$

Extending the integral of this with respect to $d\omega$ over all directions of the rays for which $\vartheta<\frac{1}{2}\pi$, we find the energy that is restored to the group $(\lambda,\ \lambda+d\lambda)$ and must be subtracted from *(69)*. Since

$$\int\cos\vartheta\,d\omega=\pi,\quad\int\cos^2\vartheta\,d\omega=\tfrac{2}{3}\pi,$$

the result of the integration is

$$\frac{1}{4}cA\left[\psi(\lambda)-\frac{4w}{3c}\left\{2\psi(\lambda)+\lambda\frac{\partial\psi}{\partial\lambda}\right\}\right]d\lambda\,dt,$$

and we have for the change of the energy existing in the cylinder, so far as it belongs to wave-lengths between λ and $\lambda+d\lambda$,

$$\frac{dJ}{dt}=-\frac{1}{3}wA\left\{2\psi(\lambda)+\lambda\frac{\partial\psi}{\partial\lambda}\right\}d\lambda.$$

But, since $\frac{dh}{dt}=w$, we see from *(68)* that

$$\frac{dJ}{dt}=wA\psi(\lambda)d\lambda+Ah\frac{\partial\psi}{\partial t}d\lambda,$$

so that

$$w\psi+h\frac{\partial\psi}{\partial t}=-\frac{2}{3}w\psi-\frac{1}{3}w\lambda\frac{\partial\psi}{\partial\lambda},$$

or, if we put

$$\frac{w}{3h}=k,$$

$$\frac{\partial\psi}{\partial t}=-k\left(5\psi+\lambda\frac{\partial\psi}{\partial\lambda}\right).\tag{71}$$

This differential equation enables us to calculate the change which the motion of the piston produces in the distribution of the energy over the different wave-lengths. In order to put it in a form more clearly showing its meaning, we shall first deduce from it the rate of change of the total energy per unit of volume

$$K=\int_0^\infty\psi\,d\lambda.$$

For this purpose we have only to multiply (*71*) by $d\lambda$, and to integrate each term from $\lambda = 0$ to $\lambda = \infty$. Since

$$\int_0^\infty \frac{\partial \psi}{\partial t} d\lambda = \frac{dK}{dt}$$

and

$$\int_0^\infty \lambda \frac{\partial \psi}{\partial \lambda} d\lambda = |\lambda\psi|_{\lambda=0}^{\lambda=\infty} - \int_0^\infty \psi d\lambda = -\int_0^\infty \psi d\lambda = -K,$$

we find

$$\frac{dK}{dt} = -4kK, \quad \frac{d\log K}{dt} = -4k.$$

In deducing this equation I have supposed that for $\lambda = \infty$ the product $\lambda\psi$ tends towards the limit 0.

Now, when the velocity w is given for every instant, k is a known function of the time and so will be K. We may therefore introduce this latter quantity as independent variable instead of t. Putting

$$\log K = \xi$$

and considering ψ as a function of this quantity and of

$$\log \lambda = \eta,$$

we find from (*71*) after division by $-k\psi$,

$$4\frac{\partial \log \psi}{\partial \xi} = 5 + \frac{\partial \log \psi}{\partial \eta}.$$

This is simplified still further if, instead of ξ and η, we introduce

$$\xi' = \xi \quad \text{and} \quad \eta' = \xi + 4\eta$$

as independent variables. The equation then becomes

$$\frac{\partial}{\partial \xi'}(\log \psi - \tfrac{5}{4}\xi') = 0,$$

showing that the expression

$$\log \psi - \tfrac{5}{4}\xi' = \log\left(\psi K^{-\frac{5}{4}}\right),$$

and therefore

$$\psi K^{-\frac{5}{4}}$$

itself must be a function of η' alone. But

$$\eta' = \xi + 4\eta = 4\log\left(\lambda K^{\frac{1}{4}}\right),$$

so that $\psi K^{-\frac{5}{4}}$ may also be represented as a function of $\lambda K^{\frac{1}{4}}$. The solution of our equation is thus seen to be

$$K^{-\frac{5}{4}}\psi(\lambda, K) = F\left(\lambda K^{\frac{1}{4}}\right), \tag{72}$$

where we have expressed that ψ is a function of λ and K, and where the function F remains indeterminate.

If, in the course of the motion of the piston, the value K' of K is reached, we shall have, similarly to (72), for any wave-length

$$K'^{-\frac{5}{4}}\psi(\lambda, K') = F(\lambda K'^{\frac{1}{4}}).$$

The right-hand side of the first equation becomes equal to that of the second, if we replace λ by

$$\left\{\frac{K'}{K}\right\}^{\frac{1}{4}}\lambda,$$

so that

$$\psi(\lambda, K') = \left(\frac{K'}{K}\right)^{\frac{5}{4}}\psi\left(\left\{\frac{K'}{K}\right\}^{\frac{1}{4}}\lambda, K\right).$$

Hence, if in the original state the distribution of energy is given by the function $\varphi(\lambda)$, i. e. if, for all values of λ,

$$\psi(\lambda, K) = \varphi(\lambda),$$

we find for the corresponding function in the final state

$$\psi(\lambda, K') = \left(\frac{K'}{K}\right)^{\frac{5}{4}}\varphi\left(\left\{\frac{K'}{K}\right\}^{\frac{1}{4}}\lambda\right).$$

31 (Page 80). Planck finds in C. G. S.-units

$$\alpha = 2{,}02 \, . \, 10^{-16},$$

(so that the mean kinetic energy of a molecule would be $2{,}02 \cdot 10^{-16} T$ ergs), for the mass of an atom of hydrogen

$$1{,}6 \cdot 10^{-24} \text{ gramm}$$

and for the universal unit of electricity expressed in the units which we have used

$$1{,}6 \cdot 10^{-20} c\sqrt{4\pi}$$

(see § 35).

32 (Page 81). In a first series of experiments Hagen and Rubens deduced the absorption by a metal from its reflective power; they found that for $\lambda = 12\mu$, 8μ and even for $\lambda = 4\mu$ the results closely agreed with the values that can be calculated from the conductivity. In later experiments made with rays of wave-length $25{,}5\,\mu$ („Reststrahlen" of fluorite), which led to the same result, the emissivity of a metal was compared with that of a black body, and the coefficient of absorption calculated by our formula (122) (p. 69).

33 (Page 81). Let us choose the axis of x at right angles to the plate, so that $x = 0$ at the front surface and $x = \Delta$ at the back;

further, let a be the amplitude of the electric vibrations in the incident beam, this beam being represented by

$$\mathfrak{d}_y = a \cos n\left(t - \frac{x}{c} + p\right) \cdot$$

The electric force $\mathbf{E}_y$ in the interior of the thin plate may be considered as having the same intensity at all points. It produces a current of conduction

$$\mathbf{J}_y = \sigma \mathbf{E}_y$$

and a dielectric displacement in the ether contained in the metal. The variations of this displacement, however, do not give rise to any thermal effect, and the heat produced will therefore correspond to the work done by the force $\mathbf{E}_y$ while it produces the current $\mathbf{J}_y$. Per unit of time and unit of volume this work is equal to

$$\mathbf{J}_y \mathbf{E}_y = \sigma \mathbf{E}_y^2,$$

so that the development of heat in a part of the plate corresponding to unit of area of its surface is given by

$$\sigma \mathbf{E}_y^2 \Delta.$$

Now, at the front surface, $\mathbf{E}_y$ is equal to the corresponding quantity in the ether outside the metal (on account of the continuity of the tangential electric force), i. e. to $\mathfrak{d}_y + \mathfrak{d}_{y(r)}$ where $\mathfrak{d}_{y(r)}$ relates to the reflected beam. Since, however, the amplitude of $\mathfrak{d}_{y(r)}$ is proportional to Δ, and since we shall neglect terms containing Δ^2, we may omit $\mathfrak{d}_{y(r)}$. In this way we find for the development of heat

$$\sigma a^2 \Delta \cos^2(nt + p),$$

and for its mean value during a time comprising many periods

$$\tfrac{1}{2} \sigma a^2 \Delta.$$

The coefficient of absorption A is found if we divide this by the amount of energy $\frac{1}{2} a^2 c$ which, per unit of time, falls upon the portion of the plate considered.

34 (Page 85). This is confirmed by the final formula for a_s^2 (p. 89), according to which this quantity is proportional to s^2, and therefore to $\frac{1}{\lambda^2}$.

35 (Page 87). The truth of this is easily seen if we consider both the metallic atoms and the electrons as perfectly elastic spheres, supposing the former to be immovable. Let a sphere whose radius R is equal to the sum of the radii of an atom and of an electron be described around the centre O of an atom, and let a line OP be drawn in a direction opposite to that in which an electron strikes against the atom. Then, the position of the point Q on the sphere where the centre of the electron lies at the instant of impact may be determined by the angle $POQ = \vartheta$ and the angle φ between the plane POQ and a fixed plane passing through OP. The probability that in a collision these angles lie between the limits ϑ and $\vartheta + d\vartheta$, φ and $\varphi + d\varphi$, is found to be

$$\frac{1}{\pi} \sin\vartheta \cos\vartheta \, d\vartheta \, d\varphi, \tag{73}$$

where ϑ ranges from 0 to $\frac{1}{2}\pi$, and φ from 0 to 2π.

Let us also represent the direction in which the electron rebounds, by the point S where a radius parallel to it intersects the spherical surface. The polar coordinates of this point are $\vartheta' = 2\vartheta$ and $\varphi' = \varphi$, and if these angles vary between the limits ϑ' and $\vartheta' + d\vartheta'$, φ' and $\varphi' + d\varphi'$, the point S takes all positions on the element

$$d\sigma = R^2 \sin\vartheta' \, d\vartheta' \, d\varphi'$$

of the sphere. But we may write for the expression (73)

$$\frac{1}{4\pi} \sin\vartheta' \, d\vartheta' \, d\varphi',$$

so that the probability of the point S lying on the element $d\sigma$ is

$$\frac{d\sigma}{4\pi R^2}.$$

This being independent of the position of $d\sigma$ on the sphere, we conclude that, after an impact, all directions of the velocity of the electron are equally probable.

36 (Page 88). Considering a single electron which, at the time t, occupies the position P, we can fix our attention on the distance $PQ = l$ over which it travels before it strikes against an atom. If an electron undergoes a great number N of collisions in a certain interval of time, we may say that the experiment of throwing it among the atoms and finding the length of this free path l is made with it N times. But, since the arrangement of the atoms is highly irregular, we may just as well make the experiment with N different electrons moving in the same direction with a common velocity u. Let us therefore consider such a group, and let us seek the number N' of it, which, after having travelled over a distance l, have not yet struck against an atom, a number that is evidently some function of l. During an interval dt a certain part of this number N' will be disturbed in their rectilinear course, and since this part will be proportional both to N' and to dt, or, what amounts to the same thing, to the distance $dl = udt$, we may write for it

$$\beta N' dl, \tag{74}$$

where β is a constant. Hence, while the distance dl is travelled over, the number N' changes by

$$dN' = -\beta N' dl,$$

so that we have

$$N' = N\varepsilon^{-\beta l},$$

because $N' = N$ for $l = 0$.

The expression (74), which now becomes

$$\beta N \varepsilon^{-\beta l} dl \tag{75}$$

gives the number of electrons for which the length of path freely travelled over lies between l and $l + dl$. The sum of their free paths is

$$\beta N l \varepsilon^{-\beta l} dl,$$

and we shall find the sum of all the free paths if we integrate from $l = 0$ to $l = \infty$. Dividing by N, we get for the mean free path

$$l_m = \beta \int_0^\infty l \varepsilon^{-\beta l} dl = \frac{1}{\beta}.$$

The number (75) of free paths whose lengths lie between l and $l + dl$ is therefore equal to

$$\frac{1}{l_m} N \varepsilon^{-\frac{l}{l_m}} dl,$$

or, since

$$N = \frac{u\vartheta}{l_m},$$

equal to

$$\frac{u\vartheta}{l_m^2} \varepsilon^{-\frac{l}{l_m}} dl.$$

37 (Page 89). This case occurs when the atoms and the electrons are rigid elastic spheres, the atoms being immovable, for it is clear that an electron may then move with different velocities in exactly the same zigzag line. Other assumptions would lead to a value of l_m depending on the velocity u, but then we should also have to modify the formula given in § 50 for the electric conductivity. The final formula for $\frac{E}{A}$ would probably remain unaltered.

38 (Page 90). It may be noticed that the numbers given in Note 31 can be said to be based on formula (148), if in calculating them one uses only the part of the radiation curve corresponding to long waves.

39 (Page 92). According to what has been said, the potential and the kinetic energy may be represented by expressions of the form

$$U = \tfrac{1}{2} a_1 p_1^2 + \cdots + \tfrac{1}{2} a_n p_n^2,$$
$$T = \tfrac{1}{2} b_1 \dot{p}_1^2 + \cdots + \tfrac{1}{2} b_n \dot{p}_n^2,$$

immediately showing that the amounts of energy belonging to each of the n fundamental modes of vibration have simply to be added. Since for small vibrations the coefficients a and b may be regarded as constants, each mode of motion is determined by an equation of Lagrange

$$\frac{d}{dt}\left(\frac{\partial T}{\partial \dot{p}_k}\right) = -\frac{\partial U}{\partial p_k},$$

or

$$b_k \ddot{p}_k = -a_k p_k,$$

the general solution of which is

$$p_k = \alpha \cos\left(\sqrt{\frac{a_k}{b_k}}\, t + \beta\right),$$

where α and β are constants.

In this state of motion there is a potential energy

$$\frac{1}{2} a_k p_k^2 = \frac{1}{2} a_k \alpha^2 \cos^2\left(\sqrt{\frac{a_k}{b_k}}\, t + \beta\right),$$

and a kinetic energy

$$\frac{1}{2} b_k \dot{p}_k^2 = \frac{1}{2} a_k \alpha^2 \sin^2\left(\sqrt{\frac{a_k}{b_k}}\, t + \beta\right),$$

both of which have the mean value

$$\tfrac{1}{4} a_k \alpha^2.$$

40 (Page 94). Taking three edges of the parallelepiped as axes of coordinates, and denoting by f, g, h the direction cosines of the electric vibrations of the beam travelling in the direction (μ_1, μ_2, μ_3), we may represent this beam by the formulae

$$\mathbf{d}_x = fa \cos n\left(t - \frac{\mu_1 x + \mu_2 y + \mu_3 z}{c} + p\right),$$

$$\mathbf{d}_y = ga \cos n\left(t - \frac{\mu_1 x + \mu_2 y + \mu_3 z}{c} + p\right),$$

$$\mathbf{d}_z = ha \cos n\left(t - \frac{\mu_1 x + \mu_2 y + \mu_3 z}{c} + p\right).$$

If we assume similar formulae with the same constants a and p for the seven other beams, replacing μ_1, μ_2, μ_3 by the values indicated in (149), and f, g, h by

$$f, -g, -h; \ -f, g, -h; \ -f, -g, h;$$
$$f, -g, -h; \ -f, g, -h; \ -f, -g, h;$$
$$f, g, h$$

respectively, the total values of d_x, d_y, d_z are given by

$$\left.\begin{aligned}
\mathsf{d}_x &= -8fa\cos\frac{n\mu_1 x}{c}\sin\frac{n\mu_2 y}{c}\sin\frac{n\mu_3 z}{c}\cos n(t+p),\\
\mathsf{d}_y &= -8ga\sin\frac{n\mu_1 x}{c}\cos\frac{n\mu_2 y}{c}\sin\frac{n\mu_3 z}{c}\cos n(t+p),\\
\mathsf{d}_z &= -8ha\sin\frac{n\mu_1 x}{c}\sin\frac{n\mu_2 y}{c}\cos\frac{n\mu_3 z}{c}\cos n(t+p).
\end{aligned}\right\} \quad (76)$$

By these the condition that d be normal to the walls is fulfilled at the planes XOY, YOZ, ZOX, for at the first plane, for example, $z=0$, and consequently $\mathsf{d}_x = 0$, $\mathsf{d}_y = 0$.

The same condition must also be satisfied at the opposite faces of the parallelepiped. This requires that, if q_1, q_2, q_3 have the meaning given in the text,

$$\sin\frac{n\mu_1 q_1}{c} = 0, \quad \sin\frac{n\mu_2 q_2}{c} = 0, \quad \sin\frac{n\mu_3 q_3}{c} = 0.$$

Therefore,

$$\frac{n\mu_1 q_1}{c}, \quad \frac{n\mu_2 q_2}{c}, \quad \frac{n\mu_3 q_3}{c}$$

must be multiples of π, and since $\frac{n}{c} = \frac{2\pi}{\lambda}$,

$$\frac{2\mu_1 q_1}{\lambda}, \quad \frac{2\mu_2 q_2}{\lambda}, \quad \frac{2\mu_3 q_3}{\lambda}$$

must be whole numbers.

41 (Page 94). If one of these states, say a state A, is determined by the formulae (*76*) of the preceding Note, in which f, g, h relate to any direction at right angles to the direction (μ_1, μ_2, μ_3), a state of things A' in which the polarization is perpendicular to the former one is represented by equations of the same form (with other constants a' and p'), in which f, g, h are replaced by the constants f', g', h' determining a direction at right angles both to (f, g, h) and to (μ_1, μ_2, μ_3). It is easily seen that any other mode of motion represented by formulae like (*76*) with values of f, g, h such that

$$\mu_1 f + \mu_2 g + \mu_3 h = 0$$

may be decomposed into two states of the kind of A and A'. The total electric field will therefore consist of a large number of fields A and A', each having a definite amplitude a and phase p. In order to find the total electric energy we must calculate for each mode of motion the integral

$$\frac{1}{2}\int \mathfrak{d}^2 dS,$$

and for each combination of two modes

$$\int (\mathfrak{d} \cdot \mathfrak{d}')\, dS \quad . \quad . \quad . \quad . \quad . \quad . \quad . \quad . \quad (77)$$

Now, it may be shown that all the integrals of the latter kind are zero. For a combination of two states such as we have just now called A and A' (which are characterized by equal values of μ_1, μ_2, μ_3 and of the frequency n), this is seen if one takes into account that in the integrals

$$\int_0^{q_1} \cos^2 \frac{n\mu_1 x}{c}\, dx, \quad \int_0^{q_1} \sin^2 \frac{n\mu_1 x}{c}\, dx, \quad \int_0^{q_2} \cos^2 \frac{n\mu_2 y}{c}\, dy \text{ etc.} \qquad (78)$$

the square of the cosine or the sine may be replaced by $\frac{1}{2}$, so that (77) becomes

$$8(ff' + gg' + hh')\, aa'\, q_1 q_2 q_3 \cos n(t+p) \cos n(t+p'),$$

which is 0 because the directions (f, g, h) and (f', g', h') are at right angles to each other.

In any other case at least one of the coefficients $\frac{n\mu_1}{c}$, $\frac{n\mu_2}{c}$, $\frac{n\mu_3}{c}$ will be different for the states $\mathfrak{d}$ and $\mathfrak{d}'$. Thus, $\frac{n\mu_1}{c}$ may have the value k for one state and the value k' for the other. The integrals

$$\int_0^{q_1} \cos kx \cos k'x\, dx = \frac{1}{2(k+k')} \sin (k+k') q_1 + \frac{1}{2(k-k')} \sin (k-k') q_1,$$

$$\int_0^{q_1} \sin kx \sin k'x\, dx = -\frac{1}{2(k+k')} \sin (k+k') q_1 + \frac{1}{2(k-k')} \sin (k-k') q_1$$

both are zero, because kq_1 and $k'q_1$ are multiples of π. Consequently, each of the three integrals

$$\int \mathfrak{d}_x \mathfrak{d}'_x\, dS, \quad \text{etc.}$$

into which (77) may be decomposed vanishes.

It is readily seen that similar results hold for the magnetic energy. It will suffice to observe that, in the state represented by the formulae (*76*), the magnetic force has the components

$$\mathsf{h}_x = 8f' a \sin\frac{n\mu_1 x}{c}\cos\frac{n\mu_2 y}{c}\cos\frac{n\mu_3 z}{c}\sin n(t+p),$$

$$\mathsf{h}_y = 8g' a \cos\frac{n\mu_1 x}{c}\sin\frac{n\mu_2 y}{c}\cos\frac{n\mu_3 z}{c}\sin n(t+p),$$

$$\mathsf{h}_z = 8h' a \cos\frac{n\mu_1 x}{c}\cos\frac{n\mu_2 y}{c}\sin\frac{n\mu_3 z}{c}\sin n(t+p),$$

where

$$f' = \mu_2 h - \mu_3 g, \quad g' = \mu_3 f - \mu_1 h, \quad h' = \mu_1 g - \mu_2 f$$

are the constants determining a direction perpendicular both to (μ_1, μ_2, μ_3) and to (f, g, h).

If further, one takes into account what has been said of the integrals (*78*), it will be found that the parallelepiped contains an amount

$$4(f^2+g^2+h^2)q_1 q_2 q_3 a^2 \cos^2 n(t+p) = 4 q_1 q_2 q_3 a^2 \cos^2 n(t+p)$$

of electric, and an amount

$$4 q_1 q_2 q_3 a^2 \sin^2 n(t+p)$$

of magnetic energy. Each of these expressions has the mean value

$$2 q_1 q_2 q_3 a^2.$$

42 (Page 97). On further consideration I think that it will be very difficult to arrive at a formula different from that of Rayleigh so long as we adhere to the general principles of the theory of electrons as set forth in our first chapter. But, on the other hand, it must be observed that Jeans's theory is certainly in contradiction with known facts. Let us compare, for example, the emissivity E_1 for yellow light of a polished silver plate at 15° C. with that (E_2) of a black body at 1200° C., confining ourselves to the direction normal to the plate. Silver reflects about 90 percent of the incident light, so that the coefficient of absorption of the plate is $\frac{1}{10}$, and by Kirchhoff's law, $E_1 = \frac{1}{10} E_3$, if E_3 denotes the emissivity of a black body at 15°. But, by Jeans's theory (see § 74) the emissivity of a black body for light of a given wave-length must be proportional to the absolute temperature, so that we have $E_3 = \frac{288}{1473} E_2 = \frac{1}{5} E_2$, and $E_1 = \frac{1}{50} E_2$.

Now, at the temperature of 1200°, a black body would glow very brilliantly, and if the silver plate at 15° had an emissivity only fifty times smaller, it ought certainly to be visible in the dark.

It must be noticed that we have based our reasoning on Kirchhoff's law, the validity of which is not doubted by Jeans. In fact, the point in the above argument was that, at temperatures at which a black body has a perceptible emissivity for the kind of rays considered, it can never be that, for some other body, *only one* of the coefficients E and A is very small. The silver plate might be expected to emit an appreciable amount of light, because its coefficient of absorption shows that in reality the exchange of energy between its particles and the ether is *not* extremely show.

From facts like that which I have mentioned it appears that, if we except the case of very long waves, bodies emit considerably less light, in proportion to their coefficient of absorption, than would be required by Jeans's formulae. The only equation by which the observed phenomena are satisfactorily accounted for is that of Planck, and it seems necessary to imagine that, for short waves, the connecting link between matter and ether is formed, not by free electrons, but by a different kind of particles, like Planck's resonators, to which, for some reason, the theorem of equipartition does not apply. Probably these particles must be such that their vibrations and the effects produced by them cannot be appropriately described by means of the ordinary equations of the theory of electrons; some new assumption, like Planck's hypothesis of finite elements of energy will have to be made.

It must not be thought, however, that all difficulties can be cleared in this way. Though in many, or in most cases, Planck's resonators may play a prominent part, yet, the phenomena of conduction make it highly probable that the metals at least also contain free electrons whose motion and radiation may be accurately described by our formulae. It seems difficult to see why a formula like Planck's should hold for the emission and absorption caused by these particles. Therefore, this formula seems to require that the free electrons, though certainly existing in the metal, be nearly inactive. Nor is this all. If we are right in ascribing the emission and the absorption by a metal to two different agencies, to that of free electrons in the case of long waves (on the grounds set forth in § 60), and to that of „resonators“ in the case of shorter ones, we must infer that for intermediate wave-lengths both kinds of particles have their part in the phenomena. The question then arises in what way the equilibrium is brought about under these complicated circumstances.

It must be added that, even in the case of long waves, there are some difficulties. To these attention has been drawn by J. J. Thomson.[1])

---

1) J. J. Thomson, The corpuscular theory of matter, p. 85.

I shall close this discussion by a remark on the final state that is required by Jeans's theory. I dare say that it will be found impossible to form an idea of a state of things in which the energy would be uniformly distributed over an infinite number of degrees of freedom. The final state can therefore scarcely be thought of as really existing, but the distribution of energy might be conceived continually to tend towards uniformity without reaching it in a finite time.

42* (Page 97) [1915]. Later researches have shown that in all probability the theorem of equipartition holds for systems subject to the ordinary laws of dynamics and electromagnetism. A satisfactory theory of radiation will therefore require a profound modification of fundamental principles. Provisionally we must content ourselves with Planck's hypothesis of quanta.

We cannot speak here of the development that has been given to his important theory, but one result ought to be mentioned.

Planck finds that the mean energy of a resonator whose number of vibrations per second is ν, is given by

$$E = \frac{h\nu}{\varepsilon^{\frac{h\nu}{kT}} - 1}.$$

If kT is much greater than $h\nu$, the denominator may be replaced by

$$\frac{h\nu}{kT},$$

and the formula becomes

$$E = kT.$$

This is the value required by the theorem of equipartition. We see therefore that this theorem can only be applied if the temperature is sufficiently high. For lower temperatures E is smaller than kT and even, if kT is considerably below $h\nu$, we may write

$$\frac{E}{kT} = \frac{h\nu}{kT}\varepsilon^{-\frac{h\nu}{kT}}$$

which is very small.

The resonators imagined by Planck are „linear", each consisting f. i. of a single electron vibrating along a straight line. If the number of degrees of freedom of a vibrator is greater, the total energy becomes greater too and it seems that we may state as a general rule that a system capable of a certain number of fundamental vibrations, when in equilibrium with bodies kept at the temperature T, takes the energy E for each of its degrees of freedom.

We may even apply this to the ether contained in the rectangular box which we considered in §§ 73 und 74.[1])

We found (pp. 94 and 95)

$$\frac{8\pi q_1 q_2 q_3}{\lambda^4} d\lambda$$

for the number of fundamental vibrations whose wave-length lies between λ and $\lambda + d\lambda$. Each of these corresponds to a degree of freedom and we have therefore to multiply

$$E = \frac{h\nu}{\varepsilon^{\frac{h\nu}{kT}} - 1}$$

by the above number. Replacing ν by $\frac{c}{\lambda}$, we find in this way

$$\frac{8\pi ch}{\lambda^5} \cdot \frac{1}{\varepsilon^{\frac{ch}{k\lambda T}} - 1} q_1 q_2 q_3 \cdot d\lambda.$$

If we want to know the energy per unit of volume we have still to divide by the volume of the parallelepiped $q_1 q_2 q_3$. The result is seen to agree with Planck's radiation formula (132).

43 (Page 102). In Zeeman's first experiments it was not found possible neatly to separate the components; only a broadening of the lines was observed, and the conclusions were drawn from the amount of this broadening and the state of polarization observed at the borders.

44 (Page 110). For great values of the coordinates, the coefficients c might be functions of them. They may, however, be treated as constants if we confine ourselves to very small vibrations.

45 (Page 112). The result of the elimination of $q_1, q_2, \ldots q_\mu$ from the equations (176) is

$$\begin{vmatrix} f_1 - m_1 n^2, & -inc_{12}, & \ldots, & -inc_{1\mu} \\ -inc_{21}, & f_2 - m_2 n^2, & \ldots, & -inc_{2\mu} \\ \cdot & \cdot & \ldots, & \\ \cdot & \cdot & \ldots, & \\ -inc_{\mu 1} & -inc_{\mu 2}, & \ldots, & f_\mu - m_\mu n^2 \end{vmatrix} = 0. \qquad (79)$$

Developing the determinant we get in the first place the principal term

$$\Pi = (f_1 - m_1 n^2)(f_2 - m_2 n^2) \ldots (f_\mu - m_\mu n^2),$$

1) P. Debye, Ann. Phys. **33** (1910), p. 1427.

and in the second place terms containing as factors two of the coefficients c. These coefficients being very small, we may neglect all further terms which contain more than two factors of the kind. One of the said terms is obtained if, in the principal term, the two factors $f_k - m_k n^2$ and $f_l - m_l n^2$ are replaced by $-inc_{kl} \cdot inc_{lk} = -n^2 c_{kl}^2$. Hence, denoting by Π_{kl} the product which remains when we omit from Π the factors $f_k - m_k n^2$ and $f_l - m_l n^2$, we may write for (79)

$$\Pi - n^2 \sum_{kl} c_{kl}^2 \Pi_{kl} = 0, \qquad (80)$$

an equation that can be satisfied by values of n^2 differing very little from the roots n_1^2, n_2^2, ... n_μ^2 of the equation

$$\Pi = 0,$$

which are determined by (172).

Thus there is a root

$$n^2 = n_k^2 + \delta, \qquad (81)$$

where δ is very small. Indeed, if this value is substituted in (80) we may replace n^2 by n_k^2 in all the products Π_{kl}, and the same may be done in the factors of the first term Π, with the exception only of $f_k - m_k n^2$, for which we must write $-m_k \delta$. By this Π becomes

$$-m_k \delta \, \Pi_k(n_k^2),$$

where the last term means the product Π after omission of the said factor, and substitution of $n^2 = n_k^2$ in the remaining ones.

In the sum occurring in (80) only those terms become different from zero, in which the factor $f_k - m_k n^2$ (corresponding to the particular value we have chosen for k) is missing. Our equation therefore assumes the form

$$-m_k \delta \, \Pi_k(n_k^2) - n_k^2 \sum_l c_{kl}^2 \Pi_{kl}(n_k^2) = 0,$$

from which the value of δ is immediately found.

This value may be positive or negative, but, as it is very small, the right-hand side of (81) is positive in any case, and gives a real value for the frequency

$$n = n_k + \frac{\delta}{2 n_k}.$$

46 (Page 113). Equation (79) is somewhat simplified when we divide the horizontal rows of the determinant by $\sqrt{m_1}$, $\sqrt{m_2}$, etc., and then treat the vertical columns in the same manner. Putting

$$\frac{c_{kl}}{\sqrt{m_k m_l}} = e_{kl}, \qquad (82)$$

so that

$$e_{kl} = -e_{lk}, \qquad (83)$$

and using (172), one finds

$$\begin{vmatrix} n_1^2 - n^2, & -ine_{12}, & \cdot\ \cdot, & -ine_{1\mu} \\ -ine_{21}, & n_2^2 - n^2, & \cdot\ \cdot, & -ine_{2\mu} \\ \cdot & \cdot & \cdot\ \cdot, & \\ \cdot & \cdot & \cdot\ \cdot, & \\ -ine_{\mu 1}, & -ine_{\mu 2}, & \cdot\ \cdot, & n_\mu^2 - n^2 \end{vmatrix} = 0. \qquad (84)$$

Let us now suppose that a certain number k, say the first k, of the frequencies $n_1, n_2, \ldots$ have a common value ν, and let us seek a value of n satisfying the condition (*84*), and nearly equal to ν. When n has a value of this kind, all the elements of the determinant with the exception of $n_{k+1}^2 - n^2, \ldots n_\mu^2 - n^2$ are very small quantities. Therefore, the part which contains these $\mu - k$ elements, namely the part

$$(n_{k+1}^2 - n^2) \ldots (n_\mu^2 - n^2) \begin{vmatrix} n_1^2 - n^2, & -ine_{12}, & \cdot\ \cdot & -ine_{1k} \\ -ine_{21}, & n_2^2 - n^2, & \cdot\ \cdot & -ine_{2k} \\ \cdot & \cdot & \cdot\ \cdot & \\ \cdot & \cdot & \cdot\ \cdot & \\ -ine_{k1}, & -ine_{k2}, & \cdot\ \cdot & n_k^2 - n^2 \end{vmatrix}$$

greatly predominates. We shall therefore replace (*84*) by

$$\begin{vmatrix} n_1^2 - n^2, & -ine_{12}, & \cdot\ \cdot & -ine_{1k} \\ -ine_{21}, & n_2^2 - n^2, & \cdot\ \cdot & -ine_{2k} \\ \cdot & \cdot & \cdot\ \cdot & \\ \cdot & \cdot & \cdot\ \cdot & \\ -ine_{k1}, & -ine_{k2}, & \cdot\ \cdot & n_k^2 - n^2 \end{vmatrix} = 0.$$

Finally, since the quantities e are very small, we shall replace n by ν wherever it is multiplied by an e, so that we find

$$\begin{vmatrix} \nu^2 - n^2, & -i\nu e_{12}, & \cdot\ \cdot & -i\nu e_{1k} \\ -i\nu e_{21}, & \nu^2 - n^2, & \cdot\ \cdot & -i\nu e_{2k} \\ \cdot & \cdot & \cdot\ \cdot & \\ \cdot & \cdot & \cdot\ \cdot & \\ -i\nu e_{k1}, & -i\nu e_{k2}, & \cdot\ \cdot & \nu^2 - n^2 \end{vmatrix} = 0, \qquad (85)$$

an equation of degree k in n^2.

Now, on account of the relations (*83*), the latter determinant is not altered when we change the signs of all the elements containing an e (the effect being merely that the horizontal rows become equal to the original vertical columns). Hence, after development, the equation can only have terms with an even number of these elements, so that it is of the form

$$(\nu^2 - n^2)^k + P_1(\nu^2 - n^2)^{k-2} + P_2(\nu^2 - n^2)^{k-4} + \cdots = 0, \qquad (86)$$

where P_1 is made up of terms containing *two* factors of the form $i\nu e$, P_2 of terms containing *four* such factors, and so on.

It follows from this that the coefficients P are real quantities. But we may go further and prove that, if $\nu^2 - n^2$ is considered as the unknown quantity, all the roots of the equation (85) or (86) are real.

For this purpose we observe that, on account of (85), if we take for $\nu^2 - n^2$ one of its roots, the equations

$$\begin{aligned} (\nu^2 - n^2)x_1 - i\nu e_{12}x_2 - \cdots - i\nu e_{1k}x_k &= 0, \\ - i\nu e_{21}x_1 + (\nu^2 - n^2)x_2 - \cdots - i\nu e_{2k}x_k &= 0, \\ \cdots\cdots\cdots\cdots\cdots\cdots\cdots\cdots \\ - i\nu e_{k1}x_1 - i\nu e_{k2}x_2 - \cdots + (\nu^2 - n^2)x_k &= 0 \end{aligned}$$

may be satisfied by certain values of $x_1, x_2 \ldots x_k$, which in general will be complex quantities. Let $\bar{x}_1, \bar{x}_2, \ldots \bar{x}_k$ be the conjugate values. Then, multiplying the equations by $\bar{x}_1, \bar{x}_2, \ldots \bar{x}_k$ respectively and adding, we find

$$(\nu^2 - n^2)\sum_j x_j\bar{x}_j - \nu\sum_{jl} i(e_{jl}x_l\bar{x}_j + e_{lj}x_j\bar{x}_l) = 0. \qquad (87)$$

Now, putting

$$x_j = \xi_j + i\eta_j, \quad \bar{x}_j = \xi_j - i\eta_j, \quad x_l = \xi_l + i\eta_l, \quad \bar{x}_l = \xi_l - i\eta_l,$$

we have

$$x_j\bar{x}_j = \xi_j^2 + \eta_j^2,$$

and, in virtue of (83),

$$i(e_{jl}x_l\bar{x}_j + e_{lj}x_j\bar{x}_l) = 2e_{jl}(\xi_l\eta_j - \xi_j\eta_l).$$

The two sums in (87) are therefore real, and $\nu^2 - n^2$ must be so likewise.

We have now to distinguish the cases of k even and k odd. In the first case (86) is an equation of degree $\frac{1}{2}k$, when $(\nu^2 - n^2)^2$ is considered as the quantity to be determined, and, since $\nu^2 - n^2$ must be real, its roots are all positive. Calling them $\alpha^2, \beta^2, \gamma^2, \ldots$, we have the solution

$$n^2 - \nu^2 = \pm\alpha, \pm\beta, \pm\gamma, \cdots$$

whence

$$n = \nu \pm \frac{\alpha}{2\nu}, \quad \nu \pm \frac{\beta}{2\nu}, \quad \nu \pm \frac{\gamma}{2\nu}, \cdots \qquad (88)$$

being k values of the frequency.

When k is odd, equation (*86*) has the factor $\nu^2 - n^2$, so that one root is

$$n = \nu,$$

corresponding to the original spectral line. After having divided the equation by $\nu^2 - n^2$, we are led back to the former case, so that now, besides $n = \nu$, there are $k - 1$ roots of the form (*88*).

In the particular case of three equivalent degrees of freedom, equation (*86*) becomes

$$(\nu^2 - n^2)^3 + (\nu^2 - n^2)\nu^2(e_{23}e_{32} + e_{31}e_{13} + e_{12}e_{21}) = 0,$$

giving $n^2 - \nu^2 = 0$ and

$$n^2 - \nu^2 = \pm \nu \sqrt{e_{23}^2 + e_{31}^2 + e_{12}^2},$$

from which (177) immediately follows, if we replace ν by n_1 and e_{23}, e_{31}, e_{12} by their values (*82*).

I am indebted to a remark made by Dr. A. Pannekoek for the extension of the foregoing theory to cases of more than three equivalent degrees of freedom.

47 (Page 113). That the distances between the magnetic components of a spectral line will be proportional to the intensity of the magnetic field (for a given direction of it) is also seen from the general equation (*86*). It suffices to observe that each quantity e is proportional to $|\mathbf{H}|$. Therefore P_1 is proportional to $\mathbf{H}^2$, P_2 to $\mathbf{H}^4$, and so on. The values of $n^2 - \nu^2$ which satisfy the equation vary as $|\mathbf{H}|$ itself, and as they are very small, the same is true of $n - \nu$.

48 (Page 120). In the following theory of the vibrations of a system of four electrons we shall denote by a the edge of the tetrahedron in the position of equilibrium, by l the distance from the centre O to one of the edges, by r the radius of the circumscribed sphere, and by ϑ the angle between the radius drawn towards one of the angles and an edge ending at that angle. We have

$$\cos\vartheta = \sqrt{\frac{2}{3}}, \quad l = \frac{1}{4}a\sqrt{2}, \quad r = \frac{1}{4}a\sqrt{6}.$$

In the state of equilibrium one of the electrons A is acted on by the repulsions of the three others, each equal to

$$\frac{e^2}{4\pi a^2},$$

and by the force due to the positive charge. The latter force is the same as when a charge $\mathsf{e} = \frac{4}{3}\pi r^3 \varrho_0$ were placed at the point O. Hence we have the condition of equilibrium

$$\frac{3e^2}{4\pi a^2}\cos\vartheta + \frac{e\mathsf{e}}{4\pi r^2} = 0,$$

or

$$\varrho_0 = -\frac{3e}{\pi a^3}.$$

The frequency of the first mode of motion is easily found by observing that, after a displacement of all the electrons to a distance $r+\delta$ from the centre, where δ is infinitely small, the resultant force acting on any one of them would remain zero, if the attraction exerted by the positive sphere were still equivalent to that of a charge e at O. As it is, there is a residual force due to the attraction of the positive charge included between the spheres whose radii are r and $r+\delta$. The amount of this charge being $4\pi r^2 \varrho\delta$, and the force exerted by it on one of the electrons $e\varrho\delta$, we have the equation of motion

$$m\frac{d^2\delta}{dt^2} = e\varrho\delta,$$

giving for the frequency

$$n^2 = -\frac{e\varrho}{m}.$$

Let us next consider the motion that has been described in the text as a twisting around the axis OX. The formula for this case is found in the simplest way by fixing our attention on the potential energy of the system. When the edges AB and CD are turned around OX through equal angles φ in opposite directions, two of the lines AC, AD, BC, BD are changed to

$$\sqrt{4l^2 + a^2\sin^2(\tfrac{1}{4}\pi - \varphi)} = a(1 - \tfrac{1}{2}\varphi - \tfrac{1}{8}\varphi^2),$$

and the two others to

$$a(1 + \tfrac{1}{2}\varphi - \tfrac{1}{8}\varphi^2).$$

The potential energy due to the mutual action of the corpuscles is therefore

$$2\cdot\frac{1}{4\pi}\left\{\frac{e^2}{a(1-\frac{1}{2}\varphi-\frac{1}{8}\varphi^2)} + \frac{e^2}{a(1+\frac{1}{2}\varphi-\frac{1}{8}\varphi^2)}\right\} = \frac{e^2}{\pi a}(1 + \tfrac{3}{8}\varphi^2).$$

The potential energy with respect to the positive sphere having not been altered (because each electron has remained at the distance r from the centre), and the kinetic energy being equal to

$$\tfrac{1}{2}ma^2\dot{\varphi}^2,$$

the equation of motion becomes

$$\tfrac{1}{2} m a^2 \dot{\varphi}^2 + \frac{3 e^2}{8 \pi a} \varphi^2 = \text{const.},$$

giving for the frequency

$$n^2 = \frac{3 e^2}{4 \pi a^3 m} = - \frac{\varrho_0 e}{4 m}.$$

In examining the vibrations for which the equations (181) and (182) are given in the text, we may treat the system as one with only two degrees of freedom, the configuration of which is wholly determined by the coordinates p and g.

This time we shall apply the general theory of a vibrating system, starting from the formulae for the potential energy U and the kinetic energy T expressed as functions of p, g, $\dot{p}$, $\dot{g}$. If we ascribe a potential energy zero to two corpuscles placed at the distance a, their potential energy at the distance $a + \delta a$ will be

$$\frac{e^2}{4 \pi (a + \delta a)} - \frac{e^2}{4 \pi a} = \frac{e^2}{4 \pi} \left\{ - \frac{\delta a}{a^2} + \frac{(\delta a)^2}{a^3} \right\}.$$

The value of δa being $2g$ for the pair AB, $-2g$ for CD, and $\frac{g^2}{a}$ for the remaining pairs, we find the following expression for the mutual potential energy of the four corpuscles

$$\frac{e^2}{\pi a^3} g^2 = - \tfrac{1}{3} e \varrho_0 g^2. \tag{89}$$

As to the potential energy u of a corpuscle with respect to the positive sphere, we may write for it $e(\varphi - \varphi_0)$, if the potential due to the sphere has the value φ_0 for the position of equilibrium of the corpuscle and the value φ for its new position. Therefore, since φ is a function of the distance r from the centre, we may write, denoting by δr the change of r,

$$u = e \left\{ \frac{d \varphi}{d r} \delta r + \frac{1}{2} \frac{d^2 \varphi}{d r^2} (\delta r)^2 \right\}.$$

Taking into account that, by Poissson's equation,

$$\frac{d^2 \varphi}{d r^2} + \frac{2}{r} \frac{d \varphi}{d r} = - \varrho,$$

and that $- \frac{d \varphi}{d r}$, the electric force acting on the electron in its original position, is equal to

$$\frac{e}{4 \pi r^2} = \frac{1}{3} \varrho_0 r,$$

we find

$$u = e \left\{ - \tfrac{1}{3} \varrho_0 r \delta r + (\tfrac{1}{3} \varrho_0 - \tfrac{1}{2} \varrho)(\delta r)^2 \right\}. \tag{90}$$

If $A'B'$ is the line AB displaced, and E' its middle point, we have

$$OE' = l + p, \quad E'A' = \tfrac{1}{2}a + g,$$

$$OA' = \sqrt{(l+p)^2 + (\tfrac{1}{2}a + g)^2},$$

and therefore for the electron A

$$\delta r = \frac{1}{2r}(2lp + ag) - \frac{1}{8r^3}(2lp + ag)^2 + \frac{1}{2r}(p^2 + g^2).$$

The same value holds for B and we get those for C and D by changing the signs of p and g. Substituting in (*90*) and taking the sum of the four values, we find

$$e\left\{\frac{1}{2}(\varrho_0 - \varrho)\frac{1}{r^2}(2lp + ag)^2 - \frac{2}{3}\varrho_0(p^2 + g^2)\right\},$$

which, added to (*89*), gives

$$U = e\left\{\frac{1}{2}(\varrho_0 - \varrho)\frac{1}{r^2}(2lp + ag)^2 - \frac{1}{3}\varrho_0(2p^2 + 3g^2)\right\}$$

$$= 2m(\alpha p^2 + 2\beta pg + \gamma g^2),$$

if we put

$$\alpha = -\frac{e\varrho}{3m}, \quad \beta = \frac{e(\varrho_0 - \varrho)\sqrt{2}}{3m}, \quad \gamma = \frac{e(\varrho_0 - 4\varrho)}{6m}.$$

The square of the velocity being $\dot{p}^2 + \dot{g}^2$ for each electron, we have

$$T = 2m(\dot{p}^2 + \dot{g}^2), \tag{91}$$

and the equations of motion

$$\frac{d}{dt}\left(\frac{\partial T}{\partial \dot{p}}\right) + \frac{\partial U}{\partial p} = 0, \quad \frac{d}{dt}\left(\frac{\partial T}{\partial \dot{g}}\right) + \frac{\partial U}{\partial g} = 0$$

assume the form

$$\ddot{p} + \alpha p + \beta g = 0, \quad \ddot{g} + \beta p + \gamma g = 0.$$

If we put

$$p = k \cos nt, \quad g = sp,$$

the constants n and s are determined by the equations

$$-n^2 + (\alpha + \beta s) = 0, \quad -sn^2 + (\beta + \gamma s) = 0$$

from which (181) and (183) are easily deduced.

In the calculation of the influence of a magnetic field on the vibrations to which the formula (183) relates, we may consider the three modes of motion, corresponding to a definite value of s, which, in the absence of a magnetic field, have the same frequency, say n_0, as the only ones of which the system is capable. Reverting to the formulae of § 90, we shall call p_1, p_2, p_3 the three displacements, common to all the electrons, which occur in the three modes, this displacement being parallel to OX in the first mode, to OY in the second and to OZ in the third. It is to be understood that p_1 is now what is called p in § 100, and that in every case the displacements p are attended with transverse displacements $g = \pm sp$.

Equation (*91*) gives for each mode

$$T = 2m(1+s^2)\dot{p}^2,$$

so that the coefficients m_1, m_2, m_3 introduced in § 89 have the common value

$$m_0 = 4m(1+s^2). \tag{92}$$

The coefficients f_1, f_2, f_3 are also equal to each other, and if we substitute

$$p_1 = q_1 \varepsilon^{int}, \quad p_2 = q_2 \varepsilon^{int}, \quad p_3 = q_3 \varepsilon^{int}$$

(cf. (175)), we find the following equations

$$\left.\begin{aligned} m_0(n_0^2 - n^2)q_1 - in_0 c_{12} q_2 - in_0 c_{13} q_3 &= 0,\\ -in_0 c_{21} q_1 + m_0(n_0^2 - n^2) q_2 - in_0 c_{23} q_3 &= 0,\\ -in_0 c_{31} q_1 - in_0 c_{32} q_2 + m_0(n_0^2 - n^2) q_3 &= 0, \end{aligned}\right\} \tag{93}$$

corresponding to (176) and giving for the frequencies of the magnetic triplet (cf. (177))

$$n_0 \text{ and } n_0 \pm \frac{1}{8m(1+s^2)} \sqrt{c_{23}^2 + c_{31}^2 + c_{12}^2}\,. \tag{94}$$

It remains to determine the coefficients c, for which purpose we have to return to (173).

The expression $P_1 \delta p_1$ represents the work done, in the case of the virtual displacement δp_1, by the electromagnetic forces that are called into play by the motion of the electrons in the magnetic field **H**. Consequently $c_{12}\dot{p}_2 \delta p_1$ is the work of these forces in so far as they are due to the velocities of the particles in the motion determined by $\dot{p}_2$. Calculating this work, we shall find the value of c_{12}.

It will be well to introduce the rectilinear coordinates of the four corpuscles in their positions of equilibrium. If the axes are properly chosen, these are for A: l, l, l, for B: $l, -l, -l$, for C: $-l, l, -l$, and for D: $-l, -l, l$.

When the coordinate p_1 is changed by δp_1, the four particles undergo a displacement equal to δp_1 in the direction of OX, combined with displacements $s\delta p_1$ directed along the line AB for A and B and along CD for C and D. Taking into acount that in the case of a positive $s\delta p_1$, the distance from OX is increased for

A and B, and diminished for C and D, and putting $s' = s\sqrt{\frac{1}{2}}$, we find for the rectangular components of the displacement

$$\left.\begin{array}{llll} \text{for } A: & \delta p_1, & s'\delta p_1, & s'\delta p_1, \\ \text{,, } B: & \delta p_1, & -s'\delta p_1, & -s'\delta p_1, \\ \text{,, } C: & \delta p_1, & -s'\delta p_1, & s'\delta p_1, \\ \text{,, } D: & \delta p_1, & s'\delta p_1, & -s'\delta p_1. \end{array}\right\} \quad (95)$$

If here, instead of δp_1, we wrote $\dot{p}_1$, we should get the components of the velocities occurring in the motion $\dot{p}_1$, Similarly, the velocities in the motion $\dot{p}_2$ are

$$\left.\begin{array}{llll} \text{for } A: & s'\dot{p}_2, & \dot{p}_2, & s'\dot{p}_2, \\ \text{,, } B: & -s'\dot{p}_2, & \dot{p}_2, & s'\dot{p}_2, \\ \text{,, } C: & -s'\dot{p}_2, & \dot{p}_2, & -s'\dot{p}_2, \\ \text{,, } D: & s'\dot{p}_2, & \dot{p}_2, & -s'\dot{p}_2. \end{array}\right\} \quad (96)$$

We have now to fix our attention on the electromagnetic forces due to these velocities, and to determine the work of these forces corresponding to the displacements (*95*). The result is found to depend on the component $\mathbf{H}_z$ only, and we shall therefore omit from the beginning all terms with $\mathbf{H}_x$ and $\mathbf{H}_y$. Thus we write

$$\frac{e}{c}\mathbf{v}_y\mathbf{H}_z, \quad -\frac{e}{c}\mathbf{v}_x\mathbf{H}_z, \quad 0$$

for the components of the electromagnetic force acting on an electron, by which, taking $\mathbf{v}_x$ and $\mathbf{v}_y$ from (*96*), we find the following forces acting on the corpuscles in the directions of OX and OY:

$$\begin{array}{lll} \text{for } A: & \frac{e}{c}\mathbf{H}_z\dot{p}_2, & -\frac{e}{c}\mathbf{H}_z s'\dot{p}_2, \\ \text{,, } B: & \frac{e}{c}\mathbf{H}_z\dot{p}_2, & \frac{e}{c}\mathbf{H}_z s'\dot{p}_2, \\ \text{,, } C: & \frac{e}{c}\mathbf{H}_z\dot{p}_2, & \frac{e}{c}\mathbf{H}_z s'\dot{p}_2, \\ \text{,, } D: & \frac{e}{c}\mathbf{H}_z\dot{p}_2, & -\frac{e}{c}\mathbf{H}_z s'\dot{p}_2. \end{array}$$

Finally, in order to find the work $c_{12}\dot{p}_2\delta p_1$, we must take the products of these quantities and the corresponding ones in the first two columns of (*95*), and add the results. This leads to the value

$$c_{12} = 4\frac{e}{c}\mathbf{H}_z(1 - s'^2) = 4\frac{e}{c}\mathbf{H}_z(1 - \tfrac{1}{2}s^2),$$

and similarly

$$c_{23} = 4\frac{e}{c}\mathbf{H}_x(1-\tfrac{1}{2}s^2), \quad c_{31} = 4\frac{e}{c}\mathbf{H}_y(1-\tfrac{1}{2}s^2),$$

so that the last term of (*94*) is equal to

$$\pm\frac{e}{2cm}|\mathbf{H}|\cdot\frac{1-\tfrac{1}{2}s^2}{1+s^2}.$$

Dividing this by the corresponding term in (164), we find

$$\omega = \frac{1-\tfrac{1}{2}s^2}{1+s^2}, \qquad (97)$$

from which the values (184) and (185) are easily deduced.

49 (Page 123). Let $\varrho - \varrho_0$ be made to approach the limit 0 from the positive side, so that, by (182), $\nu = +\infty$. Taking into account that

$$4(\varrho-\varrho_0)\sqrt{2(1+2\nu^2)} = \frac{1}{2}(2\varrho-\varrho_0)\frac{\sqrt{2(1+2\nu^2)}}{\nu}$$

and that the limit of

$$\frac{\sqrt{2(1+2\nu^2)}}{\nu}$$

is 2, one will easily find that the formulae (183)—(185) lead to the values given in the text.

The same results are also obtained when $\varrho - \varrho_0$ is supposed to approach the limit 0 from the negative side.

It must, however, be noticed that, as (*97*) shows, for one of the two solutions (namely for the one for which $\omega = -\tfrac{1}{2}$) the coefficient s determined by (181) becomes infinite, indicating that for this solution $p = 0$ (since g must be finite). The corresponding vibrations would therefore be ineffective in the limiting case (§ 99), because the radiation is due to the vibrations of the electrons in the direction of OX.

50 (Page 123). After having found the frequency n, we may deduce from the equations (*93*) the ratios between q_1, q_2, q_3, which determine the form of the vibrations, and the nature of the light emitted. We shall abbreviate by putting

$$4\frac{e}{c}(1-\tfrac{1}{2}s^2) = \sigma, \qquad (98)$$

so that

$$c_{23} = \sigma\mathbf{H}_x, \quad c_{31} = \sigma\mathbf{H}_y, \quad c_{12} = \sigma\mathbf{H}_z,$$

and, by (*94*) and (*92*), for the outer lines of the triplet

$$n^2 - n_0{}^2 = \pm\frac{n_0\sigma}{m_0}|\mathbf{H}|, \qquad (99)$$

where we shall understand by $|\mathbf{H}|$ a positive number.

If $\mathbf{h}$ is a unit vector in the direction of the magnetic force, the equations (*93*) assume the form

$$\left.\begin{aligned} \pm q_1 + i(\mathbf{h}_z q_2 - \mathbf{h}_y q_3) = 0, \\ \pm q_2 + i(\mathbf{h}_x q_3 - \mathbf{h}_z q_1) = 0, \\ \pm q_3 + i(\mathbf{h}_y q_1 - \mathbf{h}_x q_2) = 0. \end{aligned}\right\} \qquad (100)$$

Let

$$q_1 = \mathbf{a}_x + i\mathbf{b}_x, \quad q_2 = \mathbf{a}_y + i\mathbf{b}_y, \quad q_3 = \mathbf{a}_z + i\mathbf{b}_z$$

be a set of complex values satisfying these conditions and let us consider $\mathbf{a}_x$, $\mathbf{b}_x$, etc. as the components of certain vectors $\mathbf{a}$ and $\mathbf{b}$.

Separating the real and the imaginary parts of (*100*), we find the equations

$$\pm \mathbf{a} - [\mathbf{b} \cdot \mathbf{h}] = 0, \quad \pm \mathbf{b} + [\mathbf{a} \cdot \mathbf{h}] = 0,$$

showing in the first place that the vectors $\mathbf{a}$ and $\mathbf{b}$ must be at right angles both to the magnetic field and to each other, and in the second place that they must be of equal magnitude.

We are now in a position to determine the nature of the light emitted by the vibrating system. As we found in § 39, the radiation of an electron depends on its acceleration only. We infer from this that, when there are a certain number of equal electrons, the resultant radiation will be the same as if we had a single corpuscle with the same charge, whose displacement from its position of equilibrium were at every instant equal to the resultant of the displacements of the individual electrons. Now, in the first mode of motion which we have considered in what precedes, the resultant displacement is obviously $4p$ in the direction of OX. In this way it is seen that the radiation going forth from the tetrahedron when it, vibrates in the manner we have now been examining is equal to that from a single electron, the „equivalent" electron as we may call it, the components of whose displacement are given by the real parts of the expressions

$$4q_1 \varepsilon^{int}, \quad 4q_2 \varepsilon^{int}, \quad 4q_3 \varepsilon^{int},$$

i. e. by

$$\left.\begin{aligned} 4\mathbf{a}_x \cos nt - 4\mathbf{b}_x \sin nt, \\ 4\mathbf{a}_y \cos nt - 4\mathbf{b}_y \sin nt, \\ 4\mathbf{a}_z \cos nt - 4\mathbf{b}_z \sin nt. \end{aligned}\right\} \qquad (101)$$

The equivalent electron therefore has a motion compounded of two rectilinear vibrations in the directions of the vectors $\mathbf{a}$ and $\mathbf{b}$, with equal amplitudes $4|\mathbf{a}|$ and $4|\mathbf{b}|$ and with a difference of phase of a quarter period. Hence, it moves with constant velocity in a circle whose plane is perpendicular to the magnetic force, and the radiation will be much the same as in the elementary theory of the Zeeman-effect.

When we take the upper signs in our formulae we have

$$\mathbf{a} = [\mathbf{b} \cdot \mathbf{h}],$$

from which it follows that the circular motion represented by (*101*) has the direction of that of the hands of a clock, if the observer is placed on the side towards which the lines of force are directed. Therefore in this case the light emitted in the direction of the lines of force has a right-handed circular polarization. Its polarization is left-handed when we take the under signs.

Now, the equation (*99*) shows that, when σ is positive, the frequency is greatest for the right-handed, and least for the left-handed circular polarization, contrary to what we found in the elementary theory of the Zeeman-effect. The reverse, however, will be the case, when σ has a negative value. Since the charge e is negative, it follows from (*97*) and (*98*) that the signs of σ and ω are opposite. The sign of the Zeeman-effect will therefore be that which we found in the elementary theory or the reverse according as ω is positive or, negative.

51 (Page 126). When the particle has a velocity of translation $\mathbf{v}$, the forces acting on one of its electrons are

$$X = \frac{e}{c}(\mathbf{v}_y \mathbf{H}_z - \mathbf{v}_z \mathbf{H}_y), \quad Y = \frac{e}{c}(\mathbf{v}_z \mathbf{H}_x - \mathbf{v}_x \mathbf{H}_z), \quad Z = \frac{e}{c}(\mathbf{v}_x \mathbf{H}_y - \mathbf{v}_y \mathbf{H}_x)$$

Here, denoting by x, y, z the coordinates of the electron with respect to the centre of the particle, and distinguishing by the index 0 the values at that point, we may replace $\mathbf{H}_x$, $\mathbf{H}_y$, $\mathbf{H}_z$ by

$$\mathbf{H}_{0x} + x\frac{\partial \mathbf{H}_x}{\partial x} + y\frac{\partial \mathbf{H}_x}{\partial y} + z\frac{\partial \mathbf{H}_x}{\partial z}, \quad \text{etc.} \tag{102}$$

Substituting this in the expressions

$$\Sigma(yZ - zY), \quad \text{etc.}$$

for the components of the resultant couple and using the equations of § 104, we find

$$\frac{e}{c}\left[\mathbf{v}_x \frac{\partial \mathbf{H}_y}{\partial y}\Sigma y^2 - \mathbf{v}_y \frac{\partial \mathbf{H}_x}{\partial y}\Sigma y^2 - \mathbf{v}_z \frac{\partial \mathbf{H}_x}{\partial z}\Sigma z^2 + \mathbf{v}_x \frac{\partial \mathbf{H}_z}{\partial z}\Sigma z^2\right], \quad \text{etc.}$$

or, since

$$\frac{\partial \mathbf{H}_y}{\partial y} + \frac{\partial \mathbf{H}_z}{\partial z} = -\frac{\partial \mathbf{H}_x}{\partial x},$$

$$-\frac{eK}{c}\left\{\mathbf{v}_x \frac{\partial \mathbf{H}_x}{\partial x} + \mathbf{v}_y \frac{\partial \mathbf{H}_x}{\partial y} + \mathbf{v}_z \frac{\partial \mathbf{H}_x}{\partial z}\right\}, \quad \text{etc.}$$

When the field is constant and if in the symbol $\frac{d\mathbf{H}}{dt}$ we understand by $\mathbf{H}$ the magnetic force at the point occupied by the particle at the time t, the couple is given by

$$-\frac{eK}{c}\frac{d\mathbf{H}}{dt},$$

and, since the moment of inertia is $2mK$, the change of the angular velocity $\mathbf{k}$ is determined by

$$\frac{d\mathbf{k}}{dt} = -\frac{e}{2mc}\frac{d\mathbf{H}}{dt}.$$

Hence, on the assumption that the particle did not rotate so long as it was outside the field,

$$\mathbf{k} = -\frac{e}{2mc}\mathbf{H}.$$

In the above calculation no attention has been paid to the electromagnetic forces called into play by the rotation itself. In as much as the magnetic field may be considered as homogeneous throughout the extent of the particle, these forces produce no resultant couple, just because the axis of rotation is parallel to the lines of force. This is seen as follows. If $\mathbf{r}$ denotes the vector drawn from the centre to one of the electrons, we have for the linear velocity of that corpuscle

$$\mathbf{v} = [\mathbf{k} \cdot \mathbf{r}],$$

and for the electromagnetic force acting on it

$$\mathbf{F} = \frac{e}{c}[\mathbf{v} \cdot \mathbf{H}] = \frac{e}{c}\{(\mathbf{k} \cdot \mathbf{H})\mathbf{r} - (\mathbf{r} \cdot \mathbf{H})\mathbf{k}\}.$$

The moment of this force with respect to the centre is

$$[\mathbf{r} \cdot \mathbf{F}] = -\frac{e}{c}(\mathbf{r} \cdot \mathbf{H})[\mathbf{r} \cdot \mathbf{k}],$$

so that its components are

$$-\frac{e}{c}(x\mathbf{H}_x + y\mathbf{H}_y + z\mathbf{H}_z)(y\mathbf{k}_z - z\mathbf{k}_y), \quad \text{etc.} \tag{103}$$

From this we find for the components of the resultant moment

$$-\frac{e}{c}K(\mathbf{H}_y\mathbf{k}_z - \mathbf{H}_z\mathbf{k}_y), \quad \text{etc.},$$

from which it is seen that this moment is zero when $\mathbf{k}$ has the direction of $\mathbf{H}$.

The problem is more complicated when we take into account the small variations of the magnetic field from one point of the particle to another. I shall observe only that, if we use the values

(*102*), we must add to (*103*) terms of the third order with respect to x, y, z, and that the sum of these terms vanishes in many cases, for instance when, corresponding to each electron with coordinates x, y, z, there is another with the coordinates $-x, -y, -z$.

52 (Page 126). Let $\mathbf{k}$ and $\mathbf{r}$ have the same meaning as in the preceding Note and let $\mathbf{v}$ be the absolute velocity of an electron, $\mathbf{v}'$ its relative velocity with respect to the rotating particle, so that

$$\mathbf{v} = [\mathbf{k} \cdot \mathbf{r}] + \mathbf{v}'. \tag{104}$$

From this we find for the acceleration

$$\mathbf{q} = \dot{\mathbf{v}} = [\mathbf{k} \cdot \dot{\mathbf{r}}] + \dot{\mathbf{v}}' = [\mathbf{k} \cdot \mathbf{v}] + \dot{\mathbf{v}}'.$$

The change of $\mathbf{v}'$ consists of two parts

$$\dot{\mathbf{v}}' = [\mathbf{k} \cdot \mathbf{v}'] + \mathbf{q}',$$

where the second is the relative acceleration and the first the change that would be produced in $\mathbf{v}'$ if there were no such acceleration; in this case $\mathbf{v}'$ would simply turn round with the particle. Since, on account of (*104*), we may write

$$[\mathbf{k} \cdot \mathbf{v}'] = [\mathbf{k} \cdot \mathbf{v}],$$

when we neglect the square of $\mathbf{k}$, we are led to the formula

$$\mathbf{q} = \mathbf{q}' + 2[\mathbf{k} \cdot \mathbf{v}].$$

53 (Page 135). In this statement it has been tacitly assumed that the bounding surface σ of the spherical space $\mathbf{S}$ does not intersect any particles. Suppose, for instance, the molecules to be so polarized that each has a positive electron on the right and a negative one on the left-hand side, and draw the axis OX towards the first side. Then, when the surface σ passes in all its parts through the space between the particles, the integral $\int \varrho x dS$ will be equal to the sum of the electric moments of the particles enclosed, and may with propriety be called the moment of the part of the body within the surface (cf. equation (195)). If, on the contrary, molecules are intersected, the value of the integral does not merely depend on the *complete* particles lying in the space $\mathbf{S}$, but it must be taken into account that, in addition to these, σ encloses a certain number of negative electrons on the right-hand side, and a certain number of positive electrons on the opposite side. Even when these additional electrons are much less numerous than those belonging to the complete particles, they may contribute an appreciable part to the integral, because the difference between the values of x for the positive and the negative ones is comparable with the dimensions of the space **S** itself, and therefore much greater than the corresponding difference for two electrons lying in the same particle.

The following remarks may, however, serve te remove all doubts as to the validity of the relation

$$\overline{\varrho \mathbf{v}} = \dot{\mathbf{P}}.$$

When the molecules are irregularly arranged, as they are in liquids and gases, some of them (and even some electrons) are certainly intersected by the spherical surface σ used in the definition of the mean values $\overline{\varphi}$. But, on account of the assumptions made about the dimensions of σ, the intersections will be much less numerous than the molecules wholly lying within the surface, and if, in calculating $\int \varphi dS$, we omit the *parts* of particles enclosed by σ, this will lead to no error, provided that the function φ be of such a kind that the contribution to the integral from one of those parts is not very much greater than the contribution from one of the complete particles.

This condition is fulfilled in the case of the integral $\int \varrho \mathbf{v}_x dS$, because there is no reason why the velocities **v** should be exceptionally great near the surface σ. Without changing the value of the integral, we may therefore make the surface pass between the particles (by slightly deforming it), and then we may be sure that $\int \varrho \mathbf{v}_x dS = \frac{d}{dt} \int \varrho x dS$, and that the latter integral represents the total electric moment of all the complete particles in the space **S**.

54 (Page 138). We shall observe in the first place that the field in the immediate neighbourhood of a polarized particle may be determined by the rules of electrostatics, even when the electric moment is not constant. Take, for instance, the case treated in § 43. It was stated in Note 23 that at great distances the terms resulting from the differentiation of the goniometric function are very much greater than those which arise from the differentiation of $\frac{1}{r}$. These latter, on the contrary, predominate when we confine ourselves to distances that are very small in comparison with the wave-length; then (cf. (88) and (89)) we may write

$$\varphi = -\frac{1}{4\pi} \left\{ \mathbf{p}_x \frac{\partial}{\partial x} \left(\frac{1}{r}\right) + \mathbf{p}_y \frac{\partial}{\partial y} \left(\frac{1}{r}\right) + \mathbf{p}_z \frac{\partial}{\partial z} \left(\frac{1}{r}\right) \right\},$$

$$\mathbf{a} = 0,$$

$$\mathbf{d} = -\operatorname{grad} \varphi, \quad \mathbf{h} = 0,$$

from which it appears that the field is identical with the electrostatic field that would exist, if the moment **p** were kept constant.

It is further to be noted that the difference between the mean electric force $\mathbf{E}$ and the electric force existing in a small cavity depends only on actions going on at very short distances, so that we may deal with this difference as if we had to do with an electrostatic system.

Let us therefore consider a system of molecules with invariable electric moments and go into some details concerning the electric force existing in it.

The field produced by the electrons being determined by

$$\Delta \varphi = - \varrho ,$$
$$\mathbf{d} = - \operatorname{grad} \varphi ,$$

we have for the mean values

$$\Delta \overline{\varphi} = - \overline{\varrho} ,$$
$$\mathbf{E} = \overline{\mathbf{d}} = - \operatorname{grad} \overline{\varphi} ,$$

or, in words: the mean electric force is equal to the force that would be produced by a charge distributed with the mean or, let us say, the „effective" density $\overline{\varrho}$.

In the definition of a mean value $\overline{\varphi}$ given in § 113, it was expressly stated that the space S was to be of spherical form. It is easily seen, however, that we may as well give it any shape we like, provided that it be infinitely small in the physical sense. The equation

$$\overline{\varrho}\,\mathsf{S} = \int \varrho \, dS$$

may therefore be interpreted by saying that for any space of the said kind the effective charge (meaning by these words the product of $\overline{\varrho}$ and S) is equal to the total real charge.

We shall now examine the distribution of the effective charge. Suppose, for the sake of simplicity, that a molecule contains two electrons situated at the points A and B with charges $-e$ and $+e$, and denote by $\mathbf{r}$ the vector AB. There will be as many of these vectors, of different directions and lengths, as there are molecules. Now, if the length of these vectors is very much greater than the size of the electrons, we may neglect the intersections of the bounding surface of the space S with the electrons themselves, but there will be a great number of intersections with the lines AB. These may not be left out of account, because for any complete molecule $\int \varrho \, dS = 0$, whereas each of the said intersections contributes to the effective charge within σ an amount $-e$ or $+e$ according as $\mathbf{r}_n$ (where n is the normal to σ drawn outwards) is positive or negative (cf. Note 53).

Hence, the total charge within σ may be represented by a surface integral. In order to find the part of it corresponding to an element $d\sigma$ (infinitely small in a physical sense) we begin by fixing our attention on those among the lines AB which have some definite direction and some definite length. If the starting points A are irregularly distributed and if, for the group considered, their number per unit of volume is ν, the number of intersections with $d\sigma$ will be $\nu \mathbf{r}_n d\sigma$ when $\mathbf{r}_n$ is positive, and $-\nu \mathbf{r}_n d\sigma$ when it is negative. Therefore, the part contributed to the charge within σ is $-\nu e \mathbf{r}_n d\sigma$ in both cases, and the total part associated with $d\sigma$ is $-\Sigma \nu e \mathbf{r}_n d\sigma$, the sum being extended to all the groups of lines AB. But $e\mathbf{r}$ is the electric moment of a particle, $\nu e \mathbf{r}$ the moment per unit of volume of the chosen group, and $\Sigma \nu e \mathbf{r}$ the total moment per unit of volume. Denoting this by $\mathbf{P}$, we have for the above expression $-\Sigma \nu e \mathbf{r}_n d\sigma$ the value $-\mathbf{P}_n$, and for the effective charge enclosed by the surface σ

$$-\int \mathbf{P}_n d\sigma. \tag{105}$$

As the difference between $\mathbf{E}$ and the electric force in a cavity depends exclusively on the state of the system in the immediate vicinity of the point considered, we may now conceive the polarization $\mathbf{P}$ to be uniform. In this case the integral (*105*) is zero for any closed surface entirely lying within the body, so that the effective charge may be said to have its seat on the bounding surface Σ. Its surface density is found by calculating (*105*) for the surface of a flat cylinder, the two plane sides of which are on both sides of an element $d\Sigma$ at a distance from each other that is infinitely small in comparison with the dimensions of $d\Sigma$. Calling N the normal to the surface Σ, we have at the outer plane $\mathbf{P}_n = 0$ (if we suppose the body to be surrounded by ether), and at the inner one $\mathbf{P}_n = -\mathbf{P}_N$. The amount of the effective charge contained in the cylinder is therefore given by $\mathbf{P}_N d\Sigma$, and the charge may be said to be distributed over the surface with a density $\mathbf{P}_N$.

Now consider a point A of the body. By what has been said, the electric force $\mathbf{E}$ at this point is due to the charge $\mathbf{P}_N$ on the bounding surface Σ. If, however, a spherical cavity is made around A as centre, there will be at this point an additional electric force $\mathbf{E}'$, caused by a similar charge on the walls of the cavity, and obviously having the direction of $\mathbf{P}$. The magnitude of this force is found as follows. Let a be the radius of the sphere, $d\sigma$ an element of its surface, ϑ the angle between the radius drawn towards this element and the polarization $\mathbf{P}$. The surface density on $d\sigma$ being $-|\mathbf{P}|\cos\vartheta$, we have for the force produced at A

$$\frac{1}{4\pi a^2}\int |\mathbf{P}| \cos^2\vartheta \, d\sigma,$$

giving

$$\mathbf{E}' = \tfrac{1}{3}\mathbf{P}.$$

Our foregoing remarks show that the expression

$$\mathbf{E} + \tfrac{1}{3}\mathbf{P}$$

may always be used for the electric force at the centre of a spherical cavity, even though the polarization of the body change from point to point and from one instant to the next.

55 (Page 138). In the case of a cubical arrangement all the particles within the sphere may be said to have equal electric moments $\mathbf{p}$. Taking the centre A of the sphere as origin of coordinates, we have for the force exerted in the direction of x by a particle situated at the point (x, y, z), at a distance r from the centre,

$$\frac{\mathbf{p}_x}{4\pi} \cdot \frac{3x^2 - r^2}{r^5}, \quad \frac{\mathbf{p}_y}{4\pi} \cdot \frac{3xy}{r^5}, \quad \frac{\mathbf{p}_z}{4\pi} \cdot \frac{3xz}{r^5}.$$

But the sums

$$\sum \frac{3x^2 - r^2}{r^5}, \quad \sum \frac{3xy}{r^5}, \quad \sum \frac{3xz}{r^5}$$

are zero, when extended to all the particles within the sphere. For the second and the third sum this is immediately clear if we take the axes of coordinates parallel to the principal directions of the cubical arrangement. Further, for axes of this direction,

$$\sum \frac{3x^2 - r^2}{r^5} = \sum \frac{3y^2 - r^2}{r^5} = \sum \frac{3z^2 - r^2}{r^5},$$

showing that each of these expressions must be zero, because their sum is so.

56 (Page 139). It must be noticed that this magnetic force $\mathbf{H}$ produces a force

$$\frac{e}{c}[\mathbf{v} \cdot \mathbf{H}]$$

acting on an electron. Since, in a beam of light, $\mathbf{H}$ is in general of the same order of magnitude as the electric force $\mathbf{E}$ (cf. the equations (7)), this force is of the order of magnitude $\frac{|\mathbf{v}|}{c}$ in comparison with the force $e\mathbf{E}$. It may therefore be neglected because the amplitudes of the electrons are extremely small with respect to the wave-length, so that the velocity of vibration is much smaller than the speed of light.

56* (Page 141) [1915]. When the value of β (see form. (202) and (199)) corresponding to (206) is substituted in equation (230) (§ 134) which determines the index of absorption, one finds exactly the result found by Lord Rayleigh[1]) for the extinction of light by a gas. This extinction is due to the scattering of the rays by the molecules, the electrons contained in these being set vibrating by the incident light and becoming therefore centres of radiation. As the energy radiated from an electron is intimately connected with the force given by (205) (§ 40) it is natural that the amount of extinction should be determined by the coefficient (206).

57 (Page 141). In order to compare the effect of the collisions with that of a resistance of the kind represented by (197), we shall first consider the vibrations set up in an isolated particle whose electron is subjected to a periodic electric force

$$\mathbf{E}_x = p \cos nt \tag{106}$$

and to the forces determined by (196) and (197). The equation of motion

$$m\frac{d^2\xi}{dt^2} = e\mathbf{E}_x - f\xi - g\frac{d\xi}{dt}$$

is most easily solved if, following the method indicated in § 119, we replace (*106*) by

$$\mathbf{E}_x = p\varepsilon^{int}.$$

In this way we find for the forced vibrations

$$\xi = \frac{pe}{f - mn^2 + ing}\varepsilon^{int} = \frac{pe}{m(n_0^2 - n^2) + ing}\varepsilon^{int}, \tag{107}$$

where

$$n_0^2 = \frac{f}{m}.$$

Let us next suppose that there is no true resistance, but that the vibrations of the electrons are over and over again disturbed by impacts occurring at irregular intervals. In this case the motion of each particle from the last collision up to the instant t for which we wish to calculate ξ, is determined by the equation

$$m\frac{d^2\xi}{dt^2} = e\mathbf{E}_x - f\xi,$$

the general solution of which is

$$\xi = \frac{pe}{m(n_0^2 - n^2)}\varepsilon^{int} + C_1\varepsilon^{in_0t} + C_2\varepsilon^{-in_0t}, \tag{108}$$

1) Rayleigh, Phil. Mag. 47 (1899), p. 375.

where the integration constants C_1 and C_2 will vary from one particle to another. These constants are determined by the values of ξ and $\frac{d\xi}{dt}$, say $(\xi)_0$ and $\left(\frac{d\xi}{dt}\right)_0$, immediately after the last collision. Now among the great number of particles, we may distinguish a group, still very numerous, for which the last collision has taken place at a definite instant t_1. Supposing that, after the impact, all directions of the displacement and the velocity are equally probable, we shall find the mean value of ξ for this group, if in *(108)* we determine C_1 and C_2 by the conditions that for $t = t_1$ both ξ and $\frac{d\xi}{dt}$ vanish. The result is

$$\xi = \frac{pe}{m(n_0^2 - n^2)} \left\{ \varepsilon^{int} - \frac{1}{2}\left(1 + \frac{n}{n_0}\right) \varepsilon^{in_0(t-t_1)+int_1} - \frac{1}{2}\left(1 - \frac{n}{n_0}\right) \varepsilon^{-in_0(t-t_1)+int_1} \right\},$$

or, if we put

$$t - t_1 = \vartheta,$$

$$\xi = \frac{pe}{m(n_0^2 - n^2)} \varepsilon^{int} \left\{ 1 - \frac{1}{2}\left(1 + \frac{n}{n_0}\right) \varepsilon^{i(n_0-n)\vartheta} - \frac{1}{2}\left(1 - \frac{n}{n_0}\right) \varepsilon^{-i(n_0+n)\vartheta} \right\}. \quad (109)$$

This is the mean value of ξ taken for a definite instant t and for those particles for which a time ϑ has elapsed since their last collision, and we shall obtain an expression that may be compared with *(107)*, if we take the mean of *(109)* for all the groups of particles which differ from each other by the length of the interval ϑ.

Let N be the total number of particles considered, and A the number of collisions which they undergo per unit of time, so that the time τ mentioned in the text is given by

$$\frac{N}{A} = \tau.$$

The collisions succeeding each other quite irregularly, we may reckon that the number of the particles for which the interval ϑ lies between ϑ and $\vartheta + d\vartheta$ is

$$A \varepsilon^{-\frac{\vartheta}{\tau}} d\vartheta = \frac{N}{\tau} \varepsilon^{-\frac{\vartheta}{\tau}} d\vartheta; \quad (110)$$

this is found by a reasoning similar to that which we used in Note 36.

We must therefore multiply *(109)* by *(110)*, integrate from $\vartheta = 0$ to $\vartheta = \infty$, and divide by N. In this way we get for the final mean value of the displacement

$$\xi = \frac{pe}{m\left(n_0^2 + \frac{1}{\tau^2} - n^2\right) + 2\frac{imn}{\tau}} \varepsilon^{int}.$$

Neglecting the term $\frac{1}{\tau^2}$ in the denominator we see that under the influence of the collisions the phenomena will be the same, as if there were a resistance determined by

$$g = \frac{2m}{\tau}.$$

58 (Page 147). In the case of a mixture the electric moment $\mathbf{P}$ is made up of as many parts $\mathbf{P}_1, \mathbf{P}_2, \ldots$ as there are constituents. Reasoning as in §§ 116—119 we can establish for each component formulae like (200), so that, if we put $a = \frac{1}{3}$, we have for the first substance

$$m_1' \frac{\partial^2 \mathbf{P}_1}{\partial t^2} = \mathbf{E} + \frac{1}{3}\mathbf{P} - f_1'\mathbf{P}_1,$$

for the second

$$m_2' \frac{\partial^2 \mathbf{P}_2}{\partial t^2} = \mathbf{E} + \frac{1}{3}\mathbf{P} - f_2'\mathbf{P}_2,$$

and so on. Hence, if all the dependent variables vary as ε^{int},

$$\mathbf{P}_1 = \frac{\mathbf{E} + \frac{1}{3}\mathbf{P}}{f_1' - m_1'n^2}, \quad \mathbf{P}_2 = \frac{\mathbf{E} + \frac{1}{3}\mathbf{P}}{f_2' - m_2'n^2}, \ \ldots,$$

and, if we put

$$\frac{1}{f_1' - m_1'n^2} + \frac{1}{f_2' - m_2'n^2} + \cdots = \omega,$$

$$\mathbf{P} = \omega(\mathbf{E} + \tfrac{1}{3}\mathbf{P}).$$

Combining this with (192) we find

$$\mathbf{D} = \frac{1 + \frac{2}{3}\omega}{1 - \frac{1}{3}\omega}\mathbf{E}$$

and for the index of refraction

$$\mu^2 = \frac{1 + \frac{2}{3}\omega}{1 - \frac{1}{3}\omega},$$

$$\frac{\mu^2 - 1}{\mu^2 + 2} = \frac{1}{3}\omega = \frac{1}{3}\left(\frac{1}{f_1' - m_1'n^2} + \frac{1}{f_2' - m_2'n^2} + \cdots\right).$$

Now each term $\frac{1}{3(f' - m'n^2)}$ gives the value of $\frac{\mu^2 - 1}{\mu^2 + 2}$ for one of the constituents taken with the density $m\varrho$ which it has in the mixture, a value that is found when we multiply the constant r for the constituent in question by the density $m\varrho$. This immediately leads to equation (218).

59 (Page 149). According to the equations (220), if we put $a = \frac{1}{3}$, the displacements $\xi_1, \xi_2, \ldots$ are determined by

$$(f_1 - m_1 n^2)\,\xi_1 = e_1(\mathbf{E}_x + \tfrac{1}{3}\mathbf{P}_x), \ \text{etc.}$$

Consequently

$$Ne_1 \xi_1 = \frac{Ne_1^2}{f_1 - m_1 n^2}\left(\mathsf{E}_x + \frac{1}{3}\mathsf{P}_x\right), \quad \text{etc.}$$

with similar formulae for $Ne_1 \eta_1$, $Ne_1 \zeta_1$, etc. Hence, taking the sums,

$$\mathsf{P} = \left(\mathsf{E} + \frac{1}{3}\mathsf{P}\right)\left\{\frac{Ne_1^2}{f_1 - m_1 n^2} + \frac{Ne_2^2}{f_2 - m_2 n^2} + \cdots\right\},$$

from which formula (222) is easily found.

60 (Page 153). The direct result of the substitution is

$$\left(\frac{c^2}{v^2} - \frac{c^2 k^2}{n^2}\right) - i\,\frac{2 c^2 k}{v n} = 1 + \frac{1}{\alpha + i\beta} = 1 + \frac{\alpha - i\beta}{\alpha^2 + \beta^2},$$

giving

$$\mu^2 - \frac{c^2 k^2}{n^2} = 1 + \frac{\alpha}{\alpha^2 + \beta^2},$$

$$2\mu\,\frac{ck}{n} = \frac{\beta}{\alpha^2 + \beta^2},$$

from which the equations (227) and (228) are easily deduced.

61 (Page 154). The expression $\frac{\alpha}{\alpha^2 + \beta^2}$ considered as a function of α has a maximum value $\frac{1}{2\beta}$ for $\alpha = \beta$; it is therefore very small when β is large. It follows from this that even the greatest values of $\frac{2\alpha + 1}{\alpha^2 + \beta^2}$ are of the order of magnitude $\frac{1}{\beta}$, so that we may expand the square root in (227) and (228) in ascending powers of that quantity. Hence, if we neglect terms of the order $\frac{1}{\beta^3}$,

$$\sqrt{1 + \frac{2\alpha + 1}{\alpha^2 + \beta^2}} = 1 + \frac{1}{2}\cdot\frac{2\alpha + 1}{\alpha^2 + \beta^2} - \frac{1}{8}\,\frac{(2\alpha + 1)^2}{(\alpha^2 + \beta^2)^2},$$

and this may be replaced by

$$1 + \frac{1}{2}\cdot\frac{2\alpha + 1}{\alpha^2 + \beta^2} - \frac{1}{2}\cdot\frac{\alpha^2}{(\alpha^2 + \beta^2)^2},$$

because the quantity $\frac{4\alpha + 1}{(\alpha^2 + \beta^2)^2}$ never has a value greater than one of the order $\frac{1}{\beta^3}$.

Finally

$$\mu^2 = 1 + \frac{\alpha}{\alpha^2 + \beta^2} + \frac{1}{4}\,\frac{\beta^2}{(\alpha^2 + \beta^2)^2},$$

$$\frac{c^2 k^2}{n^2} = \frac{1}{4}\,\frac{\beta^2}{(\alpha^2 + \beta^2)^2}. \qquad (111)$$

We are therefore led to (229) and (230) if in μ we neglect terms of the order $\frac{1}{\beta^2}$, and in k terms of the order $\frac{1}{\beta^{3/2}}$. Indeed, if we want to know k with this degree of approximation, we may omit in k^2 and in $\frac{c^2k^2}{n^2}$ quantities of the order $\frac{1}{\beta^3}$, as we have done in (*111*).

62 (Page 156). If Jdn is the intensity of the incident light, in so far as it belongs to frequencies between n and $n+dn$, the amount of light that is absorbed by a layer with the thickness Δ, upon which the rays fall in the direction of the normal is given by the integral

$$A = \int (1 - \varepsilon^{-2k\Delta}) J dn,$$

where we have taken into account that the intensity is proportional to the square of the amplitude. If the absorption band is rather narrow, we may put

$$k = \frac{n_0'}{2c} \cdot \frac{\beta}{\alpha^2 + \beta^2}$$

and, in virtue of (231),

$$dn = -\frac{1}{2m'n_0'} d\alpha.$$

Further, we may extend the integration from $\alpha = -\infty$ to $\alpha = +\infty$, considering $\beta = n_0'g'$ and J as constants. The calculation is easily performed for a thin layer, for which

$$1 - \varepsilon^{-2k\Delta} = 2k\Delta - 2k^2\Delta^2.$$

It is found that the part of A that is due to the first term is independent of g' or g. When, however, the second term is retained, A increases with the resistance g.

63 (Page 161). This is easily found if the denominator of (239) is written in the form

$$\{\alpha(1+\alpha) - \beta^2 - \gamma^2\} + i(1 + 2\alpha)\beta$$

and then multiplied by the conjugate complex expression.

64 (Page 167). The explanation of magneto-optical phenomena becomes much easier if the particles of a luminous or an absorbing body are supposed to take a definite orientation under the action of a magnetic field. On this assumption, which makes it possible to dismiss the condition of isotropy of the particles (§ 93), Voigt[1]) has been able to account for many of the more complicated forms of

1) W. Voigt, Magneto- und Elektrooptik, Leipzig, 1908.

the Zeeman-effect; it was found sufficient to suppose that each particle contains two or more mutually connected electrons whose motion is determined by equations similar to our formulae of § 90, the rectilinear coordinates of the electrons now taking the place of the general coordinates p. The theory thus obtained must undoubtedly be considered as the best we possess at present, though the nature of the connexions remains in the dark, and though Voigt does not attempt to show in what manner the actions determined by the coefficients c are produced by the magnetic field.

I must also mention the beautiful phenomena that have been discovered by J. Becquerel.[1]) Certain crystals containing the elements erbium and didymium show a great number of absorption bands, many of which are so sharp, especially at the low temperatures obtainable by means of liquid air or liquid hydrogen[2]), that they may be compared with the lines of gaseous bodies, and these bands show in remarkable diversity the Zeeman-effect and the phenomena connected with it. Of course, in the case of these crystals the hypothesis of isotropic particles would be wholly misplaced. Voigt and Becquerel found it possible to explain the larger part of the observed phenomena on the lines of Voigt's new theory to which I have just alluded.

In § 91 it was stated that a true magnetic division of a spectral line is to be expected only when the original line is in reality a multiple one, i. e. when, in the absence of a magnetic field, there are two or more equal frequencies. Voigt has pointed out that, when originally there are two frequencies, not exactly but only nearly equal, similar effects may occur, sometimes with the peculiarity that there is a dissymmetry, more or less marked, in the arrangement of the components observed under the action of a magnetic field. Cases of this kind frequently occour in Becquerel's experiments, and Voigt is of opinion that many of the dissymmetries observed with isotropic bodies (§ 142), if not all, may be traced to a similar cause.

It is very interesting that some of Becquerel's lines show the Zeeman-effect in a direction opposite to the ordinary one (i. e. with a reversal of the circular polarization commonly observed in the longitudinal effect) and to a degree that is equal or even superior to the intensity of the effect in previously observed cases. These phenomena and similar ones occurring with certain lines of gaseous bodies[3]) have led

1) J. Becquerel, Comptes rendus **142** (1906), p. 775, 874, 1144; **143** (1906), p. 769, 890, 962, 1133; **144** (1907), p. 132, 420, 682, 1032, 1336.

2) H. Kamerlingh Onnes and J. Becquerel, Amsterdam Proceedings **10** (1908), p. 592.

3) J. Becquerel, Comptes rendus **146** (1908), p. 683; A. Dufour, ibidem, p. 118, 229, 634, 810; R. W. Wood, Phil. Mag. (6) **15** (1908), p. 274.

some physicists to admit the existence of vibrating *positive* electrons, for which the value of $\frac{e}{m}$ would be comparable with or even greater than the value found for the negative electrons of the cathode rays. They may also be explained by the assumption that in some systems of molecules, under the influence of an external magnetic field, there are motions of electricity such as to produce in the interior of the particles a field that is opposite to the external one. To this latter hypothesis Becquerel, however, objects that, like all phenomena of induced magnetization, the internal fields in question would in all probability be liable to considerable changes when the body is heated or cooled, whereas the magnetic division of spectral lines remains constant through a wide range of temperatures.

The possibility of a third explanation, though one about which I am very doubtful, is perhaps suggested by what we found in § 102, namely by the reversion of the ordinary direction of the effect caused by a particular arrangement of a number of negative electrons.

65 (Page 171). If x, y, z are the coordinates of a particle of the medium at the time t, its coordinates at the time $t + dt$ will, be equal to

$$x' = x + \mathfrak{g}_x dt, \quad y' = y + \mathfrak{g}_y dt, \quad z' = z + \mathfrak{g}_z dt.$$

Here $\mathfrak{g}_x$, $\mathfrak{g}_y$, $\mathfrak{g}_z$ may be regarded as linear functions of x, y, z so that, for instance,

$$\mathfrak{g}_x = \alpha + \beta x + \gamma y + \delta z,$$

or, as we may write as well

$$\mathfrak{g}_x = \alpha + \beta x' + \gamma y' + \delta z'.$$

The particles which originally lie in the plane

$$x = a$$

will have reached the plane

$$x' = a + (\alpha + \beta x' + \gamma y' + \delta z')\, dt$$

at the end of the interval considered. The direction constants of the normal to this plane are proportional to

$$1 - \beta dt, \quad -\gamma dt, \quad -\delta dt$$

or to

$$1 - \frac{\partial \mathfrak{g}_x}{\partial x} dt, \quad - \frac{\partial \mathfrak{g}_x}{\partial y} dt, \quad - \frac{\partial \mathfrak{g}_x}{\partial z} dt.$$

66 (Page 173). Let a sphere of radius R move with the constant velocity w through an incompressible medium, and let us suppose the motion of the latter to be irrotational. Then, if the centre of the sphere is taken as origin of coordinates, and the line of motion as axis of x, the velocity potential is given by

$$\varphi = -\frac{1}{2} R^3 w \frac{x}{r^3},$$

giving for the components of the velocity

$$\frac{\partial \varphi}{\partial x} = \frac{1}{2} R^3 w \frac{3x^2 - r^2}{r^5},$$

$$\frac{\partial \varphi}{\partial y} = \frac{1}{2} R^3 w \frac{3xy}{R^5}, \quad \frac{\partial \varphi}{\partial z} = \frac{1}{2} R^3 w \frac{3xz}{R^5}.$$

At a point of the intersection of the surface with the plane YOZ, these values become

$$-\tfrac{1}{2} w, \quad 0, \quad 0,$$

so that the relative velocity of sliding is $-\frac{3}{2} w$.

67 (Page 173). Instead of considering a uniform translation of the earth through the ether, we may as well conceive the planet to be at rest, and the ether to flow along it, so that, at infinite distance, it has a constant velocity w_0 in the direction of OZ.

Let the ether obey Boyle's law, and let it be attracted by the earth with a force inversely proportional to the square of the distance r from the centre. Then, when there is no motion of the medium, the density k and the pressure p will be functions of r, determined by the equation of equilibrium

$$-\frac{dp}{dr} = \frac{\omega k}{r^2},$$

and the relation

$$k = \mu p,$$

where ω und μ are constants.

These conditions are satisfied by

$$\log k = \frac{\mu \omega}{r} + \log k_0,$$

k_0 being the density at infinite distance.

Now, there can be a state of motion in which there is a velocity potential φ, and in which the density k has the value given by the above formula. Indeed, if we put

$$\varphi = z\left[a\left(\frac{\mu\omega}{2r} - 1\right) + b\left(\frac{\mu\omega}{2r} + 1\right)\varepsilon^{-\frac{\mu\omega}{r}}\right],$$

(understanding by a and b constants and taking the centre of the sphere as origin of coordinates), the components of the velocity

$$u=\frac{\partial\varphi}{\partial x},\quad v=\frac{\partial\varphi}{\partial y},\quad w=\frac{\partial\varphi}{\partial z}$$

satisfy the equation of continuity

$$\frac{\partial(ku)}{\partial x}+\frac{\partial(kv)}{\partial y}+\frac{\partial(kw)}{\partial z}=0.$$

The form of φ has been chosen with a view to the remaining conditions of the problem, namely:

$$\text{for } r=\infty:\ \frac{\partial\varphi}{\partial x}=0,\quad \frac{\partial\varphi}{\partial y}=0,\quad \frac{\partial\varphi}{\partial z}=w_0,$$

and

$$\text{for } r=R \text{ (i. e. at the surface of the earth): } \frac{\partial\varphi}{\partial r}=0.$$

These conditions lead to the equations

$$-a+b=w_0,$$

$$a=\left(\frac{\mu^2\omega^2}{2R^2}+\frac{\mu\omega}{R}+1\right)\varepsilon^{-\frac{\mu\omega}{R}}b.$$

Along the intersection of the planet's surface with the xy-plane there is a velocity of sliding

$$\frac{\partial\varphi}{\partial z}=\left(\frac{\mu\omega}{2R}-1\right)a+\left(\frac{\mu\omega}{2R}+1\right)\varepsilon^{-\frac{\mu\omega}{R}}b=\frac{\mu^3\omega^3}{4R^3}\varepsilon^{-\frac{\mu\omega}{R}}b.$$

This is found to be 0,011 w_0 if $\frac{\mu\omega}{R}=10$, and 0,0056 w_0 if $\frac{\mu\omega}{R}=11$. In these cases the ratio between the density near the surface and that at infinite distance would be ε^{10} or ε^{11} respectively.

68 (Page 181). Let the relative rays converge towards a point O, which we take as origin of coordinates, and let us determine the form of the waves by the construction explained in § 153. We have to compound a vector in the direction of the relative ray and having the magnitude v' with a vector $-\frac{\mathfrak{g}}{\mu^2}$. Neglecting quantities of the second order, we may also make the first vector equal to v, the wave velocity in the medium when at rest, and we may consider this velocity as constant in the immediate neighbourhood of the point O. Moreover, the second vector may be regarded as having a constant magnitude, say in the direction of OX.

Now, at a point (x, y, z), at a distance r from O, the components of the first vector are

$$-\frac{x}{r}v, \quad -\frac{y}{r}v, \quad -\frac{z}{r}v,$$

and those of the second

$$-\frac{|\mathfrak{g}|}{\mu^2}, \quad 0, \quad 0,$$

so that the components of the resultant vector, which is at right angles to the wave-front, are

$$-\left\{\frac{x}{r}v + \frac{|\mathfrak{g}|}{\mu^2}\right\}, \quad -\frac{y}{r}v, \quad -\frac{z}{r}v.$$

The equation of the surface normal to the resultant vector is therefore

$$vr + \frac{|\mathfrak{g}|}{\mu^2}x = C.$$

This is the equation of an ellipsoid, the centre of which has the coordinates

$$-\frac{\alpha C}{v^2 - \alpha^2}, \quad 0, \quad 0,$$

if

$$\alpha = \frac{|\mathfrak{g}|}{\mu^2},$$

and whose semi-axes have the directions of OX, OY, OZ and the lengths

$$\frac{vC}{v^2 - \alpha^2}, \quad \frac{C}{\sqrt{v^2 - \alpha^2}}, \quad \frac{C}{\sqrt{v^2 - \alpha^2}}.$$

Since the square of α is neglected, we may say that the waves are of spherical form. Their centre approaches the point O as the constant C diminishes.

69 (Page 191). If n is the frequency of the source of light, the frequency at a fixed point in one of the tubes will also be n, because the successive waves take equal times to reach this point. Hence, with reference to fixed axes, a beam of light may be represented by expressions of the form

$$a \cos n\left(t - \frac{x}{u} + p\right),$$

where u is the velocity in question.

Transforming to axes moving with the fluid — and confining ourselves to one of the two cases distinguished in the text —, we have to put

$$x = x' + wt,$$

by which the above expression becomes

$$a \cos n\left(t - \frac{w}{u}t - \frac{x'}{u} + p\right).$$

In this way the relative frequency is seen to be

$$n' = n\left(1 - \frac{w}{u}\right),$$

for which, denoting by μ the refractive index for the frequency n, we may write

$$n' = n\left(1 - \frac{\mu w}{c}\right),$$

because u differs from $\frac{c}{\mu}$ only by a quantity proportional to w.

The index of refraction corresponding to the frequency n' is

$$\mu - \frac{\mu w}{c} n \frac{d\mu}{dn},$$

and the corresponding velocity of propagation

$$\frac{c}{\mu - \frac{\mu w}{c} n \frac{d\mu}{dn}} = \frac{c}{\mu} + \frac{w}{\mu} n \frac{d\mu}{dn} = \frac{c}{\mu} - \frac{w}{\mu} T \frac{d\mu}{dT} = \frac{c}{\mu} - \frac{w}{\mu} \lambda \frac{d\mu}{d\lambda},$$

if λ is the wave-length.

This is the velocity to which we must add the term $w\left(1 - \frac{1}{\mu^2}\right)$.

In the case of water we have for the spectral line D

$$1 - \frac{1}{\mu^2} = 0{,}438$$

and

$$1 - \frac{1}{\mu^2} - \frac{1}{\mu} \lambda \frac{d\mu}{d\lambda} = 0{,}451$$

whereas, if the velocity relative to the fixed parts of the apparatus is represented by

$$\frac{c}{\mu} \pm \varepsilon w,$$

$\varepsilon = 0{,}434$ (with a possible error of $\pm 0{,}02$) is the value which Michelson and Morley deduced from their experiments.

69* (Page 191) [1915]. In a repetition of Fizeau's experiment Zeeman has recently found[1]) for different wave-lengths displacements of the interference fringes which agree very satisfactorily with the formula I gave in § 164. This is shown in the following table,

1) Zeeman, Proc. Amsterdam Academy, **17** (1914), p. 445; **18** (1915), p. 398.

in which Δ_{exp} is the observed shift, expressed in terms of the distance between the fringes, Δ_L the shift calculated by means of the formula, and Δ_{Fr} the result of the calculation when the term

$$\mp \frac{w}{\mu} T \frac{d\mu}{dT}$$

is omitted.

λ in $\mathring{A} \cdot U$	Number of observations	Δ_{exp}	Δ_{Fr}	Δ_L
4500	6	0,826 ± 0,007	0,786	0,825
4580	6	0,808 ± 0,005	0,771	0,808
5461	9	0,656 ± 0,005	0,637	0,660
6440	1	0,542	0,534	0,551
6870	10	0,511 ± 0,007	0,500	0,513

Zeeman adds that the calculated values of Δ may perhaps be vitiated to a small extent by inaccuracies in the measurement of the velocity of flow and of the length of the column of flowing water. These errors disappear from the ratio between the values of Δ for two different wave-lengths. Taking for these 4500 and 6870, the ratio as deduced from the experiments is found to be 1,616. According to the formula it is 1,572 when the last term is omitted, and 1,608 when it is taken into account.

70 (Page 191). For the case of a mirror the proposition is easily proved after the manner indicated in § 154. If, supposing the mirror to be made of a metallic substance, we want to deduce the same result from the theorem of corresponding states (§§ 162 and 165), we must first extend this theorem to absorbing bodies. This can really be done.[1])

71 (Page 192). Beams of light consisting of parallel rays, in a stationary and in a moving crystal, will correspond to each other when their lateral boundary is the same, i. e. when the relative rays have the same direction s. In both cases we may consider a definite line of this direction, and write down the equations for the disturbance of equilibrium at different points of this line, reckoning

---

1) See H. B. A. Bockwinkel, Sur les phénomènes du rayonnement dans un système qui se meut d'une vitesse uniforme par rapport à l'éther. Arch. néerl. (2) **14** (1908), p. 1.

the distance s from a fixed point of it. For the stationary crystal the vibrations are represented by expressions of the form

$$a \cos n \left(t - \frac{s}{u} + p\right),$$

and the corresponding expressions for the other case have the form

$$a \cos n \left(t' - \frac{s}{u} + p\right),$$

or, since along the line considered

$$t' = t - \frac{1}{c^2}(\mathbf{w}_x x' + \mathbf{w}_y y' + \mathbf{w}_z z') = t - \frac{1}{c^2}\mathbf{w}_s s,$$

$$a \cos n \left(t - \frac{\mathbf{w}_s s}{c^2} - \frac{s}{u} + p\right),$$

from which it appears that the velocity u' of the ray relative to the ponderable matter is determined by

$$\frac{1}{u'} = \frac{1}{u} + \frac{\mathbf{w}_s}{c^2}, \quad u' = u - \frac{u^2}{c^2}\mathbf{w}_s.$$

72 (Page 194). Strictly speaking, it must be taken into account that in the moving system the relative rays may slightly deviate from these lines, the theorem that their course is not altered by a translation having been proved only when we neglected terms of the second order. Closer examination shows, however, that no error is introduced by this circumstance.[1])

72* (Page 197) [1915]. If I had to write the last chapter now, I should certainly have given a more prominent place to Einstein's theory of relativity (§ 189) by which the theory of electromagnetic phenomena in moving systems gains a simplicity that I had not been able to attain. The chief cause of my failure was my clinging to the idea that the variable t only can be considered as the true time and that my local time t' must be regarded as no more than an auxiliary mathematical quantity. In Einstein's theory, on the contrary, t' plays the same part as t; if we want to describe phenomena in terms of x', y', z', t' we must work with these variables exactly as we could do with x, y, z, t. If, for instance, a point is

---

1) Lorentz, De l'influence du mouvement de la terre sur les phénomènes lumineux, Arch. néerl. **21** (1887), p. 169—172 (Abhandlungen über theoretische Physik, **1**, p. 389—392).

moving, its coordinates x, y, z will undergo certain changes dx, dy, dz during the increment of time dt and the components of the velocity $\mathbf{v}$ will be

$$\mathbf{v}_x = \frac{dx}{dt}, \quad \mathbf{v}_y = \frac{dy}{dt}, \quad \mathbf{v}_z = \frac{dz}{dt}.$$

Now, the four changes dx, dy, dz, dt will cause corresponding changes dx', dy', dz', dt' of the new variables x', y', z', t' and in the system of these the velocity $\mathbf{v}'$ will be defined as a vector having the components

$$\mathbf{v}'_x = \frac{dx'}{dt'}, \quad \mathbf{v}'_y = \frac{dy'}{dt'}, \quad \mathbf{v}'_z = \frac{dz'}{dt'}. \tag{112}$$

The substitution used by Einstein is the particular case we get when in (287) and (288) we take $l = 1$, as we shall soon be led to do (Note 75* and § 179). Provisionally, this factor will be left undeterminate.

The real meaning of the substitution (287), (288) lies in the relation

$$x'^2 + y'^2 + z'^2 - c^2t'^2 = l^2(x^2 + y^2 + z^2 - c^2t^2) \tag{113}$$

that can easily be verified, and from which we may infer that we shall have

$$x'^2 + y'^2 + z'^2 = c^2t'^2, \tag{114}$$

when

$$x^2 + y^2 + z^2 = c^2t^2. \tag{115}$$

This may be interpreted as follows. Let a disturbance, which is produced at the time $t = 0$ at the point $x = 0$, $y = 0$, $z = 0$ be propagated in all directions with the speed of light c, so that at the time t it reaches the spherical surface determined by (*115*). Then, in the system x', y', z', t', this same disturbance may be said to start from the point $x' = 0$, $y' = 0$, $z' = 0$ at the time $t' = 0$ and to reach the spherical surface (*114*) at the time t'. Since the radius of this sphere is ct', the disturbance is propagated in the system x', y', z', t', as it was in the system x, y, z, t, with the speed c. Hence, the velocity of light is not altered by the transformation (cf. § 190).

The formulae (287) and (288) may even be found, if we seek a linear substitution satisfying the condition (*113*) and such that for $x = 0$, $y = 0$, $z = 0$, $t = 0$ we have $x' = 0$, $y' = 0$, $z' = 0$, $t' = 0$. The relations being linear the point $x' = 0$, $y' = 0$, $z' = 0$ will have, in the system x, y, z, t, a velocity constant in direction and magnitude. If the axes of x and x' are chosen in the direction of this velocity, one is led to equations of the form (287), (288).

In the theory of relativity we have constantly to attend to the relations existing between the corresponding quantities that have to be introduced if we want to describe the same phenomena, first in the system x, y, z, t and then in the system x', y', z', t'. Part of these "transformation formulae" present themselves immediately; others must be properly chosen and may be considered as defining "corresponding" quantities, the aim being always to arrive, if possible, at equations of the same form in the two modes of description.

The transformation formulae for the velocities are easily found. We have only to substitute in (*112*) the values

$$dx' = kl(dx - w\,dt), \quad dy' = l\,dy, \quad dz' = l\,dz,$$

$$dt' = kl\left(dt - \frac{w}{c^2}dx\right) \qquad (116)$$

and to divide by dt the numerator and the denominator of the fractions. If we put

$$\omega = k\left(1 - \frac{w}{c^2}\mathbf{v}_x\right), \qquad (117)$$

the result is

$$\mathbf{v}'_x = k\frac{\mathbf{v}_x - w}{\omega}, \quad \mathbf{v}'_y = \frac{\mathbf{v}_y}{\omega}, \quad \mathbf{v}_z' = \frac{\mathbf{v}_z}{\omega}. \qquad (118)$$

These formulae combined with (285) lead to the following relations that will be found of use afterwards

$$(c^2 - \mathbf{v}'^2)^{\frac{1}{2}} = \frac{(c^2 - \mathbf{v}^2)^{\frac{1}{2}}}{\omega}, \qquad (119)$$

$$\omega = \frac{1}{k\left(1 + \frac{w}{c^2}\mathbf{v}'_x\right)}. \qquad (120)$$

In order to conform to the notations that have been used in the text, we shall now put

$$\mathbf{v}_x = \mathbf{u}_x + w, \quad \mathbf{v}_y = \mathbf{u}_y, \quad \mathbf{v}_z = \mathbf{u}_z.$$

By this we find

$$\mathbf{v}'_x = k\frac{\mathbf{u}_x}{\omega}, \quad \mathbf{v}'_y = \frac{\mathbf{u}_y}{\omega}, \quad \mathbf{v}'_z = \frac{\mathbf{u}_z}{\omega}, \qquad (121)$$

showing the relation between the velocity $\mathbf{v}'$ and the vector $\mathbf{u}'$ used in the text

$$\mathbf{v}' = \frac{\mathbf{u}'}{k\,\omega}. \qquad (122)$$

Finally, we may infer from (*120*) and (*122*)

$$\omega = \frac{1}{k}\left(1 - \frac{w}{c^2}\mathbf{u}'_x\right). \qquad (123)$$

We may add that ω is a positive quantity, because the velocities w and $\mathbf{v}_x$ are always smaller than c.

We shall next consider the transformation formula for what we may call a "material" element of volume.

Let there be a very great number of points very close to each other and moving in such a way that their velocities are continuous functions of the coordinates. Let us fix our attention on a definite value of t and let at that moment x, y, z be the coordinates of one of the points P_0, and $x + \mathrm{x}$, $y + \mathrm{y}$, $z + \mathrm{z}$ those of a point P infinitely near it. If

$$\overline{x'},\quad \overline{y'},\quad \overline{z'},\quad \overline{t'},$$

are the values of x', y', z', t' corresponding to x, y, z, t, we may write for those which correspond to $x + \mathrm{x}$, $y + \mathrm{y}$, $z + \mathrm{z}$, t

$$\overline{x'} + kl\mathrm{x},\quad \overline{y'} + l\mathrm{y},\quad \overline{z'} + l\mathrm{z},\quad \overline{t'} - kl\frac{w}{c^2}\mathrm{x}. \qquad (124)$$

Now, using the system x, y, z, t, we can fix our attention on all the points, lying simultaneously, i. e. at a given time t, in a certain element dS of the space x, y, z. We can consider these sane points after having passed to the system x', y', z', t'. We shall then have to consider as simultaneous the positions belonging to a definite value, say $\overline{t'}$ of the time t', and we can consider the element $\overline{dS'}$ in the space x', y', z', in which these positions are found. What we want to know, is the ratio between dS and $\overline{dS'}$.

In order to find it, we must remark that in (*124*) we have the coordinates of the point P at the instant $\overline{t'} - kl\frac{w}{c^2}\mathrm{x}$. From these we shall pass to the coordinates at the instant $\overline{t'}$ by adding the distances travelled over in the time $kl\frac{w}{c^2}\mathrm{x}$. We may write for them

$$kl\frac{w}{c^2}\mathrm{x}\mathsf{v}'_x,\quad kl\frac{w}{c^2}\mathrm{x}\mathsf{v}'_y,\quad kl\frac{w}{c^2}\mathrm{x}\mathsf{v}'_z,$$

and since $\mathrm{x}, \mathrm{y}, \mathrm{z}$ are infinitely small, we may here understand by $\mathsf{v}'_x, \mathsf{v}'_y, \mathsf{v}'_z$ the velocities of the point P_0 at the instant $\overline{t'}$. The coordinates of the different points P (having different values of $\mathrm{x}, \mathrm{y}, \mathrm{z}$) at the definite instant $\overline{t'}$ are therefore given by

$$x' = \overline{x'} + kl\left(1 + \frac{w\mathsf{v}'_x}{c^2}\right)\mathrm{x},$$

$$y' = \overline{y'} + kl\frac{w\mathsf{v}'_y}{c^2}\mathrm{x} + l\mathrm{y},$$

$$z' = \overline{z'} + kl\frac{w\mathsf{v}'_z}{c^2}\mathrm{x} + l\mathrm{z}.$$

These equations express the relations between the coordinates $\mathrm{x}, \mathrm{y}, \mathrm{z}$ of a point in the element dS and those of the corresponding point in the element $\overline{dS'}$. In virtue of a well known theorem the ratio between the elements is given by

$$\frac{\overline{dS'}}{dS} = \begin{vmatrix} \frac{\partial x'}{\partial \mathrm{x}}, & \frac{\partial x'}{\partial \mathrm{y}}, & \frac{\partial x'}{\partial \mathrm{z}} \\ \frac{\partial y'}{\partial \mathrm{x}}, & \frac{\partial y'}{\partial \mathrm{y}}, & \frac{\partial y'}{\partial \mathrm{z}} \\ \frac{\partial z'}{\partial \mathrm{x}}, & \frac{\partial z'}{\partial \mathrm{y}}, & \frac{\partial z'}{\partial \mathrm{z}} \end{vmatrix},$$

the determinant being taken with the positive sign. Working out this formula, and remembering that x, y, z are infinitely small, we find for the determinant

$$kl^3\left(1 + \frac{w \mathbf{v}'_x}{c^2}\right),$$

so that, on account of (*120*)

$$\overline{dS'} = \frac{l^3}{\omega} dS.$$

We have denoted the element by $\overline{dS'}$ in order to distinguish it from the dS' given by equation (299).

We shall now suppose that the points which we considered have equal electric charges. Then we may say that the same charge that lies in dS at the time t, is found in $\overline{dS'}$ at the time $\overline{t'}$, or as we may now write t', and this will remain true if, by increasing the number of points, we pass to a continuous distribution. The densities ϱ and $\overline{\varrho'}$ which, in the two modes of considering the phenomena, must be attributed to the electric charge, will therefore be inversely proportional to the volumes dS and $\overline{dS'}$. Hence

$$\overline{\varrho'} = \frac{\omega}{l^3} \varrho. \qquad (125)$$

We have written $\overline{\varrho'}$ in order to distinguish this density from the quantity ϱ' defined by (290). The two are related to each other in the way expressed by

$$\overline{\varrho'} = k\omega\varrho', \qquad (126)$$

to which we may add, on account of (*122*) and (*126*)

$$\overline{\varrho'}\mathbf{v}' = \varrho'\mathbf{u}'. \qquad (127)$$

The transformation formulae for the electric and the magnetic force remain as given in (291).

73 (Page 197) [1915]. It may be shown that in the theory of relativity the fundamental equations (17)—(20) are not changed in form when we pass to the system x', y', z', t'.

In virtue of (286) and (288) we have the following general relations between the differential coefficients with respect to x, y, z, t and those with respect to x', y', z', t'

$$\frac{\partial}{\partial x} = kl\frac{\partial}{\partial x'} - kl\frac{w}{c^2}\frac{\partial}{\partial t'}, \quad \frac{\partial}{\partial y} = l\frac{\partial}{\partial y'}, \quad \frac{\partial}{\partial z} = l\frac{\partial}{\partial z'}, \tag{128}$$

$$\frac{\partial}{\partial t} = kl\frac{\partial}{\partial t'} - klw\frac{\partial}{\partial x'}. \tag{129}$$

The equation (17) therefore assumes the form

$$kl\frac{\partial \mathbf{d}_x}{\partial x'} + l\frac{\partial \mathbf{d}_y}{\partial y'} + l\frac{\partial \mathbf{d}_z}{\partial z'} - kl\frac{w}{c^2}\frac{\partial \mathbf{d}_x}{\partial t'} = \varrho, \tag{130}$$

and the first of the three equations contained in (19) becomes

$$l\left(\frac{\partial \mathbf{h}_z}{\partial y'} - \frac{\partial \mathbf{h}_y}{\partial z'}\right) = \frac{kl}{c}\frac{\partial \mathbf{d}_x}{\partial t'} - kl\frac{w}{c}\frac{\partial \mathbf{d}_x}{\partial x'} + \frac{1}{c}\varrho \mathbf{v}_x. \tag{131}$$

Substituting the value of $\frac{\partial \mathbf{d}_x}{\partial t'}$ taken from this formula in (*130*), we find

$$kl\frac{\partial \mathbf{d}_x}{\partial x'} + l\frac{\partial \mathbf{d}_y}{\partial y'} + l\frac{\partial \mathbf{d}_z}{\partial z'} - l\frac{w}{c}\left(\frac{\partial \mathbf{h}_z}{\partial y'} - \frac{\partial \mathbf{h}_y}{\partial z'}\right) - kl\frac{w^2}{c^2}\frac{\partial \mathbf{d}_x}{\partial x'} = \left(1 - \frac{w\mathbf{v}_x}{c^2}\right)\varrho = \frac{\omega}{k}\varrho.$$

Hence, multiplying by $\frac{k}{l^3}$ and taking into account the values of $\mathbf{d}'_x$ etc., and $\overline{\varrho'}$

$$\frac{\partial \mathbf{d}'_x}{\partial x'} + \frac{\partial \mathbf{d}'_y}{\partial y'} + \frac{\partial \mathbf{d}'_z}{\partial z'} = \overline{\varrho'} \tag{132}$$

which is of the same form as (17).

If, on the other hand, the value of $\frac{\partial \mathbf{d}_x}{\partial x'}$ drawn from (*130*) is substituted in (*131*), one finds

$$l\left(\frac{\partial \mathbf{h}_z}{\partial y'} - \frac{\partial \mathbf{h}_y}{\partial z'}\right) - \frac{lw}{c}\frac{\partial \mathbf{d}_y}{\partial y'} - \frac{lw}{c}\frac{\partial \mathbf{d}_z}{\partial z'} = \left(\frac{kl}{c} - \frac{klw^2}{c^3}\right)\frac{\partial \mathbf{d}_x}{\partial t'} + \frac{1}{c}\varrho \mathbf{u}_x,$$

or, after multiplication by $\frac{k}{l^3}$,

$$\frac{\partial \mathbf{h}'_z}{\partial y'} - \frac{\partial \mathbf{h}'_y}{\partial z'} = \frac{1}{c}\left(\frac{\partial \mathbf{d}'_x}{\partial t'} + \overline{\varrho'}\mathbf{v}'_x\right),$$

because, on account of (*121*) and (*125*)

$$\frac{k}{l^3}\varrho \mathbf{u}_x = \overline{\varrho'}\mathbf{v}'_x.$$

We have thus found the first of the equations contained in

$$\text{rot}' h' = \frac{1}{c}\left(\frac{\partial \mathbf{d}'}{\partial t'} + \overline{\varrho'}\mathbf{v}'\right). \tag{133}$$

The remaining formulae are obtained by similar transformations.

As to the equations (292) given in the text, we have only to remark that in (*132*) $\overline{\varrho'}$ may be replaced by

$$\left(1-\frac{w\,\mathbf{u}'_x}{c^2}\right)\varrho',$$

following from (*126*) and (*123*), and that, with a view to (*127*), we may in (*133*) replace $\overline{\varrho'}\,\mathbf{v}'$ by $\varrho'\,\mathbf{u}'$.

74 (Page 198) [1915]. Since in the theory of relativity the fundamental equations have exactly the same form in the two systems x, y, z, t and x', y', z', t', we may at once apply to this latter the formulae which we gave in § 13. We may therefore determine a scalar potential $\overline{\varphi'}$ and a vector potential $\mathbf{a}'$ by the equations

$$\Delta'\overline{\varphi'}-\frac{1}{c^2}\frac{\partial^2\overline{\varphi'}}{\partial t'^2}=-\overline{\varrho'}, \quad (134)$$

$$\Delta'\mathbf{a}'-\frac{1}{c^2}\frac{\partial^2\mathbf{a}'}{\partial t'^2}=-\frac{1}{c}\overline{\varrho'}\,\mathbf{v}', \quad (135)$$

and we shall have

$$\mathbf{d}'=-\frac{1}{c}\frac{\partial\mathbf{a}'}{\partial t'}-\operatorname{grad}'\overline{\varphi'}, \quad (136)$$

$$\mathbf{h}'=\operatorname{rot}\mathbf{a}'. \quad (137)$$

Since

$$\overline{\varrho'}\,\mathbf{v}'=\varrho'\,\mathbf{u}',$$

the formulae (*135*) and (*137*) agree with the second of (294), and (296).

Further, if in (*134*) we replace $\overline{\varrho'}$ by

$$\left(1-\frac{w\,\mathbf{u}'_x}{c^2}\right)\varrho',$$

we see on comparison with (294) that a solution is

$$\overline{\varphi'}=\varphi'-\frac{w}{c}\,\mathbf{a}'_x.$$

By this (*136*) takes the form of (295).

75 (Page 203). The first three equations follow at once from (*118*), if we replace ω by $\frac{1}{k}$, as we may do in virtue of (*120*), $\frac{\mathbf{v}'_x}{c}$ being very small. The values of $\frac{d^2x'}{dt'^2}, \frac{d^2y'}{dt'^2}, \frac{d^2z'}{dt'^2}$ are found by a new differentiation in which the relation

$$\frac{dt'}{dt}=kl\left(1-\frac{w\,\mathbf{v}_x}{c^2}\right)$$

derived from (*116*), is used. We may here replace v_x by w, so that it becomes

$$\frac{dt'}{dt} = \frac{l}{k}.$$

75* (Page 203 and 205) [1915]. An important conclusion may be drawn from equations (305) if we start from the fundamental assumption that the motion of a particle can be described by means of an equation of the form

$$\mathbf{F} = \dot{\mathbf{G}}, \tag{138}$$

where $\mathbf{F}$ means the force acting on the particle and $\mathbf{G}$ is a vector, the momentum, having the direction of the velocity $\mathbf{v}$ and whose magnitude G is a function of the magnitude v of the velocity. Indeed, we may infer from this (cf. § 27) that the longitudinal mass m' and the transverse one m'' are given by

$$m' = \frac{dG}{dv}, \quad m'' = \frac{G}{v}. \tag{139}$$

The formulae (305) show that

$$m' = k^2 m'' = \frac{c^2}{c^2 - v^2} m'',$$

and we find therefore

$$\frac{dG}{dv} = \frac{c^2}{c^2 - v^2} \cdot \frac{G}{v},$$

a differential equation from which the momentum can be found as a function of the velocity.

The solution is as follows

$$d \log G = \frac{c^2 dv}{(c^2 - v^2) v} = \frac{dv}{v} - \frac{dv}{2(c+v)} + \frac{dv}{2(c-v)},$$

$$\log G = \log v - \tfrac{1}{2} \log (c + v) - \tfrac{1}{2} \log (c - v) + \log C,$$

$$G = \frac{Cv}{(c^2 - v^2)^{\frac{1}{2}}},$$

where C is a constant of integration.

Substituting in (*139*) we find

$$m' = \frac{Cc^2}{(c^2 - v^2)^{\frac{3}{2}}}, \quad m'' = \frac{C}{(c^2 - v^2)^{\frac{1}{2}}},$$

and, for the case considered in the text

$$m' = k^3 \frac{C}{c}, \quad m'' = k \frac{C}{c}.$$

Now, in passing to the limit $v = 0$, k and l both become equal to 1, from which we may conclude

$$\frac{C}{c} = m_0$$

$$m' = k^3 m_0, \quad m'' = k m_0.$$

The coefficient l must therefore have the value 1 for all values of the velocity (cf. § 179).

As to the momentum, we may write for it

$$\mathbf{G} = \frac{c m_0 \mathbf{v}}{(c^2 - \mathbf{v}^2)^{\frac{1}{2}}}$$

and for its components

$$\mathbf{G}_x = \frac{c m_0 \mathbf{v}_x}{(c^2 - \mathbf{v}^2)^{\frac{1}{2}}}, \quad \mathbf{G}_y = \frac{c m_0 \mathbf{v}_y}{(c^2 - \mathbf{v}^2)^{\frac{1}{2}}}, \quad \mathbf{G}_z = \frac{c m_0 \mathbf{v}_z}{(c^2 - \mathbf{v}^2)^{\frac{1}{2}}}.$$

Having got thus far we can immediately write down the transformation formulae for the momentum.

Indeed, using the system x', y', z', t' we shall have to put

$$\mathbf{G}'_x = \frac{c m_0 \mathbf{v}'_x}{(c^2 - \mathbf{v}'^2)^{\frac{1}{2}}}, \quad \mathbf{G}'_y = \frac{c m_0 \mathbf{v}'_y}{(c^2 - \mathbf{v}'^2)^{\frac{1}{2}}}, \quad \mathbf{G}'_z = \frac{c m_0 \mathbf{v}'_z}{(c^2 - \mathbf{v}'^2)^{\frac{1}{2}}}$$

and these quantities can be expressed in terms of $\mathbf{G}_x$, $\mathbf{G}_y$, $\mathbf{G}_z$ if we use the formulae (*118*) and (*119*).

The result is found to be

$$\mathbf{G}'_x = k\mathbf{G}_x - \frac{k c w m_0}{(c^2 - v^2)^{\frac{1}{2}}}, \quad \mathbf{G}'_y = \mathbf{G}_y, \quad \mathbf{G}'_z = \mathbf{G}_z. \qquad (140)$$

These formulae may now serve us for finding the relation between the force $\mathbf{F} = \dot{\mathbf{G}}$ in the system x, y, z, t and the force in the system x', y', z', t' for which we may write

$$\mathbf{F}' = \dot{\mathbf{G}}',$$

indicating by the dot a differentiation with respect to t'. For this purpose we shall fix our attention on the changes of the quantities in (*140*) going on in the element dt. Between these we have the relations

$$d\mathbf{G}'_x = k\, d\mathbf{G}_x - \frac{k c w m_0 v}{(c^2 - v^2)^{\frac{3}{2}}} dv, \quad d\mathbf{G}'_y = d\mathbf{G}_y, \quad d\mathbf{G}'_z = d\mathbf{G}_z.$$

If these are divided by

$$dt' = \omega\, dt,$$

which is found from (*116*) and (*117*), we get

$$\mathsf{F}'_x = \frac{k}{\omega}\mathsf{F}_x - \frac{kc}{\omega}\frac{w m_0 v}{(c^2-v^2)^{\frac{3}{2}}}\frac{dv}{dt}, \quad \mathsf{F}'_y = \frac{1}{\omega}\mathsf{F}_y, \quad \mathsf{F}'_z = \frac{1}{\omega}\mathsf{F}_z.$$

Now for the motion of the particle considered in the system x, y, z, t, $\frac{m_0 c^3}{(c^2-v^2)^{\frac{3}{2}}}$ is the longitudinal mass and $\frac{dv}{dt}$ the longitudinal acceleration. The product of these is the component of the force F in the direction of motion, and multiplying again by v we shall find the scalar product $(\mathsf{v}\cdot\mathsf{F})$. The last term in the first of the above equations may therefore be written

$$-\frac{k}{\omega}\cdot\frac{w}{c^2}(\mathsf{v}\cdot\mathsf{F}),$$

and the transformation formulae for the forces take the form

$$\mathsf{F}'_x = \frac{k}{\omega}\left\{\mathsf{F}_x - \frac{w}{c^2}(\mathsf{v}\cdot\mathsf{F})\right\}, \quad \mathsf{F}'_y = \frac{1}{\omega}\mathsf{F}_y, \quad \mathsf{F}'_z = \frac{1}{\omega}\mathsf{F}_z. \qquad (141)$$

We are now in a position to formulate the condition that must be satisfied if the principle of relativity shall hold. In trying to do so we must keep in mind that a physical theory in which we explain phenomena by the motion of small particles consists of two parts; viz. 1. the equation of motion (*138*) of the particles and 2. the rules which represent the forces as determined by the relative positions of the particles, their velocities, electric charges, etc. The principle of relativity requires that the form of the theory shall be the same in the systems x, y, z, t and x', y', z', t'. For this it will be necessary that, if, by means of the rules in question we calculate the forces F from the relative positions etc. such as they are in the system x, y, z, t, and similarly the forces F' from the relative positions etc. in the system x', y', z', t', the components of F and F' satisfy the relations (*141*). We may call this the general law of force; in so far as it is true we may be sure that the description of phenomena will be exactly the same in the two systems.

There is one class of forces of which in the present state of science we can say with certainty that they obey the general law, viz. the forces exerted by an electromagnetic field. Indeed the rule which determines the action of such a field on an electron carrying the charge e is expressed by the formula

$$\mathsf{F} = e\mathsf{d} + \frac{e}{c}[\mathsf{v}\cdot\mathsf{h}] \qquad (142)$$

in the system x, y, z, t and by

$$\mathsf{F}' = e\mathsf{d}' + \frac{e}{c}[\mathsf{v}'\cdot\mathsf{h}'] \qquad (143)$$

in the system x', y', z', t'. If in the formulae (291) and (*118*) we put $l=1$, it can be inferred from them that (*142*) and (*143*) satisfy the conditions (*141*).

In proving this we shall confine ourselves to the special case of an electron that is at rest in the system x, y, z, t. Putting $\mathsf{v}=0$ we find from (*117*) and (*118*) $\omega=k$, $\mathsf{v}'_x=-w$, $\mathsf{v}'_y=0$, $\mathsf{v}'_z=0$, so that (*143*) becomes

$$\mathsf{F}'_x = e\mathsf{d}'_x, \quad \mathsf{F}'_y = e\left(\mathsf{d}'_y + \frac{w}{c}\mathsf{h}'_z\right), \quad \mathsf{F}'_z = e\left(\mathsf{d}'_z - \frac{w}{c}\mathsf{h}'_y\right),$$

or, if we substitute the values (291)

$$\mathsf{F}'_x = e\mathsf{d}_x, \quad \mathsf{F}'_y = \frac{e}{k}\mathsf{d}_y, \quad \mathsf{F}'_z = \frac{e}{k}\mathsf{d}_z.$$

We find the same values from (*141*), if we put

$$\mathsf{v}=0, \quad \omega=k, \quad \mathsf{F}=e\mathsf{d}.$$

For other classes of natural forces we cannot positively assert that they obey the general law, but we may suppose them to do so without coming into contradiction with established facts.

If we make the hypothesis for the molecular forces, we are at once led to the conclusion to which we come at the end in § 174. It may be mentioned here that attractive or repulsive forces depending only on the distances are found not to follow the general law. Therefore the principle of relativity requires that the forces between the particles are of a somewhat different kind; their mathematical expression will in general contain small terms depending on the state of motion. Moreover the principle implies that all forces are propagated with the velocity of light.

This may be seen as follows. Let the acting body have the position $x=0$, $y=0$, $z=0$ at the time $t=0$ and let its velocity or its state be modified at that instant. If t is the instant at which the influence of this change makes itself felt at some distant point x, y, z, the velocity of propagation s will be determined by

$$x^2+y^2+z^2=s^2t^2. \qquad (144)$$

According to the principle of relativity the velocity of propagation must have the same value s in the system x', y', z', t'. The values for the place and time of starting being $x'=0$, $y'=0$, $z'=0$, $t'=0$ we must therefore have

$$x'^2+y'^2+z'^2=s^2t'^2,$$

if x', y', z', t' are the values corresponding to the x, y, z, t of (*144*). If the two equations are combined with (*113*), i. e. with

$$x^2+y^2+z^2-c^2t^2=x'^2+y'^2+z'^2-c^2t'^2$$

one finds

$$s=c.$$

These considerations apply f. i. to universal gravitation. In the theory of relativity this force is supposed to be propagated with the velocity of light and Newton's law is modified by the introduction of certain accessory terms depending on the state of motion. They are so small, however, that it will be very difficult to observe the influence they can have on the motions in the solar system.

It will be easily seen that the question whether the forces require time for their propagation from one particle to another loses its importance when there are no relative motions. In this case the theoretical considerations are greatly simplified. Let us suppose f. i. that all the particles are at rest in the system x', y', z', t', so that they have the common velocity $\mathbf{v}_x = w$ in the system x, y, z, t. Then equation (*117*) becomes $\omega = \frac{1}{k}$ and the relations (*141*) take the form

$$\mathbf{F}_x' = \mathbf{F}_x, \quad \mathbf{F}_y' = k\mathbf{F}_y, \quad \mathbf{F}_z' = k\mathbf{F}_z,$$

agreeing with (300). Indeed, in this latter equation S_0 is the system in which the coordinates are x', y', z', so that $\mathbf{F}(S_0)$ corresponds to what we have now called $\mathbf{F}'$.

Equation (300) is thus seen to be a special form of the general formulae (*141*). Though, strictly speaking, it can only be applied to systems in which there are no relative motions of the parts, it may be used with a sufficient approximation in the questions discussed in §§ 173—176.

76 (Page 207) [1915]. The somewhat lengthy calculations by which these formulae have been obtained and which were added in a note to the first edition may be omitted now after what has been said in Note 75*. Even the reasoning set forth in this article and the next one might have been considerably simplified. If we suppose that all the forces acting on the electrons, f. i. those by which they are drawn back towards their positions of equilibrium, obey the general law of force (Note 75*), we may conclude directly that the equations which determine the motion of the electrons and the field $\mathbf{d}'$, $\mathbf{h}'$ in the system x', y', z', t' have the same form as those which describe that motion and the field $\mathbf{d}$, $\mathbf{h}$ in the system x, y, z, t. Or, in the notation used in the text, the motion of the electrons and the values of $\mathbf{d}'$ and $\mathbf{h}'$, expressed in terms of x', y', z', t' can be the same in the two systems S_0 and S. This is the theorem of corresponding states which we wanted to establish.

As to the considerations which lead up to it step by step in §§ 175 and 176, we may make the following remarks.

1. In the original system x, y, z, t the electric moment of a particle is defined by the equations

$$\mathfrak{p}_x = \sum ex, \quad \mathfrak{p}_y = \sum ey, \quad \mathfrak{p}_z = \sum ez,$$

the x, y, z of the different electrons being taken for a definite value of t, so that we are concerned with simultaneous positions of the electrons. I had some trouble with the corresponding definition of $\mathfrak{p}_x'$, $\mathfrak{p}_y'$, $\mathfrak{p}_z'$ (page 206) because I did not consider t' as a real „time" and clung to the idea that in the system x', y', z', t' simultaneity had still to be conceived as equality of the values of t. In the theory of relativity, however, t' is to play exactly the same part as t; in consequence of this we have simply to understand by x', y', z' in the formulae

$$\mathfrak{p}_x' = \sum ex', \quad \mathfrak{p}_y' = \sum ey', \quad \mathfrak{p}_z' = \sum ez'$$

the coordinates of the electrons for one and the same time t'. Proceeding in this way, we can immediately write down the equations (308), which correspond exactly to (271) and (272). Indeed we have seen (Note 72*) that the fundamental equations are not changed by the substitution used in the theory of relativity. Hence, it is clear that if in the two systems x, y, z, t and x', y', z', t' the density of the electric charge (ϱ or $\overline{\varrho'}$) is the same function of the coordinates and the time (the charges moving in the same way), the same will be true of the components of the electric and the magnetic force ($\mathfrak{d}$, $\mathfrak{h}$ or $\mathfrak{d}'$, $\mathfrak{h}'$).

2. The transformation formulae for the electric moment may be obtained as follows.

Let x, y, z be the coordinates of the „centre" of a particle, $x + \mathrm{x}$, $y + \mathrm{y}$, $z + \mathrm{z}$ those of a point P where there is an electron e, all these coordinates being taken for the same time. Then if $x', y', z', \overline{t'}$ are the values corresponding to x, y, z, t (so that in the second system x', y', z' is the position of the centre at the time $\overline{t'}$), the values corresponding to $x + \mathrm{x}$, $y + \mathrm{y}$, $z + \mathrm{z}$, t will be

$$x' + kl\mathrm{x}, \quad y' + l\mathrm{y}, \quad z' + l\mathrm{z}, \quad \overline{t'} - kl\frac{w}{c^2}\mathrm{x}.$$

The first three expressions determine the place of P for the value of t' indicated by the fourth, and in order to find the coordinates of the electron for the time $\overline{t'}$, we have to take into account the changes of the coordinates in the interval $kl\frac{w}{c^2}\mathrm{x}$. Hence, if x is supposed to be infinitely small, we may write for the relative coordinates with respect to the centre, such as they are at the time $\overline{t'}$

$$kl\mathrm{x} + kl\frac{w}{c^2}\mathrm{x}\,\mathrm{v}_x', \quad l\mathrm{y} + kl\frac{w}{c^2}\mathrm{x}\,\mathrm{v}_y', \quad l\mathrm{z} + kl\frac{w}{c^2}\mathrm{x}\,\mathrm{v}_z',$$

where $\mathbf{v}'$ is the velocity of the centre, which is 0 in the case considered in the text.

We shall find the values of $\mathbf{p}_x'$, $\mathbf{p}_y'$, $\mathbf{p}_z'$ if, after having multiplied by e, we take the sums extended to all the electrons of the particle. Hence

$$\mathbf{p}_x' = kl\mathbf{p}_x, \quad \mathbf{p}_y' = l\mathbf{p}_y, \quad \mathbf{p}_z' = l\mathbf{p}_z,$$

agreeing with the formulae of p. 206.

77 (Page 211). Let $\mathbf{S}$ be a moving *electrostatic* system and $\mathbf{S}_0$ the corresponding stationary one. We have $\mathbf{a}' = 0$, $\mathbf{h}' = 0$, and, if φ' is the scalar potential in $\mathbf{S}_0$, the equations (291) and (295) give for every point of $\mathbf{S}$

$$\mathbf{d}_x = -l^2\frac{\partial\varphi'}{\partial x'}, \quad \mathbf{d}_y - \frac{w}{c}\mathbf{h}_z = -\frac{l^2}{k}\frac{\partial\varphi'}{\partial y'}, \quad \mathbf{d}_z + \frac{w}{c}\mathbf{h}_y = -\frac{l^2}{k}\frac{\partial\varphi'}{\partial z'},$$

$$\mathbf{h}_x = 0, \quad \mathbf{h}_y + \frac{w}{c}\mathbf{d}_z = 0, \quad \mathbf{h}_z - \frac{w}{c}\mathbf{d}_y = 0,$$

and consequently

$$\left.\begin{aligned} &\mathbf{d}_x = -l^2\frac{\partial\varphi'}{\partial x'}, \quad \mathbf{d}_y = -kl^2\frac{\partial\varphi'}{\partial y'}, \quad \mathbf{d}_z = -kl^2\frac{\partial\varphi'}{\partial z'}, \\ &\mathbf{h}_x = 0 \quad\quad\quad, \quad \mathbf{h}_y = kl^2\frac{w}{c}\frac{\partial\varphi'}{\partial z'}, \quad \mathbf{h}_z = -kl^2\frac{w}{c}\frac{\partial\varphi'}{\partial y'}. \end{aligned}\right\} \quad (145)$$

From this we find for the first component of the flow of energy in $\mathbf{S}$

$$\mathbf{s}_x = c(\mathbf{d}_y\mathbf{h}_z - \mathbf{d}_z\mathbf{h}_y) = k^2l^4w\left\{\left(\frac{\partial\varphi'}{\partial y'}\right)^2 + \left(\frac{\partial\varphi'}{\partial z'}\right)^2\right\},$$

and (by (53) and (302)) for the first component of the electromagnetic momentum, with which alone we are concerned,

$$\mathbf{G}_x = \frac{k^2l^4w}{c^2}\int\left\{\left(\frac{\partial\varphi'}{\partial y'}\right)^2 + \left(\frac{\partial\varphi'}{\partial z'}\right)^2\right\}dS = \frac{klw}{c^2}\int\left\{\left(\frac{\partial\varphi'}{\partial x'}\right)^2 + \left(\frac{\partial\varphi'}{\partial y'}\right)^2\right\}dS'.$$

We have therefore merely to calculate the last integral for the field of a sphere without translation with radius R and charge e. This is a very simple problem. We may observe that the three integrals

$$\int\left(\frac{\partial\varphi'}{\partial x'}\right)^2 dS', \quad \int\left(\frac{\partial\varphi'}{\partial y'}\right)^2 dS', \quad \int\left(\frac{\partial\varphi'}{\partial z'}\right)^2 dS'$$

have equal values, so that they are each equal to one third of their sum, i. e. to two thirds of the energy of the system. The latter having the value $\frac{e^2}{8\pi R}$, we have for each of the integrals $\frac{e^2}{12\pi R}$, and

$$\mathbf{G}_x = \frac{e^2}{6\pi c^2 R}klw.$$

It is clear that $\mathbf{G}_y = 0$ and $\mathbf{G}_z = 0$, so that in general

$$\mathbf{G} = \frac{e^2}{6\pi c^2 R}kl\mathbf{w}.$$

78 (Page 213). The equations (*145*) lead to the following value of the electromagnetic energy

$$\frac{1}{2} l^4 \int \left[\left(\frac{\partial \varphi'}{\partial x'}\right)^2 + k^2 \left(1 + \frac{w^2}{c^2}\right) \left\{ \left(\frac{\partial \varphi'}{\partial y'}\right)^2 + \left(\frac{\partial \varphi'}{\partial z'}\right)^2 \right\} \right] dS$$

$$= \frac{1}{2} \frac{l}{k} \int \left[\left(\frac{\partial \varphi'}{\partial x'}\right)^2 + k^2 \left(1 + \frac{w^2}{c^2}\right) \left\{ \left(\frac{\partial \varphi'}{\partial y'}\right)^2 + \left(\frac{\partial \varphi'}{\partial z'}\right)^2 \right\} \right] dS'. \qquad (146)$$

Putting $l = 1$ and remembering that each of the integrals $\int \left(\frac{\partial \varphi'}{\partial x'}\right)^2 dS'$ etc. has the value $\frac{e^2}{12 \pi R}$, we find

$$\frac{e^2}{24 \pi k R} \left[1 + 2 k^2 \left(1 + \frac{w^2}{c^2}\right) \right], \qquad (147)$$

which becomes equal to (315) when the value of k is substituted.

79 (Page 214). Indeed, when the electron is at rest, the electric force in its immediate neighbourhood is $E = \frac{e^2}{4 \pi R^2}$. As it is at right angles to the surface, there is a normal stress equal to

$$\frac{1}{2} E^2 = \frac{e^2}{32 \pi^2 R^4}. \qquad (148)$$

80 (Page 215). When, by some disturbing cause, the radius of the sphere is increased, the electric stress acting on its surface is diminished, as is seen from (*148*). As the internal stress is supposed to remain constant, it will draw the points of the sphere towards the inside, so that the original volume will be restored.

We shall next show that the equilibrium would be unstable with respect to changes of shape. Consider a deformation by which the sphere is changed to an elongated ellipsoid of revolution, the magnitude of each element of surface remaining as it was, and each element retaining its charge. Then it can be shown that in the interior, at each point of the axis, there will be an electric force directed towards the centre if the charge of the electron is negative. Let this force be equal to q at a point just inside the surface at one extremity P of the axis. By a well known theorem the electric force just outside the surface at the same extremity will be $q + \omega$, if we denote by $-\omega$ the negative surface density of the ellipsoid, which by our supposition is equal to the surface density of the original sphere. A surface element at P will be subjected to two normal electric stresses, $\frac{1}{2}(q + \omega)^2$ outward, and $\frac{1}{2} q^2$ inward; besides these there is the constant internal stress which must be equal to $\frac{1}{2} \omega^2$, because, in the original state, it counterbalanced the electric stress.

Since both q and ω are positive, there is a resultant force $q\omega$ directed towards the outside and tending still further to elongate the ellipsoid.

In order to prove what has been said about the internal electric force, we may proceed as follows. Choose a point A on the semi-axis OP, and consider a cone of infinitely small solid angle $d\varepsilon$, having this point for its vertex and prolonged through it. Let $d\sigma_1$ at the point B_1, and $d\sigma_2$ at B_2 be the elements of the ellipsoidal surface determined by the intersection with the cone, ϑ_1 and ϑ_2 the angles between the line $B_1 B_2$ and the tangent planes at the extremities, and let B_1 be the point nearest A, so that the angle $B_1 A P$ is sharp. Then, since

$$d\sigma_1 = \frac{AB_1^{\,2} \cdot d\varepsilon}{\sin\vartheta_1}, \quad d\sigma_2 = \frac{AB_2^{\,2} \cdot d\varepsilon}{\sin\vartheta_2},$$

the attraction exerted by the two elements on a unit of positive electricity at A will be equal to

$$\frac{\omega\, d\varepsilon}{4\pi \sin\vartheta_1} \quad \text{and} \quad \frac{\omega\, d\varepsilon}{4\pi \sin\vartheta_2}.$$

It may be shown by geometrical considerations that

$$\sin\vartheta_1 > \sin\vartheta_2,$$

from which it follows that, of the two attractions, the second is greatest, so that there is a residual force in the direction AB_2. A similar result is found for any other direction of the cone; the total resultant electric force must therefore be directed towards the centre.

81 (Page 220). The expressions (*146*) of Note 78 show that, if l is different from 1, the value (*147*) found for the energy must be multiplied by l. According to the hypothesis of Bucherer and Langevin, $l = k^{-\frac{1}{3}}$, which leads to the result mentioned in the text.

82 (Page 222). If in the equations (200), in which we may now omit the terms depending on the resistance and on the external magnetic field, we substitute $\mathbf{P} = \mathbf{D} - \mathbf{E}$, they take the form of a linear relation between the vectors $\mathbf{D}$ and $\mathbf{E}$, containing their differential coefficients with respect to the time.

83 (Page 224). Let the effective coordinates of P and Q be 0, 0, 0 and x', y', z'; then, by (286), the relative coordinates are 0, 0, 0 and $\frac{x'}{k}, y', z'$. Hence, if $0, t_1, t_2$ are the values of t at the instants when the signal is started from P, received by Q and again perceived at P, we have by (284) for the absolute coordinates of the points where the signal is found at these moments,

$$0, 0, 0; \quad \frac{x'}{k} + wt_1, y', z'; \quad wt_2, 0, 0,$$

and since the distance from the first to the second is travelled over in an interval t_1, and that from the second to the third in an interval $t_2 - t_1$,

$$\left(\frac{x'}{k} + wt_1\right)^2 + y'^2 + z'^2 = c^2 t_1^2,$$

$$\left\{\frac{x'}{k} + w(t_1 - t_2)\right\}^2 + y'^2 + z'^2 = c^2(t_2 - t_1)^2.$$

By means of these equations t_1 and t_2 can be calculated. It is simpler, however, to consider the quantities

$$t_1' = \frac{1}{k} t_1 - \frac{w}{c^2} x' \qquad (149)$$

and

$$t_2' = \frac{1}{k} t_2. \qquad (150)$$

Indeed, the formulae may be transformed to

$$x'^2 + y'^2 + z'^2 = c^2 t_1'^2$$

$$x'^2 + y'^2 + z'^2 = c^2(t_2' - t_1')^2,$$

giving

$$t_1' = \frac{1}{c}\sqrt{x'^2 + y'^2 + z'^2} \qquad (151)$$

and

$$t_2' = \frac{2}{c}\sqrt{x'^2 + y'^2 + z'^2}. \qquad (152)$$

But it appears from equation (288), for which we may now write

$$t' = \frac{1}{k} t - \frac{w}{c^2} x', \qquad (153)$$

that the variable t_2' defined by (*150*) is the time measured as local time of P that has elapsed between the starting and the return of the signal. On the other hand, $\sqrt{x'^2 + y'^2 + z'^2}$ is the length L which the observer A ascribes to the distance PQ, and $\frac{2L}{t_2'}$ is the value of the velocity of light which he deduces from the experiment. Equation (*152*) shows that this value will be equal to c.

84 (Page 226). It is sufficient to observe that, as is seen from (*153*) and (*149*), a clock showing the local time of Q will mark the time t_1' at the moment when Q is reached by the signal, and that, according to (*151*), this time t_1' is precisely $\frac{L}{c}$.

85 (Page 226). According to what has been said in § 189, the mass m which the moving observer ascribes to a body will be the mass which this body would actually have, if it were at rest. But, the masses being changed by the translation in the manner indicated by (305), the real mass will be $k^3 m$ if the acceleration has the direction of OX, and km if it is at right angles to that axis. Using the indices (o) and (r) to distinguish observed and real values, we may therefore write

$$m_{(r)} = (k^3, k, k)\, m_{(o)},$$

where the factors enclosed in brackets refer to accelerations parallel to OX, OY or OZ.

On the other hand it appears from the formulae (303) that for the accelerations

$$\mathbf{j}_{(r)} = \left(\frac{1}{k^3}, \frac{1}{k^2}, \frac{1}{k^2}\right) \mathbf{j}_{(o)},$$

so that, if the moving observer measures forces $\mathbf{F}$ by the products of acceleration and mass, we shall have

$$\mathbf{F}_{(r)} = \left(1, \frac{1}{k}, \frac{1}{k}\right) \mathbf{F}_{(o)}. \qquad (154)$$

Now, let two particles with equal real charges e be placed at the points of the moving system whose effective coordinates are x_1', y_1', z_1', x_2', y_2', z_2' and whose effective distance r' is therefore given by the first equation of § 171. If these particles had the corresponding positions in a stationary system, the components of the force acting on the second of them would be

$$\frac{(x_2' - x_1')e^2}{4\pi r'^3}, \quad \frac{(y_2' - y_1')e^2}{4\pi r'^3}, \quad \frac{(z_2' - z_1')e^2}{4\pi r'^3}. \qquad (155)$$

Hence, in virtue of (300), the components of the real force in the moving system will be

$$\frac{(x_2' - x_1')e^2}{4\pi r'^3}, \quad \frac{1}{k} \cdot \frac{(y_2' - y_1')e^2}{4\pi r'^3}, \quad \frac{1}{k} \cdot \frac{(z_2' - z_1')e^2}{4\pi r'^3}$$

and by (*154*) the components of the observed force will again have the values (*155*). The observer A will therefore conclude from his experiments that the particles repel each other with a force

$$\frac{e^2}{4\pi r'^2}$$

and he will ascribe to each of them a charge e equal to the real one.

Let us suppose, finally, that a charge e is placed in an electromagnetic field existing in the moving system, at a point which shares the translation. Then, on account of (293), the components of the force really acting on it are

$$e\mathfrak{d}_x', \quad \frac{1}{k}e\mathfrak{d}_y', \quad \frac{1}{k}e\mathfrak{d}_z',$$

and we may infer from (*154*) that the components of the observed force have the values

$$e\mathfrak{d}_x', \quad e\mathfrak{d}_y' \quad e\mathfrak{d}_z'.$$

It appears from this that, as has been stated in the text, the moving observer will be led to the vector $\mathfrak{d}'$ if he examines the force acting on a charged particle.

86 (Page 230) [1915]. Later experiments by Bucherer[1]), Hupka[2]), Schaefer and Neumann[3]) and lastly Guye and Lavanchy[4]) have confirmed the formula (313) for the transverse electromagnetic mass, so that, in all probability, the only objection that could be raised against the hypothesis of the deformable electron and the principle of relativity has now been removed.

1) A. H. Bucherer, Phys. Zeitschr. **9** (1908), p. 755; Ber. d. deutschen Phys. Ges. **6** (1908), p. 688.

2) E. Hupka, Ann. Phys. **31** (1910), p. 169.

3) Cl. Schaefer and G. Neumann, Phys. Zeitschr. **14**, (1913), p. 1117.

4) Ch. E. Guye and Ch. Lavanchy, Comptes rendus **161** (1915), p. 52.

INDEX.

(The numbers refer to pages.)

Catalogue of Dover SCIENCE BOOKS

DIFFERENTIAL EQUATIONS (ORDINARY AND PARTIAL DIFFERENTIAL)

INTRODUCTION TO THE DIFFERENTIAL EQUATIONS OF PHYSICS, L. Hopf. Especially valuable to engineer with no math beyond elementary calculus. Emphasizes intuitive rather than formal aspects of concepts. Partial contents: Law of causality, energy theorem, damped oscillations, coupling by friction, cylindrical and spherical coordinates, heat source, etc. 48 figures. 160pp. 5⅜ x 8. S120 Paperbound **$1.25**

INTRODUCTION TO BESSEL FUNCTIONS, F. Bowman. Rigorous, provides all necessary material during development, includes practical applications. Bessel functions of zero order, of any real order, definite integrals, asymptotic expansion, circular membranes, Bessel's solution to Kepler's problem, much more. "Clear . . . useful not only to students of physics and engineering, but to mathematical students in general," Nature. 226 problems. Short tables of Bessel functions. 27 figures. x + 135pp. 5⅜ x 8. S462 Paperbound **$1.35**

DIFFERENTIAL EQUATIONS, F. R. Moulton. Detailed, rigorous exposition of all non-elementary processes of solving ordinary differential equations. Chapters on practical problems; more advanced than problems usually given as illustrations. Includes analytic differential equations; variations of a parameter; integrals of differential equations; analytic implicit functions; problems of elliptic motion; sine-amplitude functions; deviation of formal bodies; Cauchy-Lipshitz process; linear differential equations with periodic coefficients; much more. Historical notes. 10 figures. 222 problems. xv + 395pp. 5⅜ x 8. S451 Paperbound **$2.00**

PARTIAL DIFFERENTIAL EQUATIONS OF MATHEMATICAL PHYSICS, A. G. Webster. Valuable sections on elasticity, compression theory, potential theory, theory of sound, heat conduction, wave propagation, vibration theory. Contents include: deduction of differential equations, vibrations, normal functions, Fourier's series. Cauchy's method, boundary problems, method of Riemann-Volterra, spherical, cylindrical, ellipsoidal harmonics, applications, etc. 97 figures. vii + 440pp. 5⅜ x 8. S263 Paperbound **$2.00**

ORDINARY DIFFERENTIAL EQUATIONS, E. L. Ince. A most compendious analysis in real and complex domains. Existence and nature of solutions, continuous transformation groups, solutions in an infinite form, definite integrals, algebraic theory. Sturmian theory, boundary problems, existence theorems, 1st order, higher order, etc. "Deserves highest praise, a notable addition to mathematical literature," Bulletin, Amer. Math. Soc. Historical appendix. 18 figures. viii + 558pp. 5⅜ x 8. S349 Paperbound **$2.55**

ASYMPTOTIC EXPANSIONS, A. Erdélyi. Only modern work available in English; unabridged reproduction of monograph prepared for Office of Naval Research. Discusses various procedures for asymptotic evaluation of integrals containing a large parameter; solutions of ordinary linear differential equations. vi + 108pp. 5⅜ x 8. S318 Paperbound **$1.35**

LECTURES ON CAUCHY'S PROBLEM, J. Hadamard. Based on lectures given at Columbia, Rome, discusses work of Riemann, Kirchhoff, Volterra, and author's own research on hyperbolic case in linear partial differential equations. Extends spherical cylindrical waves to apply to all (normal) hyperbolic equations. Partial contents: Cauchy's problem, fundamental formula, equations with odd number, with even number of independent variables; method of descent. 32 figures. iii + 316pp. 5⅜ x 8. S105 Paperbound **$1.75**

NUMBER THEORY

INTRODUCTION TO THE THEORY OF NUMBERS, L. E. Dickson. Thorough, comprehensive, with adequate coverage of classical literature. Not beyond beginners. Chapters on divisibility, congruences, quadratic residues and reciprocity, Diophantine equations, etc. Full treatment of binary quadratic forms without usual restriction to integral coefficients. Covers infinitude of primes, Fermat's theorem, Legendre's symbol, automorphs, Recent theorems of Thue, Siegal, much more. Much material not readily available elsewhere. 239 problems. 1 figure. viii + 183pp. 5⅜ x 8. S342 Paperbound **$1.65**

ELEMENTS OF NUMBER THEORY, I. M. Vinogradov. Detailed 1st course for persons without advanced mathematics; 95% of this book can be understood by readers who have gone no farther than high school algebra. Partial contents: divisibility theory, important number theoretical functions, congruences, primitive roots and indices, etc. Solutions to problems, exercises. Tables of primes, indices, etc. Covers almost every essential formula in elementary number theory! "Welcome addition . . . reads smoothly," Bull. of the Amer. Math. Soc. 233 problems. 104 exercises. viii + 227pp. 5⅜ x 8. S259 Paperbound **$1.60**

PROBABILITY THEORY AND INFORMATION THEORY

SELECTED PAPERS ON NOISE AND STOCHASTIC PROCESSES, edited by Prof. Nelson Wax, U. of Illinois. 6 basic papers for those whose work involves noise characteristics. Chandrasekhar, Uhlenback and Ornstein, Uhlenbeck and Ming, Rice, Doob. Included is Kac's Chauvenet-Prize winning "Random Walk." Extensive bibliography lists 200 articles, through 1953. 21 figures. 337pp. 6⅛ x 9¼. S262 Paperbound **$2.35**

A PHILOSOPHICAL ESSAY ON PROBABILITIES, Marquis de Laplace. This famous essay explains without recourse to mathematics the principle of probability, and the application of probabiilty to games of chance, natural philosophy, astronomy, many other fields. Translated from 6th French edition by F. W. Truscott, F. L. Emory. Intro. by E. T. Bell. 204pp. 5⅜ x 8. S166 Paperbound **$1.25**

MATHEMATICAL FOUNDATIONS OF INFORMATION THEORY, A. I. Khinchin. For mathematicians, statisticians, physicists, cyberneticists, communications engineers, a complete, exact introduction to relatively new field. Entropy as a measure of a finite scheme, applications to coding theory, study of sources, channels and codes, detailed proofs of both Shannon theorems for any ergodic source and any stationary channel with finite memory, much more. "Presents for the first time rigorous proofs of certain fundamental theorems . . . quite complete . . . amazing expository ability," American Math. Monthly. vii + 120pp. 5⅜ x 8. S434 Paperbound **$1.35**

VECTOR AND TENSOR ANALYSIS AND MATRIX THEORY

VECTOR AND TENSOR ANALYSIS, G. E. Hay. One of clearest introductions to increasingly important subject. Start with simple definitions, finish with sure mastery of oriented Cartesian vectors, Christoffel symbols, solenoidal tensors. Complete breakdown of plane, solid, analytical, differential geometry. Separate chapters on application. All fundamental formulae listed, demonstrated. 195 problems. 66 figures. viii + 193pp. 5⅜ x 8. S109 Paperbound **$1.75**

APPLICATIONS OF TENSOR ANALYSIS, A. J. McConnell. Excellent text for applying tensor methods to such familiar subjects as dynamics, electricity, elasticity, hydrodynamics. Explains fundamental ideas and notation of tensor theory, geometrical treatment of tensor algebra, theory of differentiation of tensors, and a wealth of practical material. "The variety of fields treated and the presence of extremely numerous examples make this volume worth much more than its low price," Alluminio. Formerly titled "Applications of the Absolute Differential Calculus." 43 illustrations. 685 problems. xii + 381pp. S373 Paperbound **$1.85**

VECTOR AND TENSOR ANALYSIS, A. P. Wills. Covers entire field, from dyads to non-Euclidean manifolds (especially detailed), absolute differentiation, the Riemann-Christoffel and Ricci-Einstein tensors, calculation of Gaussian curvature of a surface. Illustrations from electrical engineering, relativity theory, astro-physics, quantum mechanics. Presupposes only working knowledge of calculus. Intended for physicists, engineers, mathematicians. 44 diagrams. 114 problems. xxxii + 285pp. 5⅜ x 8. S454 Paperbound **$1.75**

DOVER SCIENCE BOOKS

PHYSICS, ENGINEERING

MECHANICS, DYNAMICS, THERMODYNAMICS, ELASTICITY

MATHEMATICAL ANALYSIS OF ELECTRICAL AND OPTICAL WAVE-MOTION, H. Bateman. By one of century's most distinguished mathematical physicists, a practical introduction to developments of Maxwell's electromagnetic theory which directly concern the solution of partial differential equation of wave motion. Methods of solving wave-equation, polar-cylindrical coordinates, diffraction, transformation of coordinates, homogeneous solutions, electromagnetic fields with moving singularities, etc. 168pp. 5⅜ x 8. S14 Paperbound **$1.60**

THERMODYNAMICS, Enrico Fermi. Unabridged reproduction of 1937 edition. Remarkable for clarity, organization; requires no knowledge of advanced math beyond calculus, only familiarity with fundamentals of thermometry, calorimetry. Partial Contents: Thermodynamic systems, 1st and 2nd laws, potentials; Entropy, phase rule; Reversible electric cells; Gaseous reactions: Van't Hoff reaction box, principle of LeChatelier; Thermodynamics of dilute solutions: osmotic, vapor pressures; boiling, freezing point; Entropy constant. 25 problems. 24 illustrations. x + 160pp. 5⅜ x 8. S361 Paperbound **$1.75**

FOUNDATIONS OF POTENTIAL THEORY, O. D. Kellogg. Based on courses given at Harvard, suitable for both advanced and beginning mathematicians, Proofs rigorous, much material here not generally available elsewhere. Partial contents: gravity, fields of force, divergence theorem, properties of Newtonian potentials at points of free space, potentials as solutions of LaPlace's equation, harmonic functions, electrostatics, electric images, logarithmic potential, etc. ix + 384pp. 5⅜ x 8. S144 Paperbound **$1.98**

DIALOGUES CONCERNING TWO NEW SCIENCES, Galileo Galilei. Classic of experimental science, mechanics, engineering, as enjoyable as it is important. Characterized by author as "superior to everything else of mine." Offers a lively exposition of dynamics, elasticity, sound, ballistics, strength of materials, scientific method. Translated by H. Grew, A. de Salvio. 126 diagrams. xxi + 288pp. 5⅜ x 8. S99 Paperbound **$1.65**

THEORETICAL MECHANICS; AN INTRODUCTION TO MATHEMATICAL PHYSICS, J. S. Ames, F. D. Murnaghan. A mathematically rigorous development for advanced students, with constant practical applications. Used in hundreds of advanced courses. Unusually thorough coverage of gyroscopic baryscopic material, detailed analyses of Corilis acceleration, applications of Lagrange's equations, motion of double pendulum, Hamilton-Jacobi partial differential equations, group velocity, dispersion, etc. Special relativity included. 159 problems. 44 figures. ix + 462pp. 5⅜ x 8. S461 Paperbound **$2.00**

STATICS AND THE DYNAMICS OF A PARTICLE, W. D. MacMillan. This is Part One of "Theoretical Mechanics." For over 3 decades a self-contained, extremely comprehensive advanced undergraduate text in mathematical physics, physics, astronomy, deeper foundations of engineering. Early sections require only a knowledge of geometry; later, a working knowledge of calculus. Hundreds of basic problems including projectiles to moon, harmonic motion, ballistics, transmission of power, stress and strain, elasticity, astronomical problems. 340 practice problems, many fully worked out examples. 200 figures. xvii + 430pp. 5⅜ x 8. S467 Paperbound **$2.00**

THE THEORY OF THE POTENTIAL, W. D. MacMillan. This is Part Two of "Theoretical Mechanics." Comprehensive, well-balanced presentation, serving both as introduction and reference with regard to specific problems, for physicists and mathematicians. Assumes no prior knowledge of integral relations, all math is developed as needed. Includes: Attraction of Finite Bodies; Newtonian Potential Function; Vector Fields, Green and Gauss Theorems; Two-layer Surfaces; Spherical Harmonics; etc. "The great number of particular cases . . . should make the book valuable to geo-physicists and others actively engaged in practical applications of the potential theory," Review of Scientific Instruments. xii + 469pp. 5⅜ x 8. S486 Paperbound **$2.25**

DYNAMICS OF A SYSTEM OF RIGID BODIES (Advanced Section), E. J. Routh. Revised 6th edition of a classic reference aid. Partial contents: moving axes, relative motion, oscillations about equilibrium, motion. Motion of a body under no forces, any forces. Nature of motion given by linear equations and conditions of stability. Free, forced vibrations, constants of integration, calculus of finite differences, variations, procession and mutation, motion of the moon, motion of string, chain, membranes. 64 figures. 498pp. 5⅜ x 8. S229 Paperbound **$2.35**

THE DYNAMICS OF PARTICLES AND OF RIGID, ELASTIC, AND FLUID BODIES: BEING LECTURES ON MATHEMATICAL PHYSICS, A. G. Webster. Reissuing of classic fills need for comprehensive work on dynamics. Covers wide range in unusually great depth, applying ordinary, partial differential equations. Partial contents: laws of motion, methods applicable to systems of all sorts; oscillation, resonance, cyclic systems; dynamics of rigid bodies; potential theory; stress and strain; gyrostatics; wave, vortex motion; kinematics of a point; Lagrange's equations; Hamilton's principle; vectors; deformable bodies; much more not easily found together in one volume. Unabridged reprinting of 2nd edition. 20 pages on differential equations, higher analysis. 203 illustrations. xi + 588pp. 5⅜ x 8. S522 Paperbound **$2.35**

PRINCIPLES OF MECHANICS, Heinrich Hertz. A classic of great interest in logic of science. Last work by great 19th century physicist, created new system of mechanics based upon space, time, mass; returns to axiomatic analysis, understanding of formal, structural aspects of science, taking into account logic, observation, a priori elements. Of great historical importance to Poincaré, Carnap, Einstein, Milne. 20 page introduction by R. S. Cohen, Wesleyan U., analyzes implications of Hertz's thought and logic of science. 13 page introduction by Helmholtz. xlii + 274pp. 5⅜ x 8. S316 Clothbound **$3.50**
S317 Paperbound **$1.75**

MATHEMATICAL FOUNDATIONS OF STATISTICAL MECHANICS, A. I. Khinchin. A thoroughly up-to-date introduction, offering a precise and mathematically rigorous formulation of the problems of statistical mechanics. Provides analytical tools to replace many commonly used cumbersome concepts and devices. Partial contents: Geometry, kinematics of phase space; ergodic problem; theory of probability; central limit theorem; ideal monatomic gas; foundation of thermodynamics; dispersion, distribution of sum functions; etc. "Excellent introduction . . . clear, concise, rigorous," Quarterly of Applied Mathematics. viii + 179pp. 5⅜ x 8. S146 Clothbound **$2.95**
S147 Paperbound **$1.35**

MECHANICS OF THE GYROSCOPE, THE DYNAMICS OF ROTATION, R. F. Deimel, Prof. of Mechanical Engineering, Stevens Inst. of Tech. Elementary, general treatment of dynamics of rotation, with special application of gyroscopic phenomena. No knowledge of vectors needed. Velocity of a moving curve, acceleration to a point, general equations of motion, gyroscopic horizon, free gyro, motion of discs, the damped gyro, 103 similar topics. Exercises. 75 figures. 208pp. 5⅜ x 8. S66 Paperbound **$1.65**

MECHANICS VIA THE CALCULUS, P. W. Norris, W. S. Legge. Wide coverage, from linear motion to vector analysis; equations determining motion, linear methods, compounding of simple harmonic motions, Newton's laws of motion, Hooke's law, the simple pendulum, motion of a particle in 1 plane, centers of gravity, virtual work, friction, kinetic energy of rotating bodies, equilibrium of strings, hydrostatics, sheering stresses, elasticity, etc. Many worked-out examples. 550 problems. 3rd revised edition. xii + 367pp. S207 Clothbound **$3.95**

A TREATISE ON THE MATHEMATICAL THEORY OF ELASTICITY, A. E. H. Love. An indispensable reference work for engineers, mathematicians, physicists, the most complete, authoritative treatment of classical elasticity in one volume. Proceeds from elementary notions of extension to types of strain, cubical dilatation, general theory of strains. Covers relation between mathematical theory of elasticity and technical mechanics; equilibrium of isotropic elastic solids and aelotropic solid bodies; nature of force transmission, Volterra's theory of dislocations; theory of elastic spheres in relation to tidal, rotational, gravitational effects on earth; general theory of bending; deformation of curved plates; buckling effects; much more. "The standard treatise on elasticity," American Math. Monthly. 4th revised edition. 76 figures. xviii + 643pp. 6⅛ x 9¼. S174 Paperbound **$2.95**

NUCLEAR PHYSICS, QUANTUM THEORY, RELATIVITY

MESON PHYSICS, R. E. Marshak. Presents basic theory, and results of experiments with emphasis on theoretical significance. Phenomena involving mesons as virtual transitions avoided, eliminating some of least satisfactory predictions of meson theory. Includes production study of π mesons at nonrelativistic nucleon energies contracts between π and u mesons, phenomena associated with nuclear interaction of π mesons, etc. Presents early evidence for new classes of particles, indicates theoretical difficulties created by discovery of heavy mesons and hyperons. viii + 378pp. 5⅜ x 8. S500 Paperbound **$1.95**

THE FUNDAMENTAL PRINCIPLES OF QUANTUM MECHANICS, WITH ELEMENTARY APPLICATIONS, E. C. Kemble. Inductive presentation, for graduate student, specialists in other branches of physics. Apparatus necessary beyond differential equations and advanced calculus developed as needed. Though general exposition of principles, hundreds of individual problems fully treated. "Excellent book . . . of great value to every student . . . rigorous and detailed mathematical discussion . . .. has succeeded in keeping his presentation clear and understandable," Dr. Linus Pauling, J. of American Chemical Society. Appendices: calculus of variations, math. notes, etc. 611pp. 5⅝ x 8⅜. T472 Paperbound **$2.95**

WAVE PROPAGATION IN PERIODIC STRUCTURES, L. Brillouin. General method, application to different problems: pure physics—scattering of X-rays in crystals, thermal vibration in crystal lattices, electronic motion in metals; problems in electrical engineering. Partial contents: elastic waves along 1-dimensional lattices of point masses. Propagation of waves along 1-dimensional lattices. Energy flow. 2, 3 dimensional lattices. Mathieu's equation. Matrices and propagation of waves along an electric line. Continuous electric lines. 131 illustrations. xii + 253pp. 5⅜ x 8. S34 Paperbound **$1.85**

THEORY OF ELECTRONS AND ITS APPLICATION TO THE PHENOMENA OF LIGHT AND RADIANT HEAT, H. Lorentz. Lectures delivered at Columbia Univ., by Nobel laureate. Unabridged, form historical coverage of theory of free electrons, motion, absorption of heat, Zeeman effect, optical phenomena in moving bodies, etc. 109 pages notes explain more advanced sections. 9 figures. 352pp. 5⅜ x 8. S173 Paperbound **$1.85**

SELECTED PAPERS ON QUANTUM ELECTRODYNAMICS, edited by J. Schwinger. Facsimiles of papers which established quantum electrodynamics; beginning to present position as part of larger theory. First book publication in any language of collected papers of Bethe, Bloch, Dirac, Dyson, Fermi, Feynman, Heisenberg, Kusch, Lamb, Oppenheimer, Pauli, Schwinger, Tomonoga, Weisskopf, Wigner, etc. 34 papers: 29 in English, 1 in French, 3 in German, 1 in Italian. Historical commentary by editor. xvii + 423pp. 6⅛ x 9¼. S444 Paperbound **$2.45**

FOUNDATIONS OF NUCLEAR PHYSICS, edited by R. T. Beyer. 13 of the most important papers on nuclear physics reproduced in facsimile in the original languages; the papers most often cited in footnotes, bibliographies. Anderson, Curie, Joliot, Chadwick, Fermi, Lawrence, Cockroft, Hahn, Yukawa. Unparalleled bibliography: 122 double columned pages, over 4,000 articles, books, classified. 57 figures. 288pp. 6⅛ x 9¼. S19 Paperbound **$1.75**

THE THEORY OF GROUPS AND QUANTUM MECHANICS, H. Weyl. Schroedinger's wave equation, de Broglie's waves of a particle, Jordon-Hoelder theorem, Lie's continuous groups of transformations, Pauli exclusion principle, quantization of Mawell-Dirac field equations, etc. Unitary geometry, quantum theory, groups, application of groups to quantum mechanics, symmetry permutation group, algebra of symmetric transformations, etc. 2nd revised edition. xxii + 422pp. 5⅜ x 8. S268 Clothbound **$4.50**
S269 Paperbound **$1.95**

PHYSICAL PRINCIPLES OF THE QUANTUM THEORY, Werner Heisenberg. Nobel laureate discusses quantum theory; his own work, Compton, Schroedinger, Wilson, Einstein, many others. For physicists, chemists, not specialists in quantum theory. Only elementary formulae considered in text; mathematical appendix for specialists. Profound without sacrificing clarity. Translated by C. Eckart, F. Hoyt. 18 figures. 192pp. 5⅜ x 8. S113 Paperbound **$1.25**

INVESTIGATIONS ON THE THEORY OF THE BROWNIAN MOVEMENT, Albert Einstein. Reprints from rare European journals, translated into English. 5 basic papers, including Elementary Theory of the Brownian Movement, written at request of Lorentz to provide a simple explanation. Translated by A. D. Cowper. Annotated, edited by R. Fürth. 33pp. of notes elucidate, give history of previous investigations. 62 footnotes. 124pp. 5⅜ x 8. S304 Paperbound **$1.25**

THE PRINCIPLE OF RELATIVITY, E. Einstein, H. Lorentz, M. Minkowski, H. Weyl. The 11 basic papers that founded the general and special theories of relativity, translated into English. 2 papers by Lorentz on the Michelson experiment, electromagnetic phenomena. Minkowski's "Space and Time," and Weyl's "Gravitation and Electricity." 7 epoch-making papers by Einstein: "Electromagnetics of Moving Bodies," "Influence of Gravitation in Propagation of Light," "Cosmological Considerations," "General Theory," 3 others. 7 diagrams. Special notes by A. Sommerfeld. 224pp. 5⅜ x 8. S93 Paperbound **$1.75**

STATISTICS

ELEMENTARY STATISTICS, WITH APPLICATIONS IN MEDICINE AND THE BIOLOGICAL SCIENCES, F. E. Croxton. Based primarily on biological sciences, but can be used by anyone desiring introduction to statistics. Assumes no prior acquaintance, requires only modest knowledge of math. All basic formulas carefully explained, illustrated; all necessary reference tables included. From basic terms and concepts, proceeds to frequency distribution, linear, nonlinear, multiple correlation, etc. Contains concrete examples from medicine, biology. 101 charts. 57 tables. 14 appendices. lv + 376pp. 5⅜ x 8. S506 Paperbound **$1.95**

ANALYSIS AND DESIGN OF EXPERIMENTS, H. B. Mann. Offers method for grasping analysis of variance, variance design quickly. Partial contents: Chi-square distribution, analysis of variance distribution, matrices, quadratic forms, likelihood ration tests, test of linear hypotheses, power of analysis, Galois fields, non-orthogonal data, interblock estimates, etc. 15pp. of useful tables. x + 195pp. 5 x 7⅜. S180 Paperbound **$1.45**

FREQUENCY CURVES AND CORRELATION, W. P. Elderton. 4th revised edition of standard work on classical statistics. Practical, one of few books constantly referred to for clear presentation of basic material. Partial contents: Frequency Distributions; Pearsons Frequency Curves; Theoretical Distributions; Standard Errors; Correlation Ratio—Contingency; Corrections for Moments, Beta, Gamma Functions; etc. Key to terms, symbols. 25 examples. 40 tables. 16 figures. xi + 272pp. 5½ x 8½. Clothbound **$1.49**

HYDRODYNAMICS, ETC.

HYDRODYNAMICS, Horace Lamb. Standard reference work on dynamics of liquids and gases. Fundamental theorems, equations, methods, solutions, background for classical hydrodynamics. Chapters: Equations of Motion, Integration of Equations in Special Gases, Vortex Motion, Tidal Waves, Rotating Masses of Liquids, etc. Excellently planned, arranged, Clear, lucid presentation. 6th enlarged, revised edition. Over 900 footnotes, mostly bibliographical. 119 figures. xv + 738pp. 6⅛ x 9¼. S256 Paperbound **$2.95**

HYDRODYNAMICS, A STUDY OF LOGIC, FACT, AND SIMILITUDE, Garrett Birkhoff. A stimulating application of pure mathematics to an applied problem. Emphasis is on correlation of theory and deduction with experiment. Examines recently discovered paradoxes, theory of modelling and dimensional analysis, paradox and error in flows and free boundary theory. Classical theory of virtual mass derived from homogenous spaces; group theory applied to fluid mechanics. 20 figures, 3 plates. xiii + 186pp. 5⅜ x 8. S22 Paperbound **$1.85**

HYDRODYNAMICS, H. Dryden, F. Murhaghan, H. Bateman. Published by National Research Council, 1932. Complete coverage of classical hydrodynamics, encyclopedic in quality. Partial contents: physics of fluids, motion, turbulent flow, compressible fluids, motion in 1, 2, 3 dimensions; laminar motion, resistance of motion through viscous fluid, eddy viscosity, discharge of gases, flow past obstacles, etc. Over 2900-item bibliography. 23 figures. 634pp. 5⅜ x 8. S303 Paperbound **$2.75**

ACOUSTICS AND OPTICS

PRINCIPLES OF PHYSICAL OPTICS, Ernst Mach. Classical examination of propagation of light, color, polarization, etc. Historical, philosophical treatment unequalled for breadth and readability. Contents: Rectilinear propagation, reflection, refraction, dioptrics, composition of light, periodicity, theory of interference, polarization, mathematical representation of properties, etc. 279 illustrations. 10 portraits. 324pp. 5⅜ x 8. S170 Paperbound **$1.75**

THE THEORY OF SOUND, Lord Rayleigh. Written by Nobel laureate, classical methods here will cover most vibrating systems likely to be encountered in practice. Complete coverage of experimental, mathematical aspects. Partial contents: Harmonic motions, lateral vibrations of bars, curved plates or shells, applications of Laplace's functions to acoustical problems, fluid friction, etc. First low-priced edition of this great reference-study work. Historical introduction by R. B. Lindsay. 1040pp. 97 figures. 5⅜ x 8.
S292, S293, Two volume set, paperbound **$4.00**

THEORY OF VIBRATIONS, N. W. McLachlan. Based on exceptionally successful graduate course, Brown University. Discusses linear systems having 1 degree of freedom, forced vibrations of simple linear systems, vibration of flexible strings, transverse vibrations of bars and tubes, of circular plate, sound waves of finite amplitude, etc. 99 diagrams. 160pp. 5⅜ x 8. S190 Paperbound **$1.35**

APPLIED OPTICS AND OPTICAL DESIGN, A. E. Conrady. Thorough systematic presentation of physical and mathematical aspects, limited mostly to "real optics." Stresses practical problem of maximum aberration permissible without affecting performance. Ordinary ray tracing methods; complete theory ray tracing methods, primary aberrations; enough higher aberration to design telescopes, low powered microscopes, photographic equipment. Covers fundamental equations, extra-axial image points, transverse chromatic aberration, angular magnification, similar topics. Tables of functions of N. Over 150 diagrams. x + 518pp. 5⅜ x 8⅝. S366 Paperbound **$2.98**

RAYLEIGH'S PRINCIPLE AND ITS APPLICATIONS TO ENGINEERING, G. Temple, W. Bickley. Rayleigh's principle developed to provide upper, lower estimates of true value of fundamental period of vibrating system, or condition of stability of elastic system. Examples, rigorous proofs. Partial contents: Energy method of discussing vibrations, stability. Perturbation theory, whirling of uniform shafts. Proof, accuracy, successive approximations, applications of Rayleigh's theory. Numerical, graphical methods. Ritz's method. 22 figures. ix + 156pp. 5⅜ x 8. S307 Paperbound **$1.50**

OPTICKS, Sir Isaac Newton. In its discussion of light, reflection, color, refraction, theories of wave and corpuscular theories of light, this work is packed with scores of insights and discoveries. In its precise and practical discussions of construction of optical apparatus, contemporary understanding of phenomena, it is truly fascinating to modern scientists. Foreword by Albert Einstein. Preface by I. B. Cohen, Harvard. 7 pages of portraits, facsimile pages, letters, etc. cxvi + 414pp. 5⅜ x 8. S205 Paperbound **$2.00**

ON THE SENSATIONS OF TONE, Hermann Helmholtz. Using acoustical physics, physiology, experiment, history of music, covers entire gamut of musical tone: relation of music science to acoustics, physical vs. physiological acoustics, vibration, resonance, tonality, progression of parts, etc. 33 appendixes on various aspects of sound, physics, acoustics, music, etc. Translated by A J. Ellis. New introduction by H. Margenau, Yale. 68 figures. 43 musical passages analyzed. Over 100 tables. xix + 576pp. 6⅛ x 9¼.
S114 Clothbound **$4.95**

ELECTROMAGNETICS, ENGINEERING, TECHNOLOGY

INTRODUCTION TO RELAXATION METHODS, F. S. Shaw. Describes almost all manipulative resources of value in solution of differential equations. Treatment is mathematical rather than physical. Extends general computational process to include almost all branches of applied math and physics. Approximate numerical methods are demonstrated, although high accuracy is obtainable without undue expenditure of time. 48pp. of tables for computing irregular star first and second derivatives, irregular star coefficients for second order equations, for fourth order equations. "Useful. . . . exposition is clear, simple . . . no previous acquaintance with numerical methods is assumed," Science Progress. 253 diagrams. 72 tables. 400pp. 5⅜ x 8. S244 Paperbound **$2.45**

THE ELECTROMAGNETIC FIELD, M. Mason, W. Weaver. Used constantly by graduate engineers. Vector methods exclusively; detailed treatment of electrostatics, expansion methods, with tables converting any quantity into absolute electromagnetic, absolute electrostatic, practical units. Discrete charges, ponderable bodies. Maxwell field equations, etc. 416pp. 5⅜ x 8. S185 Paperbound **$2.00**

ELASTICITY, PLASTICITY AND STRUCTURE OF MATTER, R. Houwink. Standard treatise on rheological aspects of different technically important solids: crystals, resins, textiles, rubber, clay, etc. Investigates general laws for deformations; determines divergences. Covers general physical and mathematical aspects of plasticity, elasticity, viscosity. Detailed examination of deformations, internal structure of matter in relation to elastic, plastic behaviour, formation of solid matter from a fluid, etc. Treats glass, asphalt, balata, proteins, baker's dough, others. 2nd revised, enlarged edition. Extensive revised bibliography in over 500 footnotes. 214 figures. xvii + 368pp. 6 x 9¼. S385 Paperbound **$2.45**

DESIGN AND USE OF INSTRUMENTS AND ACCURATE MECHANISM, T. N. Whitehead. For the instrument designer, engineer; how to combine necessary mathematical abstractions with independent observations of actual facts. Partial contents: instruments and their parts, theory of errors, systematic errors, probability, short period errors, erratic errors, design precision, kinematic, semikinematic design, stiffness, planning of an instrument, human factor, etc. 85 photos, diagrams. xii + 288pp. 5⅜ x 8. S270 Paperbound **$1.95**

APPLIED HYDRO- AND AEROMECHANICS, L. Prandtl, O. G. Tietjens. Presents, for most part, methods valuable to engineers. Flow in pipes, boundary layers, airfoil theory, entry conditions, turbulent flow, boundary layer, determining drag from pressure and velocity, etc. "Will be welcomed by all students of aerodynamics," Nature. Unabridged, unaltered. An Engineering Society Monograph, 1934. Index. 226 figures. 28 photographic plates illustrating flow patterns. xvi + 311pp. 5⅜ x 8. S375 Paperbound **$1.85**

FUNDAMENTALS OF HYDRO- AND AEROMECHANICS, L. Prandtl, O. G. Tietjens. Standard work, based on Prandtl's lectures at Goettingen. Wherever possible hydrodynamics theory is referred to practical considerations in hydraulics, unifying theory and experience. Presentation extremely clear. Though primarily physical, proofs are rigorous and use vector analysis to a great extent. An Engineering Society Monograph, 1934. "Still recommended as an excellent introduction to this area," Physikalische Blätter. 186 figures. xvi + 270pp. 5⅜ x 8. S374 Paperbound **$1.85**

GASEOUS CONDUCTORS: THEORY AND ENGINEERING APPLICATIONS, J. D. Cobine. Indispensable text, reference, to gaseous conduction phenomena, with engineering viewpoint prevailing throughout. Studies kinetic theory of gases, ionization, emission phenomena; gas breakdown, spark characteristics, glow, discharges; engineering applications in circuit interrupters, rectifiers, etc. Detailed treatment of high pressure arcs (Suits); low pressure arcs (Langmuir, Tonks). Much more. "Well organized, clear, straightforward," Tonks, Review of Scientific Instruments. 83 practice problems. Over 600 figures. 58 tables. xx + 606pp. 5⅜ x 8. S442 Paperbound **$2.75**

PHOTOELASTICITY: PRINCIPLES AND METHODS, H. T. Jessop, F. C. Harris. For engineer, specific problems of stress analysis. Latest time-saving methods of checking calculations in 2-dimensional design problems, new techniques for stresses in 3 dimensions, lucid description of optical systems used in practical photoelectricity. Useful suggestions, hints based on on-the-job experience included. Partial contents: strain, stress-strain relations, circular disc under thrust along diameter, rectangular block with square hold under vertical thrust, simply supported rectangular beam under central concentrated load, etc. Theory held to minimum, no advanced mathematical training needed. 164 illustrations. viii + 184pp. 6⅛ x 9¼. S137 Clothbound **$3.75**

MICROWAVE TRANSMISSION DESIGN DATA, T. Moreno. Originally classified, now rewritten, enlarged (14 new chapters) under auspices of Sperry Corp. Of immediate value or reference use to radio engineers, systems designers, applied physicists, etc. Ordinary transmission line theory; attenuation; parameters of coaxial lines; flexible cables; tuneable wave guide impedance transformers; effects of temperature, humidity; much more. "Packed with information . . . theoretical discussions are directly related to practical questions," U. of Royal Naval Scientific Service. Tables of dielectrics, flexible cable, etc. ix + 248pp. 5⅜ x 8.
S549 Paperbound **$1.50**

THE THEORY OF THE PROPERTIES OF METALS AND ALLOYS, H. F. Mott, H. Jones. Quantum methods develop mathematical models showing interrelationship of fundamental chemical phenomena wtih crystal structure, electrical, optical properties, etc. Examines electron motion in applied field, cohesion, heat capacity, refraction, noble metals, transition and di-valent metals, etc. "Exposition is as clear . . . mathematical treatment as simple and reliable as we have become used to expect of . . . Prof. Mott," Nature. 138 figures. xiii + 320pp. 5⅜ x 8. S456 Paperbound **$1.85**

THE MEASUREMENT OF POWER SPECTRA FROM THE POINT OF VIEW OF COMMUNICATIONS ENGINEERING, R. B. Blackman, J. W. Tukey. Pathfinding work reprinted from "Bell System Technical Journal." Various ways of getting practically useful answers in power spectra measurement, using results from both transmission and statistical estimation theory. Treats: Autocovariance, Functions and Power Spectra, Distortion, Heterodyne Filtering, Smoothing, Decimation Procedures, Transversal Filtering, much more. Appendix reviews fundamental Fourier techniques. Index of notation. Glossary of terms. 24 figures. 12 tables. 192pp. 5⅝ x 8⅝. S507 Paperbound **$1.85**

TREATISE ON ELECTRICITY AND MAGNETISM, James Clerk Maxwell. For more than 80 years a seemingly inexhaustible source of leads for physicists, mathematicians, engineers. Total of 1082pp. on such topics as Measurement of Quantities, Electrostatics, Elementary Mathematical Theory of Electricity, Electrical Work and Energy in a System of Conductors, General Theorems, Theory of Electrical Images, Electrolysis, Conduction, Polarization, Dielectrics, Resistance, much more. "The greatest mathematical physicist since Newton," Sir James Jeans. 3rd edition. 107 figures, 21 plates. 1082pp. 5⅜ x 8. S186 Clothbound **$4.95**

CHEMISTRY AND PHYSICAL CHEMISTRY

THE PHASE RULE AND ITS APPLICATIONS, Alexander Findlay. Covers chemical phenomena of 1 to 4 multiple component systems, the "standard work on the subject" (Nature). Completely revised, brought up to date by A. N. Campbell, N. O. Smith. New material on binary, tertiary liquid equilibria, solid solutions in ternary systems, quinary systems of salts, water, etc. Completely revised to triangular coordinates in ternary systems, clarified graphic representation, solid models, etc. 9th revised edition. 236 figures. 505 footnotes, mostly bibliographic. xii + 449pp. 5⅜ x 8. S92 Paperbound **$2.45**

DYNAMICAL THEORY OF GASES, James Jeans. Divided into mathematical, physical chapters for convenience of those not expert in mathematics. Discusses mathematical theory of gas in steady state, thermodynamics, Bolzmann, Maxwell, kinetic theory, quantum theory, exponentials, etc. "One of the classics of scientific writing . . . as lucid and comprehensive an exposition of the kinetic theory as has ever been written," J. of Institute of Engineers. 4th enlarged edition, with new material on quantum theory, quantum dynamics, etc. 28 figures. 444pp. 6⅛ x 9¼. S136 Paperbound **$2.45**

POLAR MOLECULES, Pieter Debye. Nobel laureate offers complete guide to fundamental electrostatic field relations, polarizability, molecular structure. Partial contents: electric intensity, displacement, force, polarization by orientation, molar polarization, molar refraction, halogen-hydrides, polar liquids, ionic saturation, dielectric constant, etc. Special chapter considers quantum theory. "Clear and concise . . . coordination of experimental results with theory will be readily appreciated," Electronics Industries. 172pp. 5⅜ x 8.
S63 Clothbound **$3.50**
S64 Paperbound **$1.50**

ATOMIC SPECTRA AND ATOMIC STRUCTURE, G. Herzberg. Excellent general survey for chemists, physicists specializing in other fields. Partial contents: simplest line spectra, elements of atomic theory; multiple structure of line spectra, electron spin; building-up principle, periodic system of elements; finer details of atomic spectra; hyperfine structure of spectral lines; some experimental results and applications. 80 figures. 20 tables. xiii + 257pp. 5⅜ x 8. S115 Paperbound **$1.95**

TREATISE ON THERMODYNAMICS, Max Planck. Classic based on his original papers. Brilliant concepts of Nobel laureate make no assumptions regarding nature of heat, rejects earlier approaches of Helmholtz, Maxwell, to offer uniform point of view for entire field. Seminal work by founder of quantum theory, deducing new physical, chemical laws. A standard text, an excellent introduction to field for students with knowledge of elementary chemistry, physics, calculus. 3rd English edition. xvi + 297pp. 5⅜ x 8. S219 Paperbound **$1.75**

KINETIC THEORY OF LIQUIDS, J. Frenkel. Regards kinetic theory of liquids as generalization, extension of theory of solid bodies, covers all types of arrangements of solids; thermal displacements of atoms; interstitial atoms, ions; orientational, rotational motion of molecules; transition between states of matter. Mathematical theory developed close to physical subject matter. "Discussed in a simple yet deeply penetrating fashion . . . will serve as seeds for a great many basic and applied developments in chemistry," J. of the Amer. Chemical Soc. 216 bibliographical footnotes. 55 figures. xi + 485pp. 5⅜ x 8.
S94 Clothbound **$3.95**
S95 Paperbound **$2.45**

ASTRONOMY

OUT OF THE SKY, H. H. Nininger. Non-technical, comprehensive introduction to "meteoritics" —science concerned with arrival of matter from outer space. By one of world's experts on meteorites, this book defines meteors and meteorites; studies fireball clusters and processions, meteorite composition, size, distribution, showers, explosions, origins, much more. viii + 336pp. 5⅜ x 8. T519 Paperbound **$1.85**

AN INTRODUCTION TO THE STUDY OF STELLAR STRUCTURE, S. Chandrasekhar. Outstanding treatise on stellar dynamics by one of greatest astro-physicists. Examines relationship between loss of energy, mass, and radius of stars in steady state. Discusses thermodynamic laws from Caratheodory's axiomatic standpoint; adiabatic, polytropic laws; work of Ritter, Emden, Kelvin, etc.; Stroemgren envelopes as starter for theory of gaseous stars; Gibbs statistical mechanics (quantum); degenerate stellar configuration, theory of white dwarfs; etc. "Highest level of scientific merit," Bulletin. Amer. Math. Soc. 33 figures. 509pp. 5⅜ x 8. S413 Paperbound **$2.75**

LES MÉTHODES NOVELLES DE LA MÉCANIQUE CÉLESTE, H. Poincaré. Complete French text of one of Poincaré's most important works. Revolutionized celestial mechanics: first use of integral invariants, first major application of linear differential equations, study of periodic orbits, lunar motion and Jupiter's satellites, three body problem, and many other important topics. "Started a new era . . . so extremely modern that even today few have mastered his weapons," E. T. Bell. 3 volumes. Total 1282pp. 6⅛ x 9¼.
Vol. 1 S401 Paperbound **$2.75**
Vol. 2 S402 Paperbound **$2.75**
Vol. 3 S403 Paperbound **$2.75**
The set **$7.50**

THE REALM OF THE NEBULAE, E. Hubble. One of the great astronomers of our time presents his concept of "island universes," and describes its effect on astronomy. Covers velocity-distance relation; classification, nature, distances, general field of nebulae; cosmological theories; nebulae in the neighborhood of the Milky way; etc. 39 photos, including velocity-distance relations shown by spectrum comparison. "One of the most progressive lines of astronomical research," The Times, London. New Introduction by A. Sandage. 55 illustrations. xxiv + 201pp. 5⅜ x 8. S455 Paperbound **$1.50**

HOW TO MAKE A TELESCOPE, Jean Texereau. Design, build an f/6 or f/8 Newtonian type reflecting telescope, with altazimuth Couder mounting, suitable for planetary, lunar, and stellar observation. Covers every operation step-by-step, every piece of equipment. Discusses basic principles of geometric and physical optics (unnecessary to construction), comparative merits of reflectors, refractors. A thorough discussion of eyepieces, finders, grinding, installation, testing, etc. 241 figures, 38 photos, show almost every operation and tool. Potential errors are anticipated. Foreword by A. Couder. Sources of supply. xiii + 191pp. 6¼ x 10. T464 Clothbound **$3.50**

BIOLOGICAL SCIENCES

THE BIOLOGY OF THE AMPHIBIA, G. K. Noble, Late Curator of Herpetology at Am. Mus. of Nat. Hist. Probably most used text on amphibia, most comprehensive, clear, detailed. 19 chapters, 85 page supplement: development; heredity; life history; speciation; adaptation; sex, integument, respiratory, circulatory, digestive, muscular, nervous systems; instinct, intelligence, habits, economic value classification, environment relationships, etc. "Nothing comparable to it," C. H. Pope, curator of Amphibia, Chicago Mus. of Nat. Hist. 1047 item bibliography. 174 illustrations. 600pp. 5⅜ x 8. S206 Paperbound **$2.98**

THE ORIGIN OF LIFE, A. I. Oparin. A classic of biology. This is the first modern statement of theory of gradual evolution of life from nitrocarbon compounds. A brand-new evaluation of Oparin's theory in light of later research, by Dr. S. Margulis, University of Nebraska. xxv + 270pp. 5⅜ x 8. S213 Paperbound **$1.75**

THE BIOLOGY OF THE LABORATORY MOUSE, edited by G. D. Snell. Prepared in 1941 by staff of Roscoe B. Jackson Memorial Laboratory, still the standard treatise on the mouse, assembling enormous amount of material for which otherwise you spend hours of research. Embryology, reproduction, histology, spontaneous neoplasms, gene and chromosomes mutations, genetics of spontaneous tumor formations, of tumor transplantation, endocrine secretion and tumor formation, milk influence and tumor formation, inbred, hybrid animals, parasites, infectious diseases, care and recording. "A wealth of information of vital concern. . . . recommended to all who could use a book on such a subject," Nature. Classified bibliography of 1122 items. 172 figures, including 128 photos. ix + 497pp. 6⅛ x 9¼.
S248 Clothbound **$6.00**

THE TRAVELS OF WILLIAM BARTRAM, edited by Mark Van Doran. Famous source-book of American anthropology, natural history, geography, is record kept by Bartram in 1770's on travels through wilderness of Florida, Georgia, Carolinas. Containing accurate, beautiful descriptions of Indians, settlers, fauna, flora, it is one of finest pieces of Americana ever written. 13 original illustrations. 448pp. 5⅜ x 8. T13 Paperbound **$2.00**

BEHAVIOUR AND SOCIAL LIFE OF THE HONEYBEE, Ronald Ribbands. Outstanding scientific study; a compendium of practically everything known of social life of honeybee. Stresses behaviour of individual bees in field, hive. Extends von Frisch's experiments on communication among bees. Covers perception of temperature, gravity, distance, vibration; sound production; glands; structural differences; wax production; temperature regulation; recognition, communication; drifting, mating behaviour, other highly interesting topics. "This valuable work is sure of a cordial reception by laymen, beekeepers and scientists," Prof. Karl von Frisch, Brit. J. of Animal Behaviour. Bibliography of 690 references. 127 diagrams, graphs, sections of bee anatomy, fine photographs. 352pp. S410 Clothbound **$4.50**

ELEMENTS OF MATHEMATICAL BIOLOGY, A. J. Lotka. Pioneer classic, 1st major attempt to apply modern mathematical techniques on large scale to phenomena of biology, biochemistry, psychology, ecology, similar life sciences. Partial contents: Statistical meaning of irreversibility; Evolution as redistribution; Equations of kinetics of evolving systems; Chemical, inter-species equilibrium; parameters of state; Energy transformers of nature, etc. Can be read with profit by even those having no advanced math; unsurpassed as study-reference. Formerly titled "Elements of Physical Biology." 72 figures. xxx + 460pp. 5⅜ x 8.
S346 Paperbound **$2.45**

TREES OF THE EASTERN AND CENTRAL UNITED STATES AND CANADA, W. M. Harlow. Serious middle-level text covering more than 140 native trees, important escapes, with information on general appearance, growth habit, leaf forms, flowers, fruit, bark, commercial use, distribution, habitat, woodlore, etc. Keys within text enable you to locate various species easily, to know which have edible fruit, much more useful, interesting information. "Well illustrated to make identification very easy," Standard Cat. for Public Libraries. Over 600 photographs, figures. xiii + 288pp. 5⅝ x 6½. T395 Paperbound **$1.35**

FRUIT KEY AND TWIG KEY TO TREES AND SHRUBS (Fruit key to Northeastern Trees, Twig key to Deciduous Woody Plants of Eastern North America), W. M. Harlow. Only guides with photographs of every twig, fruit described. Especially valuable to novice. Fruit key (both deciduous trees, evergreens) has introduction on seeding, organs involved, types, habits. Twig key introduction treats growth, morphology. In keys proper, identification is almost automatic. Exceptional work, widely used in university courses, especially useful for identification in winter, or from fruit or seed only. Over 350 photos, up to 3 times natural size. Index of common, scientific names, in each key. xvii + 125pp. 5⅝ x 8⅜. T511 Paperbound **$1.25**

INSECT LIFE AND INSECT NATURAL HISTORY, S. W. Frost. Unusual for emphasizing habits, social life, ecological relations of insects rather than more academic aspects of classification, morphology. Prof. Frost's enthusiasm and knowledge are everywhere evident as he discusses insect associations, specialized habits like leaf-rolling, leaf mining, case-making, the gall insects, boring insects, etc. Examines matters not usually covered in general works: insects as human food; insect music, musicians; insect response to radio waves; use of insects in art, literature. "Distinctly different, possesses an individuality all its own," Journal of Forestry. Over 700 illustrations. Extensive bibliography. x + 524pp. 5⅜ x 8.
T519 Paperbound **$2.49**

A WAY OF LIFE, AND OTHER SELECTED WRITINGS, Sir William Osler. Physician, humanist, Osler discusses brilliantly Thomas Browne, Gui Patin, Robert Burton, Michael Servetus, William Beaumont, Laennec. Includes such favorite writing as title essay, "The Old Humanities and the New Science," "Books and Men," "The Student Life," 6 more of his best discussions of philosophy, literature, religion. "The sweep of his mind and interests embraced every phase of human activity," G. L. Keynes. 5 photographs. Introduction by G. L. Keynes, M.D., F.R.C.S. xx + 278pp. 5⅜ x 8. T488 Paperbound **$1.50**

THE GENETICAL THEORY OF NATURAL SELECTION, R. A. Fisher. 2nd revised edition of vital reviewing of Darwin's Selection Theory in terms of particulate inheritance, by one of greatest authorities on experimental, theoretical genetics. Theory stated in mathematical form. Special features of particulate inheritance are examined: evolution of dominance, maintenance of specific variability, mimicry, sexual selection, etc. 5 chapters on man's special circumstances as a social animal. 16 photographs. x + 310pp. 5⅜ x 8.
S466 Paperbound **$1.85**

THE AUTOBIOGRAPHY OF CHARLES DARWIN, AND SELECTED LETTERS, edited by Francis Darwin. Darwin's own record of early life; historic voyage aboard "Beagle;" furore surrounding evolution, his replies; reminiscences of his son. Letters to Henslow, Lyell, Hooker, Huxley, Wallace, Kingsley, etc., and thoughts on religion, vivisection. We see how he revolutionized geology with concepts of ocean subsidence; how his great books on variation of plants and animals, primitive man, expression of emotion among primates, plant fertilization, carnivorous plants, protective coloration, etc., came into being. 365pp. 5⅜ x 8.
T479 Paperbound **$1.65**

ANIMALS IN MOTION, Eadweard Muybridge. Largest, most comprehensive selection of Muybridge's famous action photos of animals, from his "Animal Locomotion." 3919 high-speed shots of 34 different animals, birds, in 123 types of action; horses, mules, oxen, pigs, goats, camels, elephants, dogs, cats guanacos, sloths, lions, tigers, jaguars, raccoons, baboons, deer, elk, gnus, kangaroos, many others, walking, running, flying, leaping. Horse alone in over 40 ways. Photos taken against ruled backgrounds; most actions taken from 3 angles at once: 90°, 60°, rear. Most plates original size. Of considerable interest to scientists as biology classic, records of actual facts of natural history, physiology. "Really marvelous series of plates," Nature. "Monumental work," Waldemar Kaempffert. Edited by L. S. Brown, 74 page introduction on mechanics of motion. 340pp. of plates. 3919 photographs. 416pp. Deluxe binding, paper. (Weight: 4½ lbs.) 7⅛ x 10⅝.
T203 Clothbound **$10.00**

THE HUMAN FIGURE IN MOTION, Eadweard Muybridge. New edition of great classic in history of science and photography, largest selection ever made from original Muybridge photos of human action: 4789 photographs, illustrating 163 types of motion: walking, running, lifting, etc. in time-exposure sequence photos at speeds up to 1/6000th of a second. Men, women, children, mostly undraped, showing bone, muscle positions against ruled backgrounds, mostly taken at 3 angles at once. Not only was this a great work of photography, acclaimed by contemporary critics as work of genius, but it was also a great 19th century landmark in biological research. Historical introduction by Prof. Robert Taft, U. of Kansas. Plates original size, full of detail. Over 500 action strips. 407pp. 7¾ x 10⅝. Deluxe edition.
7204 Clothbound **$10.00**

AN INTRODUCTION TO THE STUDY OF EXPERIMENTAL MEDICINE, Claude Bernard. 90-year old classic of medical science, only major work of Bernard available in English, records his efforts to transform physiology into exact science. Principles of scientific research illustrated by specified case histories from his work; roles of chance, error, preliminary false conclusion, in leading eventually to scientific truth; use of hypothesis. Much of modern application of mathematics to biology rests on foundation set down here. "The presentation is polished . . . reading is easy," Revue des questions scientifiques. New foreword by Prof. I. B. Cohen, Harvard U. xxv + 266pp. 5⅜ x 8. T400 Paperbound **$1.50**

STUDIES ON THE STRUCTURE AND DEVELOPMENT OF VERTEBRATES, E. S. Goodrich. Definitive study by greatest modern comparative anatomist. Exhaustive morphological, phylogenetic expositions of skeleton, fins, limbs, skeletal visceral arches, labial cartilages, visceral clefts, gills, vascular, respiratory, excretory, periphal nervous systems, etc., from fish to higher mammals. "For many a day this will certainly be the standard textbook on Vertebrate Morphology in the English language," Journal of Anatomy. 754 illustrations. 69 page biographical study by C. C. Hardy. Bibliography of 1186 references. Two volumes, total 906pp. 5⅜ x 8. Two vol. set S449, 450 Paperbound **$5.00**

EARTH SCIENCES

THE EVOLUTION OF IGNEOUS BOOKS, N. L. Bowen. Invaluable serious introduction applies techniques of physics, chemistry to explain igneous rock diversity in terms of chemical composition, fractional crystallization. Discusses liquid immiscibility in silicate magmas, crystal sorting, liquid lines of descent, fractional resorption of complex minerals, petrogen, etc. Of prime importance to geologists, mining engineers; physicists, chemists working with high temperature, pressures. "Most important," Times, London. 263 bibliographic notes. 82 figures. xviii + 334pp. 5⅜ x 8. S311 Paperbound **$1.85**

GEOGRAPHICAL ESSAYS, M. Davis. Modern geography, geomorphology rest on fundamental work of this scientist. 26 famous essays present most important theories, field researches. Partial contents: Geographical Cycle; Plains of Marine, Subaerial Denudation; The Peneplain; Rivers, Valleys of Pennsylvania; Outline of Cape Cod; Sculpture of Mountains by Glaciers; etc. "Long the leader and guide," Economic Geography. "Part of the very texture of geography . . . models of clear thought," Geographic Review. 130 figures. vi + 777pp. 5⅜ x 8.
S383 Paperbound **$2.95**

URANIUM PROSPECTING, H. L. Barnes. For immediate practical use, professional geologist considers uranium ores, geological occurrences, field conditions, all aspects of highly profitable occupation. "Helpful information . . . easy-to-use, easy-to-find style," Geotimes. x + 117pp. 5⅜ x 8. T309 Paperbound **$1.00**

DE RE METALLICA, Georgius Agricola. 400 year old classic translated, annotated by former President Herbert Hoover. 1st scientific study of mineralogy, mining, for over 200 years after its appearance in 1556 the standard treatise. 12 books, exhaustively annotated, discuss history of mining, selection of sites, types of deposits, making pits, shafts, ventilating, pumps, crushing machinery; assaying, smelting, refining metals; also salt alum, nitre, glass making. Definitive edition, with all 289 16th century woodcuts of original. Biographical, historical introductions. Bibliography, survey of ancient authors. Indexes. A fascinating book for anyone interested in art, history of science, geology, etc. Deluxe Edition. 289 illustrations. 672pp. 6¾ x 10. Library cloth. S6 Clothbound **$10.00**

INTERNAL CONSTITUTION OF THE EARTH, edited by Beno Gutenberg. Prepared for National Research Council, this is a complete, thorough coverage of earth origins, continent formation, nature and behaviour of earth's core, petrology of crust, cooling forces in core, seismic and earthquake material, gravity, elastic constants, strain characteristics, similar topics. "One is filled with admiration . . . a high standard . . . there is no reader who will not learn something from this book," London, Edinburgh, Dublin, Philosophic Magazine. Largest Bibliography in print: 1127 classified items. Table of constants. 43 diagrams. 439pp. 6⅛ x 9¼. S414 Paperbound **$2.45**

THE BIRTH AND DEVELOPMENT OF THE GEOLOGICAL SCIENCES, F. D. Adams. Most thorough history of earth sciences ever written. Geological thought from earliest times to end of 19th century, covering over 300 early thinkers and systems; fossils and their explanation, vulcanists vs. neptunists, figured stones and paleontology, generation of stones, dozens of similar topics. 91 illustrations, including Medieval, Renaissance woodcuts, etc. 632 footnotes, mostly bibliographical. 511pp. 5⅜ x 8. T5 Paperbound **$2.00**

HYDROLOGY, edited by O. E. Meinzer, prepared for the National Research Council. Detailed, complete reference library on precipitation, evaporation, snow, snow surveying, glaciers, lakes, infiltration, soil moisture, ground water, runoff, drought, physical changes produced by water hydrology of limestone terranes, etc. Practical in application, especially valuable for engineers. 24 experts have created "the most up-to-date, most complete treatment of the subject," Am. Assoc. of Petroleum Geologists. 165 illustrations. xi + 712pp. 6⅛ x 9¼. S191 Paperbound **$2.95**

LANGUAGE AND TRAVEL AIDS FOR SCIENTISTS

SAY IT language phrase books

"SAY IT" in the foreign language of your choice! We have sold over ½ million copies of these popular, useful language books. They will not make you an expert linguist overnight, but they do cover most practical matters of everyday life abroad.

Over 1000 useful phrases, expressions, additional variants, substitutions.

Modern! Useful! Hundreds of phrases not available in other texts: "Nylon," "air-conditioned," etc.

The ONLY inexpensive phrase book **completely indexed.** Everything is available at a flip of your finger, ready to use.

Prepared by native linguists, travel experts.

Based on years of travel experience abroad.

May be used by itself, or to supplement any other text or course. Provides a living element. Used by many colleges, institutions: Hunter College; Barnard College; Army Ordinance School, Aberdeen; etc.

Available, 1 book per language:

Danish (T818) 75¢
Dutch (T817) 75¢
English (for German-speaking people) (T801) 60¢
English (for Italian-speaking people) (T816) 60¢
English (for Spanish-speaking people) (T802) 60¢
Esperanto (T820) 75¢
French (T803) 60¢
German (T804) 60¢
Modern Greek (T813) 75¢
Hebrew (T805) 60¢
Italian (T806) 60¢
Japanese (T807) 75¢
Norwegian (T814) 75¢
Russian (T810) 75¢
Spanish (T811) 60¢
Turkish (T821) 75¢
Yiddish (T815) 75¢
Swedish (T812) 75¢
Polish (T808) 75¢
Portuguese (T809) 75¢

MONEY CONVERTER AND TIPPING GUIDE FOR EUROPEAN TRAVEL, C. Vomacka. Purse-size handbook crammed with information on currency regulations, tipping for every European country, including Israel, Turkey, Czechoslovakia, Rumania, Egypt, Russia, Poland. Telephone, postal rates; duty-free imports, passports, visas, health certificates; foreign clothing sizes; weather tables. What, when to tip. 5th year of publication. 128pp. 3½ x 5¼. T260 Paperbound **60¢**

NEW RUSSIAN-ENGLISH AND ENGLISH-RUSSIAN DICTIONARY, M. A. O'Brien. Unusually comprehensive guide to reading, speaking, writing Russian, for both advanced, beginning students. Over 70,000 entries in new orthography, full information on accentuation, grammatical classifications. Shades of meaning, idiomatic uses, colloquialisms, tables of irregular verbs for both languages. Individual entries indicate stems, transitiveness, perfective, imperfective aspects, conjugation, sound changes, accent, etc. Includes pronunciation instruction. Used at Harvard, Yale, Cornell, etc. 738pp. 5⅜ x 8. T208 Paperbound **$ 2.00**

PHRASE AND SENTENCE DICTIONARY OF SPOKEN RUSSIAN, English-Russian, Russian-English. Based on phrases, complete sentences, not isolated words—recognized as one of best methods of learning idiomatic speech. Over 11,500 entries, indexed by single words, over 32,000 English, Russian sentences, phrases, in immediately useable form. Shows accent changes in conjugation, declension; irregular forms listed both alphabetically, under main form of word. 15,000 word introduction covers Russian sounds, writing, grammar, syntax. 15 page appendix of geographical names, money, important signs, given names, foods, special Soviet terms, etc. Originally published as U.S. Gov't Manual TM 30-944. iv + 573pp. 5⅜ x 8. T496 Paperbound **$2.75**

PHRASE AND SENTENCE DICTIONARY OF SPOKEN SPANISH, Spanish-English, English-Spanish. Compiled from spoken Spanish, based on phrases, complete sentences rather than isolated words—not an ordinary dictionary. Over 16,000 entries indexed under single words, both Castilian, Latin-American. Language in immediately useable form. 25 page introduction provides rapid survey of sounds, grammar, syntax, full consideration of irregular verbs. Especially apt in modern treatment of phrases, structure. 17 page glossary gives translations of geographical names, money values, numbers, national holidays, important street signs, useful expressions of high frequency, plus unique 7 page glossary of Spanish, Spanish-American foods. Originally published as U.S. Gov't Manual TM 30-900. iv + 513pp. 5⅝ x 8⅜. T495 Paperbound **$1.75**

SAY IT CORRECTLY language record sets

The best inexpensive pronunciation aids on the market. Spoken by native linguists associated with major American universities, each record contains:

14 minutes of speech—12 minutes of normal, relatively slow speech, 2 minutes of normal conversational speed.

120 basic phrases, sentences, covering nearly every aspect of everyday life, travel—introducing yourself, travel in autos, buses, taxis, etc., walking, sightseeing, hotels, restaurants, money, shopping, etc.

32 page booklet containing everything on record plus English translations easy-to-follow phonetic guide.

Clear, high-fidelity recordings.

Unique bracketing systems, selection of basic sentences enabling you to expand use of SAY IT CORRECTLY records with a dictionary, to fit thousands of additional situations.

Use this record to supplement any course or text. All sounds in each language illustrated perfectly—imitate speaker in pause which follows each foreign phrase in slow section, and be amazed at increased ease, accuracy of pronounciation. Available, one language per record for

French | **Spanish** | **German**
Italian | **Dutch** | **Modern Greek**
Japanese | **Russian** | **Portuguese**
Polish | **Swedish** | **Hebrew**
English (for German-speaking people) | **English (for Spanish-speaking people)**

7" (33 1/3 rpm) record, album, booklet. **$1.00 each.**

SPEAK MY LANGUAGE: SPANISH FOR YOUNG BEGINNERS, M. Ahlman, Z. Gilbert. Records provide one of the best, most entertaining methods of introducing a foreign language to children. Within framework of train trip from Portugal to Spain, an English-speaking child is introduced to Spanish by native companion. (Adapted from successful radio program of N.Y. State Educational Department.) A dozen different categories of expressions,. including greeting, numbers, time, weather, food, clothes, family members, etc. Drill is combined with poetry and contextual use. Authentic background music. Accompanying book enables a reader to follow records, includes vocabulary of over 350 recorded expressions. Two 10" 33 1/3 records, total of 40 minutes. Book. 40 illustrations. 69pp. 5¼ x 10½. T890 The set **$4.95**

LISTEN & LEARN language record sets

LISTEN & LEARN is the only extensive language record course designed especially to meet your travel and everyday needs. Separate sets for each language, each containing three 33 1/3 rpm long-playing records—1 1/2 hours of recorded speech by eminent native speakers who are professors at Columbia, New York U., Queens College.

Check the following features found only in LISTEN & LEARN:

Dual language recording. 812 selected phrases, sentences, over 3200 words, spoken first in English, then foreign equivalent. Pause after each foreign phrase allows time to repeat expression.

128-page manual (196 page for Russian)—everything on records, plus simple transcription. Indexed for convenience. Only set on the market completely indexed.

Practical. No time wasted on material you can find in any grammar. No dead words. Covers central core material with phrase approach. Ideal for person with limited time. Living, modern expressions, not found in other courses. Hygienic products, modern equipment, shopping, "air-conditioned," etc. Everything is immediately useable.

High-fidelity recording, equal in clarity to any costing up to $6 per record.

"Excellent . . . impress me as being among the very best on the market," Prof. Mario Pei, Dept. of Romance Languages, Columbia U. "Inexpensive and well done . . . ideal present," Chicago Sunday Tribune. "More genuinely helpful than anything of its kind," Sidney Clark, well-known author of "All the Best" travel books.

UNCONDITIONAL GUARANTEE. Try LISTEN & LEARN, then return it within 10 days for full refund, if you are not satisfied. It is guaranteed after you actually use it.

6 modern languages—FRENCH, SPANISH, GERMAN, ITALIAN, RUSSIAN, or JAPANESE *—one language to each set of 3 records (33 1/3 rpm). 128 page manual. Album.

Spanish	the set $4.95	**German**	the set $4.95	**Japanese***	the set $5.95
French	the set $4.95	**Italian**	the set $4.95	**Russian**	the set $5.95

* Available Oct. 1959.

TRÜBNER COLLOQUIAL SERIES

These unusual books are members of the famous Trübner series of colloquial manuals. They have been written to provide adults with a sound colloquial knowledge of a foreign language, and are suited for either class use or self-study. Each book is a complete course in itself, with progressive, easy to follow lessons. Phonetics, grammar, and syntax are covered, while hundreds of phrases and idioms, reading texts, exercises, and vocabulary are included. These books are unusual in being neither skimpy nor overdetailed in grammatical matters, and in presenting up-to-date, colloquial, and practical phrase material. Bilingual presentation is stressed, to make thorough self-study easier for the reader.

COLLOQUIAL HINDUSTANI, A. H. Harley, formerly Nizam's Reader in Urdu, U. of London. 30 pages on phonetics and scripts (devanagari & Arabic-Persian) are followed by 29 lessons, including material on English and Arabic-Persian influences. Key to all exercises. Vocabulary. 5 x 7½. 147pp. Clothbound **$1.75**

COLLOQUIAL ARABIC, DeLacy O'Leary. Foremost Islamic scholar covers language of Egypt, Syria, Palestine, & Northern Arabia. Extremely clear coverage of complex Arabic verbs & noun plurals; also cultural aspects of language. Vocabulary. xviii + 192pp. 5 x 7½. Clothbound **$1.75**

COLLOQUIAL GERMAN, P. F. Doring. Intensive thorough coverage of grammar in easily-followed form. Excellent for brush-up, with hundreds of colloquial phrases. 34 pages of bilingual texts. 224pp. 5 x 7½. Clothbound **$1.75**

COLLOQUIAL SPANISH, W. R. Patterson. Castilian grammar and colloquial language, loaded with bilingual phrases and colloquialisms. Excellent for review or self-study. 164pp. 5 x 7½. Clothbound **$1.75**

COLLOQUIAL FRENCH, W. R. Patterson. 16th revised edition of this extremely popular manual. Grammar explained with model clarity, and hundreds of useful expressions and phrases; exercises, reading texts, etc. Appendixes of new and useful words and phrases. 223pp. 5 x 7½. Clothbound **$1.75**

Mount Union College Libraries
539.72 L869t
Lorentz, H. A./The theory of electrons a
3 7048 00023 9836